Research in Arctic life and earth sciences: present knowledge and future perspectives

Proceedings of a symposium held 4–6 September, 1985, at Abisko, Sweden

Edited by
Mats Sonesson

Ecological Bulletins

ECOLOGICAL BULLETINS are published in cooperation with the ecological journals Holarctic Ecology and Oikos. Ecological Bulletins consist of monographs, reports and symposia proceedings on topics of international interest, published on a non-profit making basis, in many cases in cooperation with agencies such as Unesco, UNEP, and SCOPE. Orders for the volumes should be placed with the publisher. Discounts are available for standing orders.

Editor-in-Chief and Editorial Office:
Pehr H. Enckell
Ecology Building
University of Lund
S-223 62 Lund
Sweden

Published and distributed by:
Munksgaard International Booksellers
and Publishers,
P. O. Box 2148, DK-1016 Copenhagen K,
Denmark
Under the auspices of he
Swedish Natural Science Research Council
and the
Swedish Council for Planning and Coordination of Research
Suggested citation:
Author's name. 1987. Title of paper. – Ecol. Bull. (Copenhagen) 38: 000–000.

Cover photo
Abisko Scientific Research Station.
Photo O. Nordell.
© 1987, ECOLOGICAL BULLETINS
ISSN 0346-6868
ISBN 87-16-10034-4

Ecological Bulletins still available:

9. Bird Census Work and Environmental Monitoring (1970). Editor S. Svensson. Price DKK 40.

11. Ecology in Semi-arid East Africa (1971). S. Ulfstrand. Price DKK 60.

12. Natural Resources Research in East Africa (1971). M. Zumer. Price DKK 60.

15. Ecology of the Swedish Coniferous Forest landscape – a Research Programme (1972). Editor F. Andersson. Price DKK 60.

18. Scandinavian Aerobiology (1973). Editor S. Nilsson. Price DKK 60.

19. Biocontrol of Rodents (1975). Editors L. Hansson and B. Nilsson. Price DKK 130.

21. Man and the Boreal Forest (1976). Editor C. O. Tamm. Price DKK 110.

22. Nitrogen, Phosphorus and Sulphur – Global Cycles. SCOPE Report 7 (1979, 2nd reprinted edition). Editors B. H. Svensson and R. Söderlund. Price DKK 130.

23. Energetical Significance of the Annelids and Arthropods in a Swedish Grassland Soil (1977). T. Persson and U. Lohm. Price DKK 120.

24. Can Desert Encroachment be Stopped? (1976). Editors A. Rapp, H. N. Le Houérou and B. Lundholm. Price DKK 170. Peut-on-Arrêter l'Extension des Deserts? (1976). Rédacteurs A. Rapp, H. N. le Houérou et B. Lundholm.

25. Soil Organisms as Components of Ecosystems (1977). Editors U. Lohm and T. Persson. Price DKK 250.

26. Environmental Role of Nitrogen-fixing Blue-green Algae and Asymbiotic Bacteria (1978). Editor U. Granhall. Price DKK 190.

27. Chlorinated Phenoxy Acids and Their Dioxins. Mode of Action, Health Risks and Environmental Effects (1978). Editor C. Ramel. Price DKK 170.

28. Energy, Economic and Ecological Relationships for Gotland, Sweden – A Regional Systems Study (1978). A. M. Jansson and J. Zucchetto. Price DKK 130.

30. Ecology of a Subarctic Mire (1980). Editor M. Sonesson. Price DKK 200.

31. Environmental Protection and Biological Forms of Control of Pest organisms (1980). Editors B. Lundholm and M. Stackerud. Price DKK 150.

32. Structure and Function of Northern Coniferous Forests – an Ecosystem Study (1980). Editor T. Persson. Price DKK 300.

34. Fish Gene Pools. Preservation of Genetic Resources in Relation to Wild Fish Stocks (1981). Editor N. Ryman. Price DKK 110.

35. Environmental Biogeochemistry (1983). Editor R. Hallberg. Price DKK 300.

36. Ecotoxicology (1984). Editor L. Rasmussen. DKK 300.

37. Lake Gårdsjön. An acid forest lake and its catchment (1985). Editors F. Andersson and B. Olsson. Price DKK 370.

Preface

Abisko Scientific Research Station, situated in the mountains of subarctic Sweden (68°21′N; 18°49′E), is one of the oldest and largest field stations north of the Arctic Circle. Its history dates back to 1903 when the first research station was established in the area. Since 1935 it has been under the auspices of the Royal Swedish Academy of Sciences. Its purpose is "… to provide Swedish and foreign visiting researchers with the opportunity of conducting scientific work based on the specific conditions of the environment surrounding the station, and to conduct such research with its own personnel." It is also used for university courses, symposia and similar scientific meetings.

Research at the station covers a wide range of the biological, geological and geographic sciences, and scientific interest in the area has increased steadily since its establishment. The facilities of the station have, therefore, been substantially expanded in recent years, for both research and accommodation.

In 1985, the station celebrated the 50th anniversary of its affiliation with the Academy with a symposium entitled Research in Arctic Life and Earth Sciences: Present Knowledge and Future Perspectives. Seven invited papers were presented covering subjets on which research is being done at the station. The abiotic environment of the Arctic, and related areas, was described in a series of three papers which discussed mountain climatology, geology and periglacial geomorphology. Four remaining papers considered the biota of the Arctic, from their origins through soil microbiology and plant resource utilisation to population biology. These presented papers are published in this volume together with an additional article discussing Man's direct and indirect influence on the ecosystems of the area, an influence which must, or should be, considered when evaluating environmental data today. This subject is also an important part of the research programme of the station.

I wish to thank all the authors for their contributions to the conference, both by the lectures and their participation in the discussions. Thanks are also due to the chairmen who moderated the stimulating discussions, Professor Gunnar Hoppe, The Committe for Polar Research of the Academy of Sciences, Stockholm; Professor Paavo Kallio, Kevo Subarctic Research Institute, Turku, Finland; Professor Anders Rapp, Department of Physical Geography, Lund and Professor Eilif Dahl, Department of Botany, The Agricultural University of Norway, Ås.

Financial support for the symposium was provided by the Wallenberg Foundation, Stockholm and LKAB, Stockholm-Kiruna.

I wish to thank the Academy for financing the publication.

Abisko
June 1987

Mats Sonesson

Contents

Ecological Bulletins 38: 5–16. Copenhagen 1987

Periglacial geomorphology in North America: current research and future trends

Hugh M. French

French, H. M. 1987. Periglacial geomorphology in North America: current research and future trends. – Ecol. Bull. (Copenhagen) 38: 5–16.

Periglacial geomorphology in North America is a rigorous branch of process geomorphology with important applied applications. Since frost action and permafrost are central themes, periglacial geomorphology must be regarded as part of the science of geocryology. Current research problems include the cryogenic weathering of bedrock, frost heave and ice segregation, the nature and origins of ground ice, and active layer processes.

H. M. French, Dept of Geography, Univ. of Ottawa, Ottawa, Ontario, Canada K1N 6N5.

Introduction

Periglacial geomorphology seeks to explain the geomorphic processes and landforms of cold non glacial environments. Approximately one quarter of the land surface of the earth currently experiences periglacial conditions. There are two criteria which identify periglacial regions. These are (1) the existence of intense freezing and thawing of the ground, either on a seasonal or daily basis, and (2) the formation and preservation of perennially frozen ground, or permafrost.

In the last fifteen years, the necessity to plan, design and construct major engineering structures in Arctic regions has led to significant advances in our understanding of periglacial processes and landforms. In this review, some current North American research priorities are highlighted.

Cryogenic weathering

Perhaps the least understood and at the same time most fundamental area of research lies in the nature of cold climate rock weathering. For long it was assumed that repeated and intense freeze-thaw cycles characterised periglacial regions and that frost wedging was the dominant mode of rock disintegration. In the last twenty years, increasing field evidence challenges this supposition. Not only is the frequency of freeze-thaw cycles remarkably low, but hydration shattering, by adsorption-desorption of water molecules, has been advanced to explain the production of angular rock fragments (e.g., White 1976, Washburn 1980, French 1981). At the same time, chemical weathering processes have been assumed to be generally unimportant, on account of the coldness and aridity of many periglacial regions.

Recent empirical and laboratory-oriented studies (e.g., Fahey and Gowan 1979, Konischev 1982, Lautridou and Ozoef 1982) have emphasised physical weathering processes. The results have been largely inconclusive. The problem is not helped by the lack of supporting field data. Those data that are available in North America tend to highlight the relative importance of chemical weathering as first suggested by Rapp (1962) for northern Sweden. In Northern Canada, for example, where coarse grained metamorphic and igneous rocks outcrop widely, salt hydration and crystallisation following evaporation of rainwater may be the cause of micro-fracturing, weathering pits, and grus formation (Watts 1983) (Fig. 1). Similarly, on a granodiorite nunatak in the Juneau Icefields of Alaska, chemical weathering processes, notably dissolution and clay mineral transformation, occur in coarse textured rocks, and are not necessarily slowed by low temperatures (Dixon et al. 1984). Even in the relatively simple example of limestone solutional weathering, there is debate as to the significance of chemical weathering processes in cold regions, especially in those areas where permafrost prevents or restricts the underground percolation of groundwater (e.g., van Everdingen 1981, Ford 1984).

The existence of bedrock outcrops, or tors, highlights

Fig. 1. Granitic terrain, Ellesmere Island, N.W.T., Canada. Note the weathering pit in foreground with hammer for scale. (Photo courtesy of W. Blake, Jr.).

the uncertainty concerning rock weathering, and its efficacy, both today and in the past. In some areas of the High Arctic, frost shattering and tor formation is undoubtedly active (Dyke 1983). By contrast, similar features in the unglaciated northern Yukon (Fig. 2), developed upon extremely hard igneous and metamorphic sediments (Hughes et al. 1972) show no apparent signs of current formation and may be inherited features from even colder conditions during the Pleistocene.

Recent studies also question the whole concept of nivation, or snowbank weathering (Thorn 1979, 1987, Thorn and Hall 1980). A comparison of bedrock temperatures beneath and adjacent to snowbanks to the various laboratory-established criteria for effective freeze-thaw weathering, suggests that moisture-rich micro-sites lack adequate freezing intensity, while adequately frozen sites lack moisture. These results feed scepticism about the reality of such features as cryoplanation terraces. Although large rock-cut benches do exist in parts of unglaciated Siberia and interior Alaska and Yukon (Reger and Péwé 1976), their origin as the result of mechanical weathering associated with perennial or late-lying snowbanks is highly questionable.

In summary therefore, one must agree with Washburn (1985: 171) that there is still much that is unknown about the efficacy of cold climate rock weathering.

Frost heave and ice segregation

Intimately associated with the freezing of the ground surface are the phenomena of frost heave and ice segregation. These processes occur wherever moisture is present. Annual ground displacements of several centimetres with cyclic differential ground pressures of many kilopascals per square centimetre are common.

The process of ice segregation involves complex inter-relationships between the ice, an unfrozen liquid phase, and the bulk pore water (Polar Research Board 1984).

Complex latent heats of phase change as well as variable interfacial energies between phases are involved. These are not well understood. Because of its relevance to current engineering and resource development concerns in North America, frost heave is an area of priority research in both the United States and Canada.

The starting point for any discussion of frost heave must be the recognition of both primary and secondary heave (e.g., Miller 1972, Smith 1985a). Primary heave is due to capillary action and occurs as the ground begins to freeze. Secondary heave occurs at temperatures below 0°C and refers to water redistribution within existing frozen ground. Included in secondary heave are the unstable conditions occurring immediately adjacent to the frost line in the zone which is sometimes termed the 'frozen fringe'.

The fact that not all water in a soil freezes at 0°C has led to a major terminological problem. Since it has been demonstrated that in certain frost-susceptible soils, as much as 40% of the water content may be in an unfrozen state at −1.0°C (Williams 1976, 1977), it now becomes necessary to distinguish between the thermal (i.e., temperature) and state (i.e., frozen or unfrozen) conditions of earth materials. To address this problem, the terms 'non-cryotic' and 'cryotic' are now gaining acceptance in North America. These terms refer to conditions above and below 0°C respectively (van Everdingen 1976, 1985). Fig. 3 is a hypothetical graph showing the liquid water content versus ground temperature of a soil. It indicates the relationships between these new terms which describe the temperature and phase conditions. Under this scheme, perennially cryotic earth materials, that is, permafrost, may be sub-divided into one of three categories: *unfrozen cryotic, partially frozen cryotic,* and *frozen cryotic.*

It is also known that unfrozen water in frozen ground can move in the direction along which the ground temperature decreases in response to an imposed gradient. This has important implications for ice distribution

Fig. 2. Tor formed in highly resistant high grade metamorphic shale, Klondike (Yukon) Plateau, west of Dawson City. There is no apparent evidence of current formation.

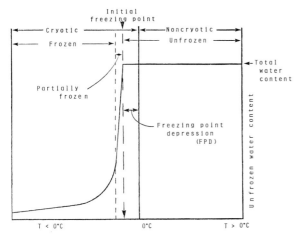

Fig. 3. Hypothetical graph of liquid water content versus ground temperature showing relationships between temperature and phase conditions of permafrost (from van Everdingen 1976).

within both the active layer and the upper few metres of permafrost. For example, the ice content in the upper part of the active layer will increase when a positive ground temperature gradient occurs in winter (i.e., the ground is warmer than the air). Field data from the U.S.S.R., Canada and China provide convincing proof that significant changes in water (ice) content occur in the active layer in the winter months (e.g., Parmuzina

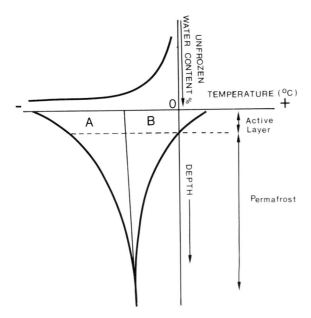

Fig. 4. Relationship between ground temperature envelopes and curves of unfrozen water content versus temperature of frozen soil (from Cheng 1983). A. Region of positive ground temperature gradient. B. Region of negative ground temperature gradient.

1978, Cheng 1983, Mackay 1983, Smith 1985b). For the same reasons, under a negative temperature gradient in summer, unfrozen water will migrate downwards, causing late summer heave of the active layer.

The upward and downward movement of unfrozen water in any one year is not equal. This is conceptually illustrated in Fig. 4. The upward migration of unfrozen pore water takes place in a time period when there is a low unfrozen pore water content (i.e., in winter, Region A, Fig. 4). By contrast, the amount of downward migration of unfrozen pore water caused by the negative ground temperature gradient (i.e., in summer, Region B, Fig. 4) is greater. The result is that more water migrates downward to the permafrost in the thaw cycle than migrates upwards in the freezing cycle.

These considerations now explain the well known fact that the highest ground ice amounts usually occur in the top 1–5 m of frozen ground (e.g., Pollard and French 1980), and that an ice-rich zone characterises the boundary between the base of the active layer and permafrost. Geomorphic indicators of frost heaving include the upheaving of bedrock blocks (Dyke 1984), the upfreezing of objects (Mackay 1984a), and the sorting and migration of soil particles.

Frost heave causes problems in the construction of roads, buildings, bridges and other structures in cold environments. These are relatively well documented in the geotechnical literature (e.g., Ferrians et al. 1969, Johnston 1981: 247–320).

Nowhere has the frost heave problem been more critical than in the recent design of proposed chilled buried gas pipelines in Arctic regions. Since they will operate at sub-zero temperatures, water and vapour will migrate towards the pipe. A 'frost-bulb' will form and ice lensing will develop leading to upward heave around the pipe. This becomes critical when the pipe passes through areas of discontinuous permafrost since the

Fig. 5. View of the frost heave test facility owned and operated by Northwest Alaskan Pipeline Company, at Fairbanks, Alaska. A series of cooling devices (Cryo-Anchors) are in the foreground.

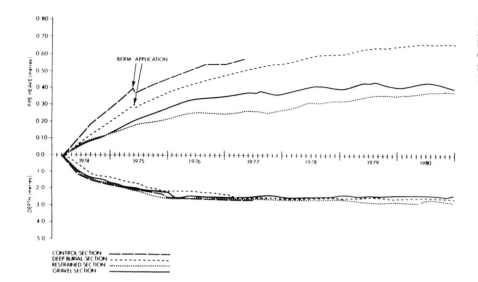

Fig. 6. Observed pipe heave and depth of frost below bottom of pipe at the Calgary frost heave test facility. (From Carlson et al. 1982).

possibility exists for long-continued frost heave around the pipe leading to eventual rupture.

In an attempt to find solutions to these problems, a number of natural scale experimental projects have been initiated to study the behaviour of soil around a buried refrigerated pipe. At Fairbanks, Alaska, for example, a sophisticated frost heave test facility has been constructed by Northwest Alaskan Pipeline (Fig. 5). The site possesses areas of both frozen and unfrozen terrain and a 1.2 m diameter pipe circulates cold air through a series of different pipe-burial modes. Results from this facility are not yet public knowledge. However, results from an earlier test facility constructed at Calgary, Alberta and operated jointly by Foothills Pipeline and the Federal Government of Canada are available. At this facility, air was recirculated at −10°C and various insulation and burial modes were monitored. Results indicate (Fig. 6) that since 1974, the pipe has heaved more than 60 cm and that frost depths have penetrated at least 3 m beneath the pipe (Carlson et al. 1982). A third facility has recently been completed at Caen, France. This is an enclosed facility and is a joint Canada/France research effort. A non-insulated pipe was installed in initially unfrozen soil with a lateral transition from a frost-susceptible silt to a non-frost-susceptible sand, thereby simulating a major boundary of soil types common in permafrost terrain. A first freezing experiment was conducted in 1982–1983 with the pipe refrigeration at −2°C and the chamber air temperature at −7°C (Burgess 1985). During this experiment the pipe heaved 16 cm over the 16 m long test section and the frost line penetrated to 45 cm beneath the pipe in the sand and to 30 cm beneath the pipe in the silt. Further experiments are currently underway.

Until the magnitude of the frost heave problem is identified, and the processes better understood, the construction of chilled gas pipelines cannot proceed.

The repair of frost damage to roads, buildings and other structures will continue to be costly.

Ground ice

The nature and extent of ground ice is of significance to three areas of periglacial research (Harry 1987). First, the thaw of ground ice and ice-rich permafrost terrain is of geotechnical significance. Second, the stratigraphic analysis of ground ice bodies and the cryotextures of their enclosing sediments are important tools in reconstructing Quaternary environmental history. The technique of cryostratigraphy, well developed in the Soviet Union, is increasingly being utilised in North America (e.g., Mackay 1978, French et al. 1982). Third, within regions beyond the present permafrost limit, the recognition of certain ground ice pseudomorphs provides firm evidence of the former existence of permafrost and thus contributes to Pleistocene palaeogeographic studies in Europe. In a recent report on permafrost research needs in the United States (Polar Research Board 1984), ground ice was identified as a priority area.

The most widely used classification of ground ice is based upon the source of water prior to freezing and the mechanism whereby it is transferred to the freezing plane (Mackay 1972). A number of ice types can be recognised, the more important being pore ice, segregated ice, intrusive ice and wedge ice. A recent trend in North America is to consider buried surface ice, that is, buried glacier, lake, river or snowbank ice, as an additional form of ground ice, as is the case in the Soviet Union.

A significant body of research now exists relating to the crystallography and petrofabrics of ground ice, as revealed by the microscopic examination of thin sections under cross-polarised light. Recent studies in North America have documented the ice petrofabrics associated with ice wedges (e.g., Black 1978, Gell 1978a, Péwé 1978), massive segregated ice (Gell 1978b), and ice cored mounds (e.g., Gell 1978c, Pollard and French 1985). This technique may prove to be of particular use in discriminating between bodies of massive segregated ice and buried ice of either glacial or snowbank origin (French and Pollard 1986). Analyses of the isotope chemistry of permafrost waters may also yield information regarding the origin and freezing history of ground ice (e.g., Michel and Fritz 1982, Lorrain and Demeur 1985, Burn et al. 1986).

During the past decade considerable research in North America has been directed to the origins of specific ice types and the evolution of ground-ice related landforms. Special attention has focussed upon the growth of ice wedges, and on the origin and classification of ice-cored terrain. The latter includes not only the morphologically distinctive ice-cored features such as pingos, palsas and seasonal frost mounds, but also flat or undulating terrain which is underlain by tabular bodies of massive ice. The thaw degradation of ice-rich permafrost terrain is also attracting attention because of its geotechnical significance.

Fig. 7. Ice wedge exposed along coast, Mackenzie Delta region.

Each of these three areas of research is briefly summarised below.

Ice wedges

Ice wedges (Fig. 7) grow by the incremental accumulation of single ice veins, formed by the freezing of meteoric water which penetrates thermal contraction cracks. In certain areas, ice wedge ice may constitute as much as 60% by volume of the upper 1–3 m of permafrost.

Many active wedges exhibit a complex structure, with one or more narrow growth stages superimposed upon the primary wedge. This structure is believed to develop in response to a recent climatic cooling trend, the top of the primary wedge marking the former permafrost table. In the Western Canadian Arctic, measurements of a large number of ice wedges imply an active layer attenuation of between 20 and 40% (Mackay 1976, Harry et al. 1985). This is a relatively recent phenomenon, probably limited to the last 50 yr.

Our understanding of ice wedge growth mechanisms owes much to the recent research of J. R. Mackay who has undertaken unique and detailed field studies since 1969 at Garry Island (Fig. 8) and elsewhere in the Mackenzie Delta (Mackay 1974, 1975, 1984b). Early work indicated that only approximately 40% of ice wedges cracked in any one year, and that cracking frequency varied inversely with snowdepth. In addition, the mean annual ice increment is highly variable thereby suggesting that it is unwise to estimate the age of an ice wedge solely on the basis of its size. Most recent research has focussed upon the direction, both vertically and laterally, of the cracking process by the installation of electronic crack detectors along and beneath ice wedge troughs (see Fig. 8). It has traditionally been assumed that thermal contraction cracks are initiated at the ground surface and propagate downwards through frozen ground. However, it is hard to understand how cracks initiated at the surface could repeatedly penetrate the centres of buried wedges. Presumably, an ice wedge does not retain a 'memory' from one year to the next. Systematic field observations between 1974 and 1982 are still inconclusive. Data indicate that both upward and downward cracking occurs and the direction of cracking varies. Collectively, these results suggest that thermal contraction cracking is a complex process, probably influenced by site-specific and year-to-year variations in the physical and thermal conditions of the wedges, and their enclosing sediments. Clearly, continued field research is required.

Ice-cored terrain

Certain permafrost regions are underlain by varying thicknesses of massive ice or icy sediments (Rampton and Mackay 1971, Mackay and Black 1973). Probably the most well known examples of massive icy bodies are associated with pingos (Fig. 9). Their growth mech-

Fig. 8. Typical terrain and instrumentation at the ice wedge monitoring site of J. R. Mackay at Garry Island, Pleistocene Mackenzie Delta. Breaking cables and electronic crack direction indicators are installed.

Fig. 9. Ice exposed in small growing pingo near Tuktoyaktuk, Mackenzie Delta.

anisms are reasonably well understood following the classic studies of J. R. Mackay in the Tuktoyaktuk area of the Mackenzie Delta (Mackay 1979).

An outcome of this research is the suggestion that pore water expulsion from sediments during closed system freezing gives rise to a continuum of ground ice landforms, ranging from sill-like sheets of intrusive ice, through conical pingos, to bodies of massive segregated ice. In a pingo, for example, pore ice, segregated ice and intrusive ice may be present (Mackay 1985), each reflecting different stages of pingo growth. To these ice types can now be added dilation crack ice, formed in the dilation cracks which open at the summit of a pingo as it grows. The existence of a distinctive pingo ice type, as proposed in the genetic classification of ground ice outlined earlier, is therefore questionable.

It appears that the morphological approach to the study of ground-ice related landforms is simplistic and periglacial geomorphology needs genetic, process mechanisms.

An illustration of this necessity is provided by recent work upon seasonal frost mounds (van Everdingen 1982, Pollard and French 1984, 1985). Differentiation between seasonal frost mounds and palsas can be extremely difficult on morphological grounds, and it has been suggested (Washburn 1983) that the term 'palsa' be expanded to include a range of frost features. However, there is no confusion when the internal structure of a seasonal frost mound is seen to consist of a body of injected ice (Fig. 10) rather than layers of mineral soil and segregated ice, as is the case for a palsa. Furthermore, if piezometers are inserted within seasonal frost mounds during their winter growth periods they provide convincing proof that the features are groundwater discharge phenomena resulting from increased hydraulic potential which develops in the active layer during winter freeze-back (Pollard and French 1984).

One must conclude that the last ten years has seen a significant increase in our understanding of frost mounds, and the differences between pingos, palsas and seasonal frost mounds can be readily appreciated.

Fig. 10. Ice exposed in seasonal frost mound, North Fork Pass area, Yukon Territory. (Photo courtesy of W. H. Pollard).

10

Fig. 11. Deformed massive segregated ice body exposed south of Nicholson Island, Pleistocene Mackenzie Delta, June 1986.

By contrast, the origin of large layers of massive ground ice remains problematic. Excellent exposures are present in coastal bluffs throughout the Western Canadian Arctic. In certain localities, the ice exhibits deformation structures (Fig. 11) which may have been formed when the permafrost was overridden by Pleistocene glaciers (Mackay et al. 1972). J. R. Mackay concludes that these icy bodies are primarily of a segregated ice nature, formed by pore water expulsion from adjacent coarse-grained sediments as the ice retreated and permafrost aggraded. Several recent studies however, question this interpretation and suggest that at least some of these massive icy bodies may represent buried surface ice. For example, based upon isotope chemistry and ice crystallography, Japanese studies conclude that massive ice exposed near Tuktoyaktuk may be 'superimposed' ice associated with the last glaciation (Fujino et al. 1983). Similarly, massive icy bodies underlying Wisconsin age till on northwest Victoria Island may be of glacial origin, according to Belgian studies upon the isotopic composition of the ice (Lorrain and Demeur 1985).

Thermokarst

The thaw degradation of ice-rich permafrost results in subsidence, erosion and the development of hummocky thermokarst topography. Because of its geotechnical significance, there is continued research into the forms and processes of thermokarst.

Several recent studies have focussed upon the dynamics of ground ice slumps, a form of backwearing thermokarst frequently observed in parts of northern Canada (e.g., Pufahl and Morgenstern 1980, Lewkowicz 1985). In the High Arctic, such processes may constitute the most rapid erosional processes operating on slopes. Rapid erosion along ice wedges can also create striking badland thermokarst terrain and the undercutting of coastal bluffs can cause rapid, often catastrophic, coastal retreat (e.g., Harry et al. 1983) (Fig. 12).

Such processes constitute hazards to northern development, primarily because of their rapidity and widespread occurrence. Continued research into the magnitude and frequency of such processes is clearly inevitable.

Brief mention must also be made of the problem of thaw lakes, and their oriented nature. First described in detail from the Alaskan Coastal Plain in the late 1940s, it is remarkable that relatively little progress has been made in our understanding of these widely occurring phenomena. Recent studies have merely confirmed earlier ideas. For example, on southwest Banks Island it is now possible to relate the size and depth of thaw basins to ground ice volumes in the underlying sediments (French and Harry 1983). Also, the preferred D-shaped equilibrium morphology can be related to prevailing wind direction during the open water season (Harry and French 1983), thus supporting the ideas of Carson and Hussey (1962) and others.

Active layer processes

The active layer refers to the layer of ground in areas underlain by permafrost which is subject to annual freezing and thawing (Brown and Kupsch 1974). In recent years significant advances have been made in our understanding of the thermal and physico-mechanical properties of this layer.

Two concepts are fundamental to any understanding of active layer processes. First is the recognition of two-sided freezing of the active layer whereby freezing occurs from both the surface downwards and from the permafrost table upwards. Second is the recognition, stressed earlier, that moisture can migrate through frozen material and that unfrozen water can be present at temperatures below 0°C. The seasonal dynamics of the active layer, using geocryological terminology, are summarised in Fig. 13.

In the context of the active layer, one must differentiate between the seasonally thawed layer possessing a

Fig. 12. Coastal erosion and block slumping along ice wedges, Maitland Bluff, Mackenzie Delta region, Canada.

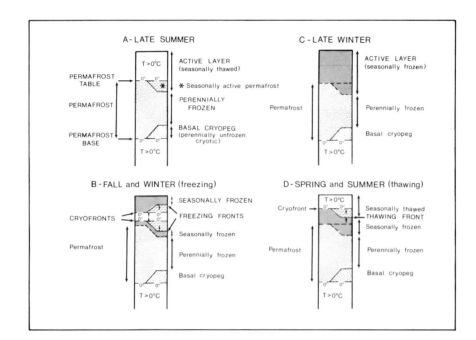

Fig. 13. Diagram illustrating seasonal changes in the active layer using geocryological terminology proposed by R. O. van Everdingen (1985). The temperature relation to 0°C and the state of water are also indicated. A. Late summer, B. Autumn and early winter (freezing), C. Late Winter, D. Spring and summer (thawing).

temperature below >0°C. The seasonal dynamics of the active layer, using geocryological terminology, are summarised in Fig. 13.

In the context of the active layer, one must differentiate between the seasonally thawed layer possessing a temperature >0°C (*seasonally cryotic*) and the upper layer of permafrost which thaws seasonally but remains below 0°C (*seasonally active permafrost*). It is also useful to distinguish between the *freezing front* (the boundary between frozen and unfrozen soil) and the *cryofront* (the 0°C boundary) when considering the freezing of the active layer in the autumn and winter. In the case of the spring and summer thaw, the distinction must be between the *cryofront* and the *thawing front* (the boundary between seasonally frozen and seasonally thawed soil).

Mass wasting

Mass wasting processes which operate in the active layer include frost creep, gelifluction (solifluction) and certain forms of rapid mass movement.

The traditional concept of frost creep involves one-sided freezing with movement decreasing from the surface downwards. This mechanism is best suited to periglacial areas of seasonal frost and/or frequent daily freeze-thaw, such as in temperate and alpine environments. When dealing with periglacial areas underlain by permafrost, two-sided freezing is a more appropriate concept. In the latter environments actual frost creep may be considerably greater than in non-permafrost environments. This is because the growth of ice lenses at the top of permafrost during freeze-back means that potential frost creep varies from a maximum in the thickest part of the lens to zero at the periphery. In

addition, towards the end of the thaw period, the presence of a residual ice lens in a soupy matrix may accelerate lateral movement.

Linked to frost creep is the gelifluction or solifluction component (Washburn 1980). Gelifluction refers to solifluction (Andersson 1906) which occurs in areas underlain by permafrost. Several long term studies recently completed in northern Canada now provide data upon rates of gelifluction movement and permit the identification of different mechanisms of active layer movement. In the Mackenzie Delta area for example, average rates of movement on hillslopes possessing numerous vegetation-covered hummocks (Fig. 14) are approximately 1.0 cm yr^{-1} (Mackay 1981). However, contrary to most other studies of mass wasting, which

Fig. 14. Vegetated earth hummocks, Arctic coastal plain, Yukon Territory.

Fig. 15. Active mudboils developed upon silty marine sands, Rea Point area, Melville Island, N.W.T.

indicate that movement decreases with depth (e.g., Washburn 1980: 200–213), the movement of hummocks is convex downslope, or plug-like. The hummocks appear to slide over the water-saturated sediments lying immediately above the permafrost table, progressively burying inter-hummock peat to form a buried organic layer. The movement is attributed to creep which is promoted by the thaw of the ice-rich layer at the base of the active layer formed by upfreezing in winter, and augmented by ice lensing in the summer thaw period. Similar movement rates and mechanisms have been described from Banks Island by Egginton and French (1985).

A second style of mass wasting identified in recent years is associated with the localised occurrence of high hydraulic pressures within the active layer. Such pressures result from water confinement between the underlying permafrost and an overlying semi-rigid carapace. The carapace is produced either by desiccation and hardening of the surface soil layers in late summer, or by downward freezing in the early winter. Hydrostatic or artesian pressures on slopes, and excess pore water pressures created by rain, are usually the causes of the high hydraulic potentials. If the overburden strength is exceeded mud may burst through the overlying carapace to form a mudboil (Shilts 1978, Egginton and Dyke 1982) (Fig. 15). Occasionally, mudbursts may produce small scale mudflow phenomena extending downslope for several metres.

Exceptionally rapid mass movements may also occur within the active layer with the permafrost table acting as a lubricated slip plane and controlling the depth of the failure plane (Fig. 16). Such failures, termed 'skin flows' or 'detachment failures' (Hughes 1972), are usually attributed to local conditions of soil moisture saturation and high pore water pressures (McRoberts and Morgenstern 1974). The thawed or thawing active layer and vegetation mat detaches from the underlying permafrost surface. In some instances, failure takes the

form of a mudflow; in others, a distinct scar or hollow is formed. In several of the Arctic islands, where the active layer is thin and fine-grained ice-rich sediments are widespread (e.g., see Fig. 16), active layer failures are both common and difficult to predict (e.g., Hodgson 1982, Stangle et al. 1982).

An important advance in our understanding of mass wasting has been the identification of the process of thaw consolidation (Morgenstern and Nixon 1971). This term refers to the time-dependent compression of frozen ground resulting from the melting of ground ice and the subsequent drainage of pore water which occurs in the active layer during spring. Many engineers regard gelifluction as one form of thaw consolidation. In all probability, a process continuum exists between the relatively slow mass wasting and the various rapid mass movements in the active layer with thaw consolidation being the central common mechanism. It is also clear that the amount and distribution of ice and unfrozen water within the active layer prior to thaw are critical factors, as are the time and speed of thaw. The existence of instability conditions on very low angled slopes in permafrost regions is best explained by thaw consolidation.

It appears therefore, that mass wasting is a complex process operating primarily, although not exclusively, in the active layer. A number of different styles of movement can be recognised:

(1) 'Classic solifluction' (i.e., frost creep and gelifluction), usually in association with one-sided freezing;
(2) Plug-like flow, associated with two-sided freezing and an ice-rich layer at the base of the active layer;
(3) Rapid mass movements confined to the active layer, and caused by the process of thaw consolidation;
(4) Mudburst and mudflow activity associated with the localised occurrence of high hydraulic potentials.

Fig. 16. Active layer failure on low angled slope underlain by ice-rich and unconsolidated shale of the Christopher Formation, Thomsen River area, northern Banks Island.

Fig. 17. Non sorted circles (mud hummocks) in the boreal forest (*Picea mariana*), near Inuvik, N.W.T.

Patterned ground

Although numerous descriptive studies of patterned ground phenomena exist in the periglacial literature, the processes of patterned ground formation have been largely neglected. The last few years has seen a redefinition of the cryoturbation process as the principal mechanism for much patterned ground phenomena.

By far the most common patterned ground feature, and until recently by far the most neglected one, is the non-sorted circle (Fig. 17), or 'hummock' (Zoltai and Tarnocai 1974, Zoltai et al. 1978). Beneath the hummock, the late summer frost table is bowl-shaped, and the hummocks grade from those which are completely vegetated (earth hummocks) to those with bare centres (mud hummocks). Often, the centre of the hummock possesses organic material intruded from the sides.

The mound form has traditionally been attributed to an upward displacement of material resulting from cryostatic (i.e., freeze-back) processes generated in a confined, wet unfrozen pocket in the active layer. However, the existence of substantial cryostatic pressures in the field has yet to be convincingly demonstrated (Mackay and MacKay 1976). On more general grounds, it can be argued that the presence of voids in the soil, the occurrence of frost cracks in winter, and the weakness of the confining soil layers lying above prevent pressures of any magnitude from forming. Moreover, on theoretical grounds, cryostatic pressures should not develop in a frost-sensitive hummock soil because ice lensing at the top and bottom of the active layer will desiccate the last unfrozen pocket so that the pore water is under tension, not under pressure.

An equilibrium model of hummock growth has been proposed by Mackay (1979b, 1980). Under this model, the upward displacement of material is caused by the freeze and thaw of ice lenses at the top and bottom of the active layer, with a gravity-induced, cell-like movement. The latter occurs because the top and bottom of the freeze-thaw zones have opposite curvatures. The central part of the active layer experiences dilation in summer and contraction in winter to drive the cell-like circulation. Although such a model does not account for the initiation of non-sorted circles, it does provide a general explanation for their continued development. As such, it represents one further step towards an understanding of these ubiquitous features of the periglacial environment.

Conclusions

While periglacial geomorphology in Europe developed mainly as a branch of Pleistocene and Quaternary studies, periglacial geomorphology in North America has developed as a rigorous branch of process geomorphology. It has important applied applications and must be regarded as part of the science of geocryology since frost action and permafrost are central themes.

References

Andersson, J. G. 1906. Solifluction: a component of subaerial denudation. – J. Geol. 14: 91–112.
Black, R. F. 1978. Fabrics of ice wedges in central Alaska, U.S.A. – In: Proc. Third Int. Conf. Permafrost, Edmonton, Canada, Vol. 1, National Research Council of Canada, Ottawa, pp. 247–253.
Burgess, M. 1985. Large scale permafrost research at Calgary and Caen. – Geos 1985 (2): 19–22.
Burn, C., Michel, F. A. and Smith, M. W. 1986. Stratigraphic, isotopic and mineralogical evidence for an early Holocene thaw unconformity at Mayo, Yukon Territory. – Can. J. Earth Sci. 23: 794–803.
Carlson, L. E., Ellwood, J. R., Nixon, J. F. and Slusarchuk, W. W. 1982. Field test results of operating a chilled, buried pipeline in unfrozen ground. – In: French, H. M. (ed.), Proc. Fourth Can. Permafrost Conf., National Research Council of Canada, Ottawa, pp. 475–480.
Carson, C. E. and Hussey, K. M. 1962. The oriented lakes of Arctic Alaska. – J. Geol. 70: 417–439.
Cheng, G. 1983. The mechanism of repeated-segregation for the formation of thick layered ground ice. – Cold Regions Sci. Technol. 8: 57–66.
Dixon, J. C., Thorn, C. E. and Darmody, R. G. 1984. Chemical weathering processes on the Vantage Peak Nunatak, Juneau Icefield, southern Alaska. – Phys. Geogr. 5: 111–131.
Dyke, A. S. 1983. Quaternary geology of Somerset Island, District of Franklin. – Geol. Surv. Can. Memoir 404.
Dyke, L. D. 1984. Frost heaving of bedrock in permafrost regions. – Bull. Ass. Engineer. Geol. 21 (4): 389–405.
Egginton, P. A. and Dyke, L. D. 1982. Density gradients and injection structures in mudboils in central District of Keewatin. – Geol. Surv. Can. Paper 82-1B: 173–176.
– and French, H. M. 1985. Solifluction and related processes, eastern Banks Island, N.W.T. – Can. J. Earth Sci. 22: 1671–1678.
van Everdingen, R. O. 1976. Geocryological terminology. – Can. J. Earth Sci. 13: 862–867.
– 1981. Morphology, hydrology and hydrochemistry of karst in permafrost terrain near Great Bear Lake, N.W.T. – Nat. Hydrol. Res. Inst., Paper No. 11, Inland Waters Directorate, Calgary.
– 1982. Frost blisters of the Bear Rock spring area near Fort Norman, N.W.T. – Arctic 35: 243–265.
– 1985. Unfrozen permafrost and other taliks. – Proc. Work-

shop on Permafrost Geophysics, Golden, Colorado, October 1984, U.S. Army CRREL, Special Report 85–5, pp. 101–105.

Fahey, B. and Gowan, R. 1979. Application of the sonic test to experimental freeze-thaw studies in geomorphic research. – Arct. Alp. Res. 11: 253–260.

Ferrians, O. J., Kachadoorian, R., and Greene, G. W. 1969. Permafrost and related engineering problems in Alaska. – United States Geol. Surv. Prof. Paper 678.

Ford, D. C. 1984. Karst groundwater activity and landform genesis in modern permafrost regions of Canada. – In: La-Fleur, R. C. (ed.), Groundwater as a geomorphic agent. Binghampton Symp. in Geomorphology, Int. Ser. No. 13, Allen and Unwin, Boston, pp. 340–350.

French, H. M. 1981. Periglacial geomorphology and permafrost. – Progr. Phys. Geogr. 5: 267–273.

– and Harry, D. G. 1983. Ground ice conditions and thaw lakes, Sachs River Lowlands, Banks Island, Canada. – In: Poser, H. and Schunke, E. (ed.), Mesoformen des Reliefs im heutigen Periglazialraum. Abh. Akad. Wiss. Göttingen, Math. – Phys. Klasse Nr. 35, pp. 70–81.

– and Pollard, W. H. 1986. Ground ice investigations, Klondike District, Yukon Territory. – Can. J. Earth Sci. 23: 450–460.

– , Harry, D. G., and Clark, M. J. 1982. Ground ice stratigraphy and Late-Quaternary events, south-west Banks Island, Canadian Arctic. – In: French, H. M. (ed.), Proc. Fourth Can. Permafrost Conf., National Research Council of Canada, Ottawa, pp. 81–90.

Fujino, K., Horiguchi, K., Shinbori, M. and Kato, K. 1983. Analysis and characteristics of cores from a masive ice body in Mackenzie Delta, N.W.T., Canada. – In: Proc. Fourth Int. Conf. Permafrost, Vol. 1, National Academy Press, Washington, D.C., pp. 316–321.

Gell, W. A. 1978a. Ice-wedge ice, Mackenzie Delta – Tuktoyaktuk Peninsula area, N.W.T., Canada. – J. Glaciol. 20: 555–562.

– 1978b. Thermal contraction cracks in massive segregated ice, Tuktoyaktuk Peninsula, N.W.T., Canada. Proc. Third Int. Conf. Permafrost, Edmonton, Canada, Vol. 1, National Research Council of Canada, Ottawa, pp. 277–281.

– 1978c. Fabrics of icing mound and pingo ice in permafrost. – J. Glaciol. 20: 563–569.

Harry, D. G. 1987. Permafrost and ground ice. – In: Clark, M. J. (ed.), International Perspectives in periglacial research, Wiley, U.K., in press.

– and French, H. M. 1983. The orientation and evolution of thaw lakes, southwest Banks Island, Canadian Arctic. – In: Proc. Fourth Int. Conf. Permafrost, Fairbanks Alaska, Vol. 1, National Academy Press, Washington, D.C., pp. 456–461.

– , French, H. M., and Clark, M. J. 1983. Coastal conditions and processes, Sachs Harbour, Banks Island, Western Canadian Arctic. – Z. Geomorphol. Suppl. Band 47: 1–26.

– , French, H. M., and Pollard, W. H. 1985. Ice wedges and permafrost conditions near King Point, Beaufort Sea coast, Yukon Territory. – Geol. Surv. Can. Paper 85–1A, pp. 111–116.

Hodgson, D. A. 1982. Surficial materials and geomorphological processes, Western Sverdrup and adjacent islands, District of Franklin. – Geol. Surv. Can. Paper 81–89.

Hughes, O. L. 1972. Surficial geology and land classification, Mackenzie Valley Transportation Corridor. – In: Proc. Can. Northern Pipeline Res. Conf., Ottawa, Canada, National Research Council of Canada, Technical Memorandum 104, pp. 17–24.

– , Rampton, V. N., and Rutter, N. W. 1972. Quaternary geology and geomorphology, southern and central Yukon. – Guidebook for field excursion A-11, 24th Int. Geol. Congr., Montreal.

Johnston, G. H. (ed.) 1981. Permafrost: Engineering Design and Construction. National Research Council of Canada, Toronto: Wiley.

Konischev, V. N. 1982. Characteristics of cryogenic weathering in the permafrost zone of the European U.S.S.R. – Arct. Alp. Res. 14: 261–265.

Lautridou, J.-P. and Ozouf, J.-C. 1982. Experimental frost shattering: 15 years of research at the Centre de Géomorphologie du CNRS. – Progr. Phys. Geogr. 6: 215–232.

Lewkowicz, A. G. 1985. Use of an ablatometer to measure short-term ablation of exposed ground ice. – Can J. Earth Sci. 22: 1767–1773.

Lorrain, R. D. and Demeur, P. 1985. Isotopic evidence for relic Pleistocene glacier ice on Victoria Island, Canadian Arctic Archipelago. – Arct. Alp. Res. 17: 89–98.

Mackay, J. R. 1972. The world of underground ice. – Ann. Ass. Am. Geogr. 62: 1–22.

– 1974. Ice-wedge cracks, Garry Island, Northwest Territories. – Can. J. Earth Sci. 11: 1366–1383.

– 1975. The closing of ice-wedge cracks in permafrost, Garry Island, Northwest Territories. – Can. J. Earth Sci. 12: 1668–1674.

– 1976. Ice wedges as indicators of recent climatic change, Western Arctic coast. – Geol. Surv. Can., Paper 76–1A, pp. 233–234.

– 1978. Freshwater shelled invertebrate indicators of palaeoclimate in Northwestern Canada during late-glacial times: Discussion. – Can. J. Earth Sci. 15: 461–462.

– 1979a. Pingos of the Tuktoyaktuk Peninsula area, Northwest Territories. – Géogr. physique Quaternaire 33: 3–61.

– 1979b. An equilibrium model for hummocks (non-sorted circles), Garry Island, Northwest Territories. – Geol. Surv. Can., Paper 79–1A, pp. 165–167.

– 1980. The origin of hummocks, western Arctic coast. – Can. J. Earth Sci. 17: 996–1006.

– 1981. Active layer slope movement in a continuous permafrost environment, Garry Island, Northwest Territories, Canada. – Can. J. Earth Sci. 18: 1666–1680.

– 1983. Downward water movement into frozen ground, western arctic coast, Canada. – Can. J. Earth Sci. 20: 120–134.

– 1984a. The frost heave of stones in the active layer above permafrost with downward and upward freezing. – Arct. Alp. Res. 16: 439–446.

– 1984b. The direction of ice-wedge cracking in permafrost: downward or upward? – Can. J. Earth Sci. 21: 516–524.

– 1985. The composition of pingo ice. – Can. J. Earth Sci. 22: 1452–1464.

– and Black, R. F. 1973. Origin, composition and structure of perennially frozen ground and ground ice. – Permafrost, North American Contribution, Second Int. Conf., Yakutsk, National Academy of Sciences Publication 2115: 185–192.

– and MacKay, D. K. 1976. Cryostatic pressures in non-sorted circles (mud hummocks), Inuvik, Northwest Territories. – Can J. Earth Sci. 13: 889–897.

– , Rampton, V. N., and Fyles, J. G. 1972. Relic Pleistocene permafrost, Western Arctic, Canada. – Science 176: 1321–1323.

McRoberts, E. C. and Morgenstern, N. R. 1974. The stability of thawing slopes. – Can. Geotechn. J. 11: 447–469.

Michel, F. A. and Fritz, P. 1982. Significance of isotope variations in permafrost waters at Illisarvik, N.W.T. – Proc. Fourth Can. Permafrost Conf., National Research Council of Canada, Ottawa, pp. 173–181.

Miller, R. D. 1972. Freezing and heaving of saturated and unsaturated soils. – Highway Res. Rec. 393: 1–11.

Morgenstern, N. R. and Nixon, J. F. 1971. One-dimensional consolidation of thawing soils. – Can. Geotechn. J. 8: 558–565.

Parmuzina, O. Yu 1978. The cryogenic structure and certain features of ice separation in a seasonally thawed layer (in

Russian). – In: Popov, A. I., (ed.), Problemy kriolotologii (Problems of cryolithology), Izdatel' stvo Moskovslogo Universiteta, 7: 141–163.

Péwé, T. L. 1978. Tyndall figures in ice crystals of ground ice in permafrost near Fairbanks, Alaska. – Proc. Third Int. Conf. Permafrost, Edmonton, Canada, Vol. 1, National Research Council of Canada, Ottawa, pp. 312–317.

Polar Research Board 1984. Permafrost Research: An assessment of future needs. Comm. Permafrost, Polar Res. Bd., National Research Council, National Academy Press, Washington, DC.

Pollard, W. H. and French, H. M. 1980. A first approximation of the volume of ground ice, Richards Island, Pleistocene Mackenzie Delta, Northwest Territories, Canada. – Can. Geotechn. J. 17: 509–516.

– and French, H. M. 1984. The groundwater hydraulics of seasonal frost mounds. – Can. J. Earth Sci. 21: 1073–1081.

– and French, H. M. 1985. Internal structure and ice crystallography of seasonal frost mounds. – J. Glaciol. 31: 157–162.

Pufahl, D. E. and Morgenstern, N. R. 1980. The energy balance at a landslide near Fort Simpson, N.W.T. – Proc. Workshop on Permafrost Engineering, National Research Council of Canada, Technical Memorandum 130: 31–39.

Rampton, V. N. and Mackay, J. R. 1971. Massive ice and icy sediments throughout the Tuktoyaktuk Peninsula, Richards Island and adjacent areas, District of Mackenzie. – Geol. Surv. Can. Paper 71–21.

Rapp, A. 1960. Recent development of mountain slopes in Karkevagge and surroundings, northern Sweden. – Geogr. Annaler 42: 71–200.

Reger, R. D. and Péwé, T. L. 1976. Cryoplanation terraces: indicators of a permafrost environment. – Quaternary Res. 6: 99–109.

Shilts, W. W. 1978. Nature and genesis of mudboils, Central Keewatin, Canada. – Can. J. Earth Sci. 15: 1053–1068.

Smith, M. W. 1985a. Models of soil freezing. – In: Church, M. and Slaymaker, O. (eds), Lectures in Geocryology, Vancouver, B.C., University of British Columbia Press, pp. 96–120.

– 1985b. Observations of soil freezing and frost heave at Inuvik, Northwest Territories, Canada. – Can. J. Earth Sci. 22: 283–290.

Stangle, K. O., Roggensack, W. D., and Hayley, D. W. 1982.

Engineering geology of surficial soils, eastern Melville Island. – In: French, H. M. (ed.), Proc. Fourth Can. Permafrost Conf. National Research Council of Canada, Ottawa, pp. 136–150.

Thorn, C. E. 1979. Bedrock freeze-thaw weathering regime in an alpine environment, Colorado Front Range. – Earth Surface Proc. 4: 211–228.

– 1987. Nivation – a geomorphic chimera. – In: Clark, M. J. (ed.), Int. Perspectives on periglacial geomorphology, Wiley, U.K., in press.

– and Hall, K. 1980. Nivation: an arctic-alpine comparison and reappraisal. – J. Glaciol. 25: 109–124.

Washburn, A. L. 1956. Classification of patterned ground and review of suggested origins. – Bull. Geol. Soc. Am. 67: 823–865.

– 1980. Geocryology: a survey of periglacial processes and environments. Edward Arnold, London.

– 1983. What is a Palsa? – In: Poser, H. and Schunke, E. (eds), Mesoformen des Reliefs im heutigen Periglazialraum, Abh. Akad. Wiss. Göttingen, Math.-Physik. Klasse Nr. 35, pp. 34–47.

– 1985. Periglacial problems. – In: Church, M. and Slaymaker, O. (eds), Lectures in Geocryology, Vancouver, B.C., University of British Columbia Press, pp. 166–202.

Watts, S. H. 1983. Weathering pit formation in bedrock near Cory Glacier, southeastern Ellesmere Island, N.W.T. – Geol. Surv. Can. Paper 83–1A, pp. 487–491.

White, S. E. 1976. Is frost action really only hydration shattering? A review. – Arct. Alp. Res. 8: 1–6.

Williams, P. J. 1976. Volume change in frozen soils. – Laurits Bjerrum Memorial Volume, Norw. Geotechn. Inst., Oslo, pp. 233–246.

– 1977. General properties of freezing soils. – In: Williams, P. J. and Fremond, M. (eds), Soil freezing and highway construction, Ch. II, Paterson Centre, Carleton Univ., Ottawa, pp. 7–12.

Zoltai, S. C. and Tarnocai, C. 1974. Soils and vegetation of hummocky terrain. – Environmental-Social Committee, Northern Pipelines, Task Force on Northern Oil Development, Report 74–5, Ottawa.

– , Tarnocai, C., and Pettapiece, W. W. 1978. Age of cryoturbated organic materials in earth hummocks from the Canadian Arctic. – Proc. Third Int. Conf. Permafrost, National Research Council of Canada, Vol. 1, pp. 325–331.

Ecological Bulletins 38: 17–37. Copenhagen 1987

Northernmost Scandinavia in the geological perspective

Maurits Lindström

Lindström, M. 1987. Northernmost Scandinavia in the geological perspective. – Ecol. Bull. (Copenhagen) 38: 17–37.

Northernmost Scandinavia has two main bedrock units, the Precambrian Basement (with rocks mainly in the range 2,500–1,500 Myr) and the Caledonian Mountain Range (age about 550–350 Myr). The Caledonides cut discordantly across Basement structures. The Basement owes its main sedimentary and volcanic rocks, as well as its most important structures and voluminous magmatic intrusions, to the Svecokarelian Orogeny (1,950–1,750 Myr) and associated events that preceded this Orogeny and followed upon it. The Kiruna ore, which is one of the world's largest iron ore bodies, formed in the course of these events together with other, economically important mineral enrichments. The Svecokarelian orogeny affected a much older continent the remains of which are still extensively exposed. The Caledonides also include major massives of older bedrock. The principal Caledonian structure consists of very extensive overthrust nappes. These are several hundred meters to a few kilometers thick sheets of rock of sedimentary and magmatic origin that have been pushed horizontally over distances of as much as hundreds of kilometers. As a result of these movement the nappes rest on the top of one another. Individual nappes can be identified over tens to many thousands of square kilometers. The original root areas of the nappes are now covered by the North Atlantic. Metamorphism tends to be greatest in some of the higher and more westerly nappes, reflecting the circumstance that they came from central parts of the Caledonian Orogen. The Caledonian Orogeny is the expression of plate tectonic movements of Cambrian to Devonian age. Later plate tectonism has moved the continental crust of Scandinavia from the southern hemisphere, where it was in the early Paleozoic, to its present, northerly position.

M. Lindström, Geology Dept, Univ. of Stockholm, S-106 91 Stockholm, Sweden.

Introduction

The geological history of norternmost Scandinavia can be traced back in its broad features almost 3,000 Myr (million years). The earth's crust in this part of the world has a heterogeneous origin and bears witness of often dramatic events. Much of the geology is very clearly expressed in landscape morphology and exerts a profound influence on the ecosystems; in many areas, however, these relationships are far from obvious and can bear a great deal of explaining.

The two great natural units of the North Scandinavian bedrock are the Precambrian basement that underlies the southeastern and major part of the region, and the Caledonides that outcrop in the broad belt of moderately high mountains along the North Atlantic and Barents Sea coasts. Precambrian is a concept that covers all rocks that are older than the Cambrian Period, which is taken to have begun between 550 and 600 Myr ago. Because the Caledonides contain many rock sequences that are of Cambrian and younger age, they must have formed at a later date than the Precambrian basement.

Both of the units referred to above are mainly composed of rocks that have undergone physical and chemical processes at great depth in the earth's crust. The modified character and old age of these rocks made them appear untractable to geological research with the methods and theoretical framework available until the end of the 19th century. Modern geological investigations in the old basement became possible only after it had been shown to contain rocks that can be recognized as the precise counterparts of deposits still forming today, and that the processes involved in the early history of these rocks are perfectly understandable by comparison with commonplace, modern processes. Among instances of such rocks are pebble beds, sandstones with rippled surfaces, beds with mudcracks, and volcanic ashfall tuffs. The foremost proponent of these ideas was the Finnish geologist J. J. Sederholm (1897).

Before the breakthrough of actualistic methods in the Precambrian, geological investigations in northernmost Scandinavia were mainly of reconnaissance and exploration character, which is not to say that they were without significant success. The discoveries of several Precambrian ores, most notably the Kiruna and Gällivare iron ores (Svenonius 1892, Lundbohm 1910) belonged to this earlier phase, and in the Caledonides Petterssen (1878, 1887) demonstrated broad aspects of the regional structure. In the field of geological theory the farthest reaching significance to be assigned to any discovery in northern Scandinavia in the 19th century belongs to Reusch's (1891) finding of fossil, petrified boulder clay (tillite) at Varanger fjord. This discovery was a major victory of the actualist cause, because it demonstrated that the ice age theory must be extended from the relatively modern to the ancient history of the planet. But a few decades earlier, science had come to accept that much of Europe had been covered by inland ice in geologically recent time (Still "stinking of varnish", as one prominent English geologist put it). Now it became evident that this Quaternary glaciation was not unique but only the latest of a family of great events of similar kind that occurred on different occasions throughout earth history.

Landmarks in the investigation of the Precambrian basement after 1900 were to no small extent surveys prompted by economic interest in the ores of northern Scandinavia. To this category belongs Lundbohm's (1910) account of the geology of Kiruna, to be compared with Geijer's (1960) analysis of the same area, furthermore Geijer's (1931) description of the geology of the ore fields of Norrbotten, in which the duality of the Svecokarelide orogen was established for northernmost Scandinavia. A comprehensive survey of the Precambrian of the Swedish portion of northernmost Scandinavia was published, with abundant new observations, by Ödman (1957). The existence of very old basement below the Karelide Precambrian in northeastern Finland was established by Mikkola (1941), who also made fundamental studies of the granulite arch (1932). The particular high-pressure, high-temperature conditions under which the granulite formed provided the basis for theoretical studies by Eskola (1952). However, the most spectacular progress towards an understanding of the Precambrian was provided by radiometric dating (Kuovo 1958, Welin and Blomqvist 1964, Welin 1970).

A summary review of modern research in the Caledonides can start with Törnebohm's (1888) overthrust hypothesis. This hypothesis stated, against an ample background of documentation compiled by its author, that the Caledonian bedrock consisted of vast horizontal slices, termed nappes or allochthon in modern terminology, that had been pushed by unknown forces over distances of hundreds of kilometres from unknown source areas in the northwest to their present position on top of non-transported, "rooted" basement (or autochthon). Törnebohm's ideas have been confirmed not only in principle but in surprisingly great detail as well. However, as a matter of objective truth, they were bold in the extreme and were hotly contested until further proof was delivered by Asklund (1933) in central Scandinavia and, among others, Kulling (1930) in the north. The phase of reconnaissance research that led to these discoveries can be said to have ended about 1960, when major summaries on the geology of the northern Caledonides were published for Norway (Holtedahl 1960) and Sweden (Kulling 1964).

Among the important works of this phase one may mention the one by Holmquist (1910), who gave a detailed and timely analysis of the geology of the Abisko area that had just been opened up to tourism and extensive, scientific exploration by the construction of the railroad to Narvik. Kulling (1964), Föyn (1937) and Holtedahl (1931) demonstrated that the pile of overthrust nappes rests on very extensive, autochthonous sedimentary rocks laid down on the Precambrian basement. Furthermore, the nappes could be divided into a lowermost, less-transported portion that outcropped in extensive areas along the southeastern margin of the mountain chain, and higher nappes of more distant and exotic derivation that dominated in the higher mountains to the northwest and could be shown to rest on the lower units where the nappes occurred in contact.

The higher nappes and their relations to underlying units were extensively mapped and described by, among others, Foslie (1941), Vogt (1941) and Kautsky (1953). As a result of these investigations it became apparent that the higher nappes consist of sedimentary and volcanic rocks that had formed in areas situated far to the northwest and now presumably covered by ocean.

Owing to the fortunate discovery of diverse fossils, the age of certain far-travelled, overthrust sedimentary rocks could be demonstrated to be Ordovician to Silurian, that is, very distinctly younger than the Precambrian. Thereby the age of the latest overthrust movements could be defined as not older than Silurian.

The last two decades of research have been characterized by increasing use of methods founded on modern technology and by cooperative efforts in field and laboratory work by an increasing number of research teams from different nations. This intensified effort has a background in the theoretical importance of northernmost Scandinavia as a region in which global orogen systems intersect (Gorbatschev 1985), but the economic potential of the hydrocarbon resources hidden in Norwegian shelf deposits might provide the greater driving force.

A reference to modern geological research in the region would be grossly incomplete without mentioning the influence of plate tectonic theory. The overthrust nappes contain fragments torn from different geological terrains. It is an important objective of geological research to reconstruct the original spatial relations between these terrains. The results of such efforts almost inevitably are phrased in plate tectonic terms. Last but not least, the plate tectonic reconstruction of the history of the northern oceans provides the framework for the geological history of northernmost Scandinavia.

The shaping up of the Precambrian Basement

The broadest features of the Precambrian geological evolution of northernmost Scandinavia can be described as follows. If the Earth's history goes back to between 5,000 and 4,000 Myr (probably closer to 5,000), the first approximately 2,000 Myr of this history left little preserved record in Scandinavia. Around 2,800–2,600 Myr there existed a major continent and perhaps also smaller areas with continental crust in northernmost and easternmost Scandinavia. The principal remains of this *Pre-Svecokarelian Basement* (Fig. 1) form the Kola Peninsula and large areas to the south and west of the White Sea; however, central and northern Finland and northern Sweden also contain good evidence of this continental complex that also was eroded and gave origin to diverse sediments, as continents tend to do. Between the minor continental areas (or islands) there existed seas in which the crust had the basaltic composition of normal oceanic areas. The massive, eastern occurrences of this Presvecokarelian Basement are summarized by Simonen (1980); occurrences in northern Sweden have been identified principally to the north of Kiruna (Welin et al. 1971) and along the border between Finland and Sweden, between Karesuando and Huuki (Lindroos and Henkel 1978).

The crust existing at this early stage was strongly moved, deformed and heated during the following *Svecokarelian Orogeny*. Under this name a succession of events is comprised that began with volcanism and thick sedimentary deposition in the interval about 2,200–2,000 Myr (Jatulian Group of the Finnish geologists). In the eastern ("Karelian") areas of northern Scandinavia these and younger Svecokarelian deposits are influenced principally by the delivery of sediments from the adjacent continent; in certain areas they were laid down directly on continental crust either as river or lake sediments, or on the continental shelf. In areas farther to the Southwest ("Svecofennian") the sediments were laiddown in the deep open ocean. This sedimentation was in some areas coupled with intensive volcanism.

The Svecokarelian Orogeny is frequently spoken of as a cycle. The concept of cyclicity implies that orogenies tend to take a certain course for which there is empirical evidence. A cycle runs from the early development of depositional troughs, often with much evidence of basaltic magmatism, through a culminating phase of strong beating, great crustal deformation and

intrusion of granites, to late phases of rising and erosional breakdown of the mountain chain, frequently coupled with further granitic intrusions. After this process that may take 200 Myr or more, the affected portion of the earth's crust tends to be stabilized and relatively immune to further orogenic deformation. The cycle following next in time will therefore have its full effects in other, perhaps neighbouring areas. According to the plate tectonic model the early phase corresponds to the phase of rifting and drifting apart of continents, the culminating phase corresponds to the processes of constriction of ocean basins and collision of plates, and the final phase is when two continental plates have collided and horizontal movement perforce comes to a stop.

The Svecokarelian orogeny culminated about 1,900–1,800 Myr ago. Probably a major east-dipping subduction zone was responsible for this process. The subducted plate may have left the surface along a north-south belt now extending through southern Sweden and moved eastwards at depth generating magmatism and crustal deformation in areas now occupied by Finland and the remainder of northern Scandinavia (Lundqvist 1979).

The culminating phase of the orogeny was marked by the injection into the crust of great volumes of magma of different composition, from gabbroic to granitic. After the principal metamorphism, deformation and mountain building had taken place, the time span from 1,700 to 1,500 Myr was characterized by sedimentation of the products of erosional breakdown of the mountains, very strong volcanism, fracturing, faulting and the intrusion of further magmas at deeper levels of the crust. After about 1,500 Myr the Precambrian basement of northern Scandinavia outside the Caledonides has been practically stable

The Presvecokarelian Basement

The basement carries the imprint of earlier orogenies as well as much evidence of shearing, folding and crushing during the Svecokarelidian Orogeny. It consists of diverse magmatic rocks, among which granodiorites are dominant, and gneisses that are the products of deformation and metamorphism of magmatic as well as sedimentary rocks.

Intercalated among the gneisses are quartzites, magnetite banded schists, black schists, and amphibolites, indicating the sedimentary and volcanic origin of many of these rocks.

Particular attention has been given to the geology of the socalled granulite arch, a structure that runs southward from the Caledonian front to the southern area about Lake Inari, and from there southeastwards and ultimately eastwards, over a distance of more than 200 km. This arch includes old basement together with overlying sediments, the whole of which was subjected to extreme shear, flattening, and granulite grade metamorphism at great depth in the crust during the earliest

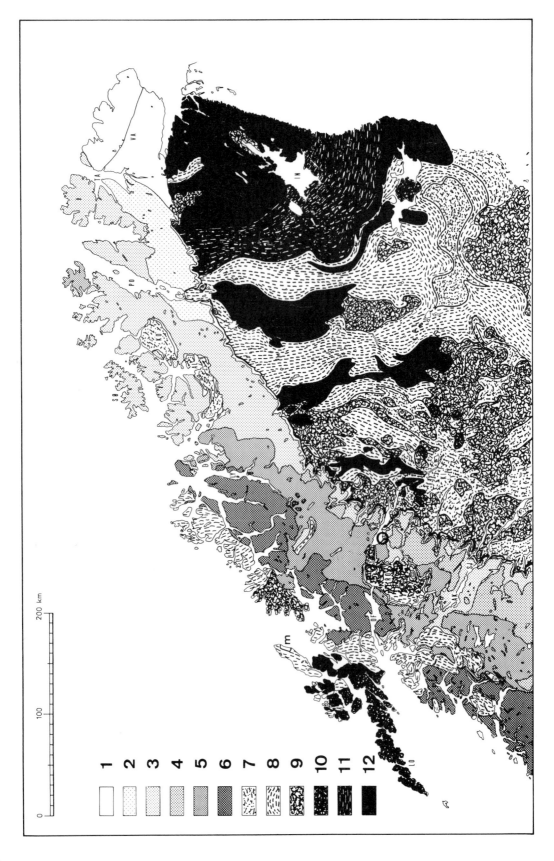

stages of the Svecokarelian Orogeny (Hörmann et al. 1980).

Beginnings and culmination of the Svecokarelian Orogeny

Erosion of the old basement and the beginning of Svecokarelian sedimentation is locally marked by conglomeratic deposits with pebbles derived from the underlying basement. Throughout much of northernmost Finland and Sweden the earliest formed part of the Karelian deposits otherwise consists of basic volcanics ("greenstones") with interlayered sediments, such as quartzites and dolomite. In Sweden this succession is known under the name Kiruna Greenstone; in Finland it forms much of the Jatulian succession. Dolomite of the greenstone succession bears evidence of formation by algae in very shallow water. It contains the concentrically laminated structures that are known as stromatolites. The Kiruna Greenstone contains iron and manganese ores, as well as sulphide ores, although these ore bodies are subordinate in importance to ores formed during the final stages of the Svecokarelian. During the culmination of orogeny the Karelian and older formation were intruded by extensive magmas that range in composition from gabbroic to granitic. One of the principal complexes of intrusions has been named the Haparanda granite suite. Its age is about 1,840 Myr (Welin et al. 1970).

Late Svecokarelian bedrock, and younger

Granitic intrusions continued to mark the progress of the Svecokarelian orogeny, with formation of major rock masses, such as the oldest portion of the Lina granite. Several intrusions were concentrated about the time interval 1,780–1,770 Myr (Welin et al. 1977).

The early stages of the Svecokarelian orogenic cycle are likely to have deposits that form the "Snavva-Sjöfall Formation". This succession occupies an extensive tract along the eastern margin of the Caledonides, from the upper reaches of Stora Lule Älv (Great Lule River) and southwards. It includes volcanics, basic as well as acidic.

Early Svecofennian sediments are not very prominent in northernmost Scandinavia; contrary to the Karelian deposits they are relatively poor in quartz and carry the evidence of deposition in deep marine throughs. Their main distribution is in central and southern parts of the orogenic belt. In the aftermath of the orogeny, heavy sedimentation of conglomerates and sandstones followed, along with acidic volcanism. The results of these processes can be studied for instance in the Kiruna area. The volcanism (Kiruna porphyries) was accompanied by emplacement of a few of the world's leading iron ores, most notably Kiruna and Gällivare. These relationships have been discussed for instance by Frietsch (1979). After formation of the Kiruna porphyries and associated sediments the bedrock was thoroughly squeezed, sheared and flattened in generally east-west directions. Further intrusions of granitic (younger Lina granite), intermediate, and basaltic magmas marked the definitive end of the Svecokarelian cycle toward about 1,500 Myr.

The Caledonides

The Caledonian Orogeny

The Caledonian orogenic cycle began with the rifting of a major continental complex consisting of northern Europe, Greenland, and the older portions of North America, as well as other, less well known continental blocks. This rifting began in the late Precambrian, 800–700 Myr ago and was accompanied by strong, gabbroic and basaltic magmatism.

The drifting apart of northern Europe on one side of the main rift zone and Greenland and North America on the other side led to the opening of a forerunner of the North Atlantic, called the Iapetus Ocean. The ultimate dimensions of the Iapetus Ocean may have been similar to those of the North Atlantic.

In the late Cambrian to earliest Ordovician parts of the Iapetus Ocean began to contract, with plate collision, crustal deformation, metamorphism and magmatism as the main results. This process is called the Finnmarkian phase (Sturt et al. 1978) of the Caledonian orogeny. Other parts of the Iapetus Ocean remained open, and the north European continent was still very far removed from North America and Greenland. The Scandian orogenic phase in the Silurian brought about the end of this situation. The Old World collided with the New World, and the Iapetus Ocean vanished from

Fig. 1. Geological features of northernmost Scandinavia. 1–6: Caledonian Orogen. 1: Autochthon. 2: Lower Allochthon. 3: Middle Allochthon. 4: Upper Allochthon: Seve Nappe Complex. 5: Upper Allochthon: Köli Nappe Complex. 6: Uppermost Allochthon. 7–12: Precambrian Basement, including Basement within the Caledonian Orogen. 7–10: Svecokarelides. 7: Sedimentary and volcanic rocks, largely with recognizable original structure. 8: Gneisses and more or less foliated granites, 9: Granites, largely with massive structure. 10: Basic magmatic rocks. 11: Rocks of the Granulite Arc. 12: Pre-Svecokarelian Basement. – m: Mesozoic of Andøya. – AK: Akkajaure. AL: Alta Window. IN: Lake Inari. KA: Karesuando. KI: Kiruna. KO: Komagfjord Window. LO: Lofoten. LY: Lyngenfjord. OF: Ofotenfjord. PO: Porsangerfjord. RO: Rombak-Sjangeli Window. SJ: Stora Sjöfallet. SØ: Sørøya. TA: Tanafjord. VA: Varanger Peninsula. – The position of Abisko is indicated by a circlet.

the map, with a mountain chain – the Caledonides – occupying its place. Final Caledonian deformations and magmatism occurred in the Devonian (between 360 and 400 Myr (Roberts and Gee 1985).

The major structures

Because much of the Precambrian basement forms flat terrain, the boundary of the Caledonides is geomorphologically apparent as a rise in elevation and degree of dissection of the landscape. However, the coincidence between geomorphological expression and geological structure is far from precise: the foremost outcrops of Caledonian overthrust nappes frequently are preserved on the tops of the westernmost of a zone of high and steep hills carved out of Precambrian basement. From their eastern and southeastern boundary the nappes dip moderately toward the west and northwest. In doing so they are gradually reduced in thickness until they all but pinch out under the load of still higher nappes to the far west.

At depth the overthrust (or allochthonous) rocks must rest on rocks that are not overthrust (i.e. "rooted" or autochthonous). The "rooted" autochthon that comprises the lower and much the thicker portion of the continental crust, is mainly Precambrian basement under the Caledonian nappes. As its uppermost layer we frequently find a ten to hundreds of meters "thick" (actually very thin) succession of late Precambrian to Cambrian and, on the Digermul Peninsula in northernmost Norway, earliest Ordovician sediments. Whereas the entire mountain chain has been massively eroded so that only its basalmost structures still remain, in some areas erosion has cut deeper into the structure than in others. Such areas that occur in isolation within the nappe terrain are referred to as windows, because they allow us to look through into the lower structure. Windows that expose Precambrian basement exist in northern Norway (Komagfjord and Alta Windows) and on the Norwegian-Swedish border (Rombak-Sjangeli Window). The Lofoten archipelago is one extensive exposure of basement. In all of these cases the autochthony of the Precambrian basement is fraught with question marks for it is very difficult to prove that the exposed basement is not undercut by a further, subhorizontal thrust plane. For instance, this appears to be the case with the Rombak-Sjangeli-Window.

The autochthon of northernmost Norway contains one somewhat exotic element the main portion of which has been named the Barents Sea Group (Siedlecka and Siedlecki 1967, Johnson et al. 1978). This extremely thick (14 km) succession of sandy, pebbly, and argillaceous sediments was deposited during the late Precambrian (Riphean) at some distance from Scandinavia. In the course of Caledonian earth movements it was transported at least a few hundred kilometers southeastwards as a block along a major vertical crustal fracture, the Trollfjord-Komagelv Fault. This fault divides the Varanger Peninsula into a northeastern and a southwestern half with quite different geological successions. The lowermost and least far-travelled of the nappes are mainly exposed along the eastern front of the mountain range. They contain late Precambrian to early Cambrian sediments that were deposited on the northwestern seaboard of Scandinavia, in continuity with the sediments of the autochthon, to which they bear great resemblance. In Norway large areas about the southern end of Porsangerfjord are occupied by the Gaissa Nappe that contains a thick sedimentary succession. In northern Sweden the corresponding unit is the Rautas Nappe Complex that contains well-preserved sediments as well as thick, entrained slabs of the continental basement on which the sediments were deposited. In Swedish geological literature these lower nappes are referred to as Lower Allochthon (Stephens et al. 1985). The nappes that follow immediately above the Lower Allochthon have travelled a few hundred km (perhaps as much as 500 km) over the underlying bedrock. The great vertical and horizontal forces exerted on these rocks during the transport have crushed and deformed them to an extent that can make it difficult to recognize their origin as sedimentary rocks and rocks of the crystalline basement. Metamorphism, induced by the orogenic heating, has contributed to the transformation of the rocks into schists of diverse kinds. These nappes are collectively called Middle Allochthon by geologists working in Sweden. The Swedish Middle Allochthon is characterized by intensive squeezing and crushing but relatively moderate metamorphism. In northern Norway the corresponding nappes are exposed extensively and in great thickness and diversity. There the collective name for them is the Kalak Nappe Complex. This complex also includes rocks with well preserved original structure and others with a high degree (amphibolite grade) of metamorphism. The metamorphism tends to rise from lower, easterly into higher, westerly nappes, indicating that the easterly and presumably more peripheral parts of the orogen were characterized by lower temperatures (Ramsay et al. 1985).

By logic, the Swedish geologists must recognize an Upper Allochthon above their Middle Allochthon. This Upper Allochthon is quite extensive and forms the highest mountains in northernmost Sweden. Its eastern, lower portion is called the Seve Nappe Complex. It thins out and disappears in areas north of Lake Torneträsk and in the western parts of the mountain chain but still is very thick in the area of Mt Kebnekaise that consists mainly of amphibolite belonging to this unit. The western – and higher – portion is called the Köli Nappe Complex. It consists of several nappes that repeat a Lower Paleozoic sedimentary and volcanic succession that formed in seas far northwest of Scandinavia. The Köli continues without interruption into Norway, where equivalent units are known under names such as Rombak Group, Vaddas Nappe, and others.

Progress in the analysis of the orogenic structure has

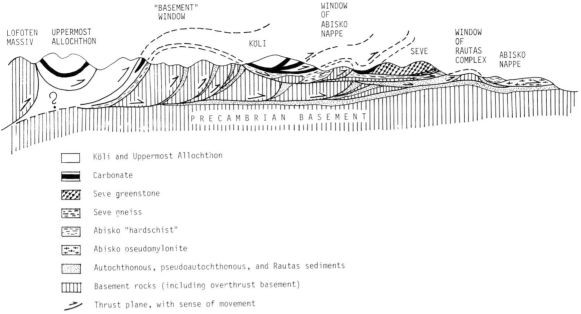

Fig. 2. Sketch of a putative cross section through the Caledonides about the level of Ofotenfjord to Torneträsk. The structures occurring in the basement are exposed only in the Rombak-Sjangeli Window, from which they are recorded in a forthcoming work by Gerhard Bax. Note that for want of deep-reaching exposure it could be difficult to tell if the basement exposed in the windows is strictly autochthonous (i.e., represents Precambrian Basement), or not (we believe they are overthrust, as shown in the sketch).

brought the realization that the Upper Allochthon is not uppermost (Roberts and Gee 1985). Thus, it has become necessary to distinguish as Uppermost Allochthon a broad belt of nappe terrain extending from Grong in central Norway to the areas about Lyngenfjord in northern Norway. The Uppermost Allochthon contains late Precambrian to Silurian sedimentary rocks, as well as magmatic rocks formed during the Caledonian orogeny. Its total distance of horizontal transport from the west can be of the order of 1,000 km. Whereas no rocks younger than Cambrian have been discovered in the Lower and Middle Allochthon, the Upper and Uppermost Allochthon contain rocks of Ordovician and Silurian age. Most likely this age difference is due to a difference in orogenic history. The Lower and Middle Allochthon of northernmost Scandinavia are believed to have participated in an early phase of the Caledonian orogeny, called Finnmarkian (about 540–490 Myr). The Upper and Uppermost Allochthon, however, were metamorphosed, deformed and overthrust 50–100 Myr later, during the Scandian phase (Ramsay et al. 1985).

Autochthon and basement windows

Along the eastern margin of the mountain range the Precambrian basement simply disappears under the pile of overthrust nappes. It is exposed under precipitous cliffs of overthrust rocks at the bottom of many a mountain valley, but even such exposures disappear westwards under west-dipping Caledonian schists. This autochthonous basement of the eastern mountain front is at the same time the westernmost outcrop of continuous Svecokarelian (and older) rocks and is covered by the description of the Precambrian basement.

Farther to the west relatively well-preserved basement rocks occur in the windows. In these cases it remains debatable whether the basement is strictly autochthonous or has been overthrust some distance without getting its fabric destroyed. The uncertainty is illustrated by Fig. 2. If there is an underlying thrust plane that is everywhere covered by overlying rock sequences it can, in fact, be impossible to identify the thrust.

With this reservation the Rombak-Sjangeli Window with its gneisses and greenstones and generally north-south striking folds represents the westernmost outcrop of relatively well preserved Svecokarelian basement. The Alta and Komagfjord windows contain pre-Svecokarelian basement as well as Karelian schists. The most interesting major basement outcrop is, perhaps, the Lofoten archipelago in which well-preserved granodiorite 2,600 Myr old cuts through still older rock sequences. Whether rooted or overthrust some distance from the west, this massif thus contains extensive, pre-Svecokarelian rocks. It demonstrates that the Caledonides include a broad strip of very old Scandinavian continental crust (Gorbatschev 1985).

The sedimentary deposits resting on the basement vary greatly in thickness, depending on how far from the sediment sources they formed, and how rapidly the earth's crust accommodated to further sedimentation by sinking while deposition was going on. The greatest mobility and most rapid sedimentation occurred in the southern half of the Varanger Peninsula in northernmost Norway, where about 5,000 m thick sediments were deposited between about 800 and 500 Myr (Riphean to earliest Ordovician time) (Føyn 1985). During the first 100 Myr or so, corresponding to the Riphean period, some 600 m of sand and silt were deposited on the sinking Precambrian Basement, after which tectonic mobility of the region led to weak but perceptible tilting of the north Norwegian segment of the earth's crust. During the following stage, probably corresponding to the Vendian period (about 700–570 Myr) a more varied succession of sediments came to rest in the area, still on a slightly unstable crust. Sands, dolomitic carbonate, clays and conglomerates are typical members of the suite, the thickness of which is 2,500–3,000 m. The most spectacular members are two discrete boulder beds, corresponding to two continental ice ages. The existence of these so-called tillites (lithified moraines) in about 650 Myr old, sedimentary successions greatly influenced the philosophical outlook on Earth History. Because much older glaciations are now known from different parts of the world, it is accepted theory that ice ages are a normal feature of the evolution of our planet.

Upon the Vendian sediments there follow about 1,500 m of Cambrian to earliest Ordovician (Tremadocian) fossiliferous sandstones and shales that are collectively known as the Digermul Group. Their top is truncated by the lowermost Caledonian thrust plane.

In other areas the corresponding sediment succession is thinner. Going westwards in Norway to the areas about southern Porsangerfjord it decreases to about 800 m, but at the same time the sequence gets undercut by a fracture plane on which increasing amounts of movement have taken place as one proceeds in the westward direction. The circumstance that the same succession is autochthonous in the east but increasingly overthrust (as the Gaissa Nappe) in its western parts might at first appear paradoxical and difficult to understand from a geometrical point of view. However, the apparent contradiction disappears if one considers that a major sedimentary succession is highly plastic if regarded on a sufficiently large scale. Thus, the rupture under the base of the western part of the sediments that cover the Precambrian Basement was necessitated by the circumstance that this flank of the sediment belt was bent out of its original orientation.

Along the very margin of the overthrust terrain there is a strip of sediments that remained autochthonous. Where this strip reaches the Torneträsk area and areas still farther to the southwest, the sediments of Vendian and Cambrian age are about 200 m thick and less. They are dominated by sandstones and claystones that were deposited on the inner parts of a relatively immobile shelf. The most dramatic episode in the history of this succession might have been the dislodgement of a mass flow, the Vakkejokk breccia, on the north side of Torneträsk. It contains huge slabs of basement granite that were entrained with the surging mud. The succession also contains preserved tracks and burrows made by a rich and varied fauna that lived not long before the beginning of the Cambrian (Vidal 1981, Thelander 1982, Stodt 1987).

The late Precambrian and Cambrian sediments of the windows as a rule have been greatly thinned, crushed and flattened by the overriding nappes. Only the Alta and Komagfjord windows have a succession that approaches 200 m thickness, consisting of sandstone and shale in the lower part and tillite, purple and green shale, and sandstone in the upper part.

The sediments to the north of the Trollfjord-Komagelv Fault in the northern part of the Varanger Peninsula were deposited perhaps 500–1,000 km farther to the northwest than where they are now; the whole crustal block on which they were deposited moved southeastwards along the fault (Siedlecka 1975). The sedimentary succession consists of conglomerates, sandstones and mudstones forming the 9,000 m thick Barents Sea Group, and the overlying Løkvikfjell Group that is over 5,000 m thick. It was deposited during the Riphean and Vendian periods, on the rapidly sinking margin of a continent. The environment can be reconstructed as floodplains near the sea and expanses of shallow sea that received the erosion products of still unknown mountains.

The Lower Allochthon

As mentioned above, the origin of Lower Allochthon by increasing deformation of the autochthonous succession is evident at the eastern flank of the Gaissa Nappe that is continuous with the Autochthon of the Varanger Peninsula.

The Rautas Complex of the areas about Torneträsk differs from the Gaissa Nappe by its much thinner sedimentary succession that may amount to a couple of hundred m, and by the circumstance that huge chunks of Precambrian crystalline basement were entrained at its basal thrust, together with the overlying sediments. The sedimentary succession of the Rautas Complex is comparable with the Autochthon occurring in the same area, but also with the sedimentary cover present on the basement rocks of the Alta Window. These similarities are to be expected because the Rautas complex was torn from the western continuation of the same Autochthon and has not travelled very far, perhaps only a few tens of kilometers.

The Middle Allochthon

The Middle and Lower Allochthon were first unrooted and deformed in the Finnmarkian orogenic phase in the late Cambrian and earliest Ordovician (540–490 Myr ago).

Like the Lower Allochthon the Middle Allochthon covers much more extensive terrain in northern Norway than in Swedish areas farther to the south. The north Norwegian nappes belonging to the Middle Allochthon also are much more diverse and thicker than their Swedish counterparts. The Middle Allochthon is derived from areas farther to the west than the Lower Allochthon. In spite of the remoteness of their hypothetical source areas, these areas still belonged to the north European continent formed by the Svecokarelian and other Precambrian orogenies. This statement can be made because the Middle Allochthon contains not only deformed sedimentary rocks (that, by the way, quite evidently are of continental origin) but also thick and extensive slices of Precambrian Basement. When a sheet of crystalline rocks from an earlier Precambrian orogeny occurs within a succession of younger sedimentary rocks the conclusion is inescapably that the lower boundary plane of such a sheet delimits a nappe. Older rocks resting extensively on younger rocks must be overthrust. At least eight nappes can be distinguished within the Middle Allochthon of northernmost Norway according to this and other criteria (Ramsay et al. 1985).

Of the eight nappes forming the Middle Allochthon on northernmost Norway, the one at the bottom (Laksefjord Nappe) has a relatively small areal extent in the Laksefjord-Tanafjord area. Its succession differs from the other units i.a. by the existence of a questionable tillite. The remaining seven units are collectively called Kalak Nappe Complex. Within this complex, the three lowermost units (Garggia, Leirbotn and Skillefjord Nappes) are considerably less far-travelled than the others. Especially the Garggia Nappe is noteworthy for its thick sedimentary succession that was deposited relatively near land, in not too deep water and thus is comparable to the underlying Lower Allochthon.

The upper four nappes of the Kalak Complex (Nalgannas, Navitdalen, Gildetun and Sørøy Nappes) show a development from shallow-water sandy deposits to deposits from a foundering continental slope. This evolution bears evidence of the gradual involvement of the far continental margin with the Finnmarkian orogenic movements. The best known instance of this kind is from the Sørøy Nappe, which is also the uppermost of the Kalak units. The Sørøy succession begins with the 2,000 m thick Klubben Group that is dominated by quartz sandstones deposited in a shallow sea. The following units, Storelv Group, Falkenes Marble Group and Aafjord Group are considerably thinner and dominated by more slowly deposited mudstones and carbonate, the occurrence of which is often a sign of slow deposition of continent-derived material. The succession ends with the Hellefjord Group in which greywacke turbidites play a dominant role. This is again a relatively thick unit, deposited from turbidity currents that were released by the occasional collapse of sediments piling up on a developing continental slope. In connection with the Finnmarkian folding this succession was massively and also in numerous fractures intruded by melts from a very great depths underneath the destabilized and deforming continental margin. The intrusives are represented by layered gabbros, diorites, peridotites, nepheline syenites and carbonatites (the Seiland igneous province).

In the areas about Torneträsk, farther to the south, the aggregate thickness of the Middle Allochthon is comprised within the Abisko Nappe that is but a few hundred meters thick at the most. Its dominant lithology is a complex of : quartzofeldspathic schists ("hardschists"), black schists and dolomite marble, all of which are tectonically laminated and crushed to very fine grain. Laminated crush rocks of this kind are properly called mylonites. The described complex of mylonite schists originated as predominantly continent-derived sedimentary rocks of the kinds known from the Autochthon, Lower Allochthon, and other parts of the Middle Allochthon. Locally the basal portion of the Abisko "hardschists" contains slabs of mylonitized gneiss that was torn from the Precambrian basement in some westerly zone of the continent. In other places, particularly near the eastern front of the Abisko Nappe, the base contains huge lenses of greenish grey, very hard and primarily massive crush rock of probably mixed granitic and sedimentary origin. This crush rock is commonly called mylonite, although it is questionable if the term is adequate in this case.

Very extensive outcrop of the Middle Allochthon is known from the areas about Akkajaure about 100 km to the south of Torneträsk (Björklund 1985). This so-called Akkajaure Nappe Complex consists of six slices of Precambrian Basement of a granitic composition, each overthrust on top of the other and with a thin cover of sedimenary rocks riding on top of it. Although each nappe can be followed for about 100 km from east to west across the mountain chain, its maximum thickness will not exceed several hundred meters. Because the uppermost nappe must have moved a distance that equals the aggregate width of the underlying nappes in the movement direction, the top of the Akkajaure Nappe Complex came from at least 500 km farther to the west, provided that the main movement responsible for the stacking up of the nappes was indeed directed approximately at right angles to the mountain chain and not nearly parallel to it.

The Upper Allochthon

As mentioned in the general overview of the mountain chain the Upper Allochthon can be divided into two principal units, the Seve, consisting mainly of Precambrian rocks, forming an easterly belt of relatively high mountains, and the Köli, consisting of Lower Paleozoic sedimentary rocks, and forming somewhat less rugged topography farther to the west. Both units were emplaced during the Scandian orogenic phase in the Silurian. The upper Köli could not have experienced any deformation and metamorphism in the preceding Finnmarkian phase, because much of its sedimentary succession had not yet been deposited when the Finnmarkian orogeny came to its end.

The Seve complex is best known from the central part of the Swedish Caledonides. (Stephens et al. 1985). Detailed knowledge about the Seve of northernmost Scandinavia is available only from the Torneträsk area. From what is known in this and other areas one can outline a general upward succession beginning with Precambrian gneisses that are strongly sheared. Upon the gneisses there follows a complex of metamorphosed basaltic magmatites that reaches considerable thickness and areal extent for instance in the Sarek and Kebnekaise mountains, and in the southern Abisko mountains. The magmatites occur largely as more or less schistose amphibolites but also as swarms of diabase dykes, some of which have intruded an overlying complex of sedimentary rocks. These sediments are particularly well exposed and in an excellent state of preservation to the north of Torneträsk, where they begin with continent-derived sandstones and mudstones, to be followed upwards by limestones and marlstones. At the boundary between the Seve and overlying Köli there then follows a mylonitized quartz sandstone with numerous inclusions of amphibolite.

One important aspect of this Seve succession is its close affinity to continental areas. In spite of its abundance of magmatic rocks of gabbroic and basaltic composition that frequently signal an oceanic origin for the rock suites to which they belong, this Seve succession most probably was torn from a northwestern fringe area of the north European continent. The basic magmatism may have belonged to a late Precambrian phase of rifting that initiated the formation of the Iapetus Ocean and thereby the beginning of the Caledonian orogenic cycle. The Köli Nappe Complex and equivalent nappes form a continuous belt (interrupted only by the Akkajaure Complex) from the central Scandinavian Caledonides northwards to areas east of Lyngenfjord. There is a small but important, isolated outlier on Magerøy. Thus, the northernmost point of continental Europe consists of rocks belonging to the Köli. The Köli succession is well known from the central Scandinavian Caledonides, where it has yielded Ordovician and lower Silurian fossils. Ordovician and/or Silurian fossils are also known from the Sulitjelma area, and Lower Silur-

ian fossils from Magerøy (Henningsmoen 1961, Andersen 1981).

To begin from the north, the Magerøy Upper Allochthon consists of an over 5 km thick succession that begins with turbidites. These deposits formed by gravity-induced suspension currents, probably at depth and at the foot of a major, submarine slope. The following succession bears evidence of shoaling that might be due to the filling up of the sedimentary basin with sediments. The shallow sea that became the result of this process was the site of abundant growth of corals and other organisms with calcareous skeletons, the remains of which are preserved as carbonate deposits. Renewed tectonic movements thereupon led to an increase of topographic contrast. Sediment-spending mountains rose in the vicinity of the depositional area which itself subsided to some depth at which it became the recipient of a new, vigorous phase of turbidite deposition. All of these early Silurian events took place, of course, in areas several hundred kilometers removed from the present position of the nappe.

In North Troms the Upper Allochthon is represented by the Vaddas and Kåfjord Nappes (Ramsay et al. 1985). The complex includes a medium to high metamorphic basement with evidence of Precambrian and Finnmarkian orogenic activity, on which there rests a distinctive quartz conglomerate that probably marks the Ordovician phase of erosion that separated the Finnmarkian and Scandian orogenic phases. On the conglomerate there follow further metasediments of sandy and muddy origin.

As will be discussed in somewhat greater detail below, the Köli succession of the Torneträsk area is dominated by metamorphic sandstones and mudstones that received their sedimentary components from continental areas of moderate topography (Still the North European continent, eventually with superimposed Finnmarkian structure?) and, to a lesser extent by dark carbonates. The latter were deposited in relatively deep, marine basins. The age of these Köli rocks is uncertain, but they probably are somewhat older than the Magerøy succession.

The Köli of areas to the south of Akkajaure has been preliminarily described in a pioneering paper by Kautsky (1953). It consists of limestones, sandstones, mudstones and volcanic rocks of acid to intermediate composition. Whereas some of the limestones are almost certainly Ordovician, others could be Lower Silurian. The limestones include beds that probably formed in relatively shallow water, because they contain coral and bryozoan colonies. Published sources do not as yet provide definitive information, to what extent basic and ultrabasic rocks are included in the Köli proper, although a number of peridotite bodies have generally been regarded as Köli of a lower Ordovician age.

In areas still farther to the south the commencement of the Scandian orogeny is signalled by the intrusion

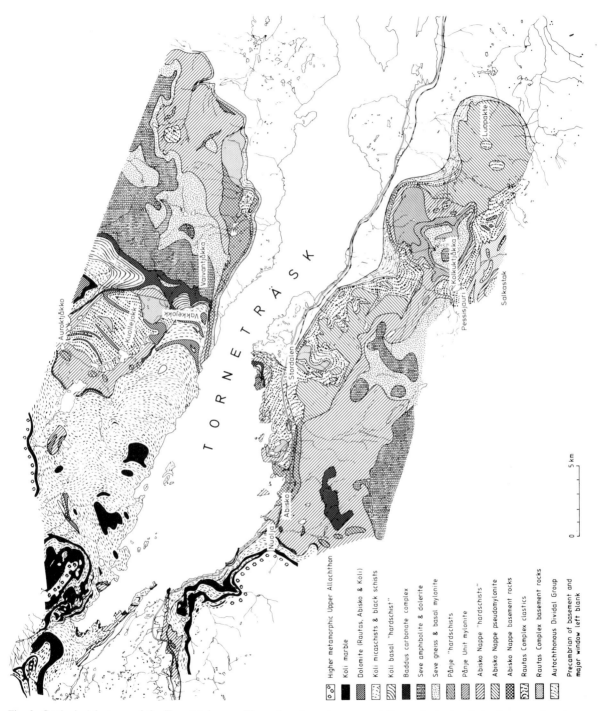

Fig. 3. Geological features of the Torneträsk area. The carbonate rocks are specially emphasized as index layers and environmentally important rock units.

into the Köli successions of granitic magmas of Ordovician age (Stephens et al. 1985).

The Uppermost Allochthon

The Uppermost Allochthon occupies two extensive and roughly boat-shaped down-folded throughs along the strikes of the mouintain chain (the troughs are not entirely ship-shape, because the "keels" undulate in a precarious way). The southern trough does not concern us so much here. It extends from Grong in central Norway to the area about Nordfold. The northern trough follows to the north in the continuation of the length axis of the southern trough. It has a somewhat more complexly lobate shape, is confined to the Norwegian part of the mountain chain, and begins to the south of Ofotfjord and has its northern end on the islands to the north of Lyngenfjord.

The basal portion of the Uppermost Allochthon generally consists of rocks that were involved in the Finnmarkian and even Precambrian orogenies. Extensively outcropping rocks of this category are strongly sheared gneisses. The Narvik Schists appear to belong to this lower portion of the Uppermost Allochthon. One of the most spectacular rock complexes occurring near the base of the Uppermost Allochthon is the "Lyngen Gabbro". It is a 100 km long slab that consists of a suite of gabbros, sheeted diabase dykes, and other basic magmatic rocks. These rocks evidently belonged to the crust underlying a part of the Iapetus Ocean during the Finnmarkian orogeny. As a consequence of relatively late Finnmarkian, crustal movements they were overthrust ("obducted") on bedrock deformed during earlier, Finnmarkian tectonism. In the interval between the Finnmarkian and Scandian phases the Lyngen Gabbro was elevated above the sea and forcefully eroded. As a result, thick deposits of erosion-products developed on its flanks and now contribute to the sedimentary succession of the Uppermost Allochthon (Bjørklykke and Olaussen 1981). Fortunate finds of fossils have made it possible to date this pre-Scandian sedimentation as Ordovician to Silurian.

In the areas about Ofotfjord there appears to be the record of an analogous succession of events. In a huge synclinal fold the metamorphosed mudstones, sandstones, and limestones of the Salangen Group rest with an intervening, erosional conglomerate on the gneissose schists of the Narvik Group. The conglomerate (Elvenes Conglomerate) might well correspond to an Ordovician phase of erosion.

In the southern trough of Uppermost Allochthon referred to above the principal nappe units tend to contain Precambrian gneisses in their basal parts, followed by thick carbonate successions with occasional sedimentary iron óres of late Precambrian age. The uppmost parts of these successions are likely to be of early Paleozoic age.

Caledonian geology at Torneträsk

The area about Torneträsk has become scientifically important through work based on the Abisko Station. It might be appropriate to focus some particular attention on the geology of this segment of the mountain chain (Fig. 3). The Torneträsk area was one of the first areas in the Scandinavian Caledonides to be subjected to relatively detailed, geological mapping (Holmquist 1910). Kulling (1964) published a map of the whole area. However, both Holmquist and Kulling had to base their geology on old-fashioned and partly inadequate, topographic maps, and by modern standards their work can be said to have been of reconnaissance character. Nevertheless, both maps represent the broad features correctly and are admirably accurate in many details.

The first detailed geological map from the Torneträsk area that was based on mapping on a large scale was published by Lindström (1955). This map reveals, among other things, that the Köli succession near the northwest end of Torneträsk contains four extensive, isoclinal recumbent folds, i.e., folds with both limbs flat-lying and essentially parallel. Moreover, these folds had been repeatedly re-folded. Running uphill across the structure one would encounter first mica-schist (forming the lower limb of the first fold), then grey calcitic marble (the core of the first fold), then mica-schist again (the upper limb of the first fold and at the same time the core of the second fold and the lower limb of the third fold), then once more marble (the core of the third fold), then mica-shist (the upper limb of the third fold and the core of the fourth fold) and finally marble again (the upper limb of the fourth fold). The reconnaissance transect would give the impression that there were three different units of marble. Only the detailed map can show that the whole succession consists of but one mica-schist and one marble unit that are repeated by folding.

From 1970 on, a project of detailed geological mapping in the Torneträsk area was pursued at the University of Marburg in Western Germany. Diploma students and past-graduates have mapped in principle every rock outcrop in their areas. The scale chosen is 1:10,000, which allows a satifactory resolution, and continuous areas of all tectonic units from the Autochthon to the Upper Allochthon are covered by the map.

The autochthon is exposed in a narrow strip of mainly steeply sloping terrain. To the south of Torneträsk the sandstones and mudstones of the Dividal Group can be followed along a descending line from the classical section at Luopakte, where their thickness totals 190 m, to Stordalen, where they reach the level of the lake and only the basal conglomerate remains of the whole succession. On the north shore of the lake the Vakkejokk Breccia is a spectacular leading layer.

The Lower Allochthon is represented by the Rautas Complex. In the Stordalen area to the south of Torneträsk and in the window of Auroktjåkko and Kuolle-

Fig. 4. View of the north side of Torneträsk, looking norheastward from Abisko. The general, westerly dip of the rock units is expressed in the morphology. Mt. Vaivantjåkka occupies the right one-third of the photo. The brook descending from it toward the middle of the figure has excellent exposures of the uppermost Seve. The white stripes descending toward the left through the birch forest in the left part of the picture are dolomite cliffs of the lower Köli; they are repeated owing to subordinate thrust-faults. Photo: Benno Kathol.

jokk (Avrrukvarri and Čuonjajohka) to the north of the lake the Rautas Complex has entrained thick slabs of well-preserved Svecokarelian Basement in its overthrusting. The basement is the same on which the sediments of the Rautas Complex were deposited, for the basal conglomerate of the sedimentary succession is preserved in many places to the south of Stordalen, resing on the Svecokarelian rocks. In areas to the south of Pessisjaure the crystalline basement rocks belonging to the Rautas Complex were thoroughly sheared during the Caledonian overthrusting.

The sedimentary succession of the Rautas Complex can be correlated in some detail with the Dividal Group of the Autochthon. A key level in the middle part of the succession is in both cases a purple and greenish grey mudstone unit. One important difference from the Autochthon is that the Rautas Complex contains thick beds and major lenses of dolomite that are conspicuous in the terrain by their yellowish white colour. In the Auroktjåkko-Kuollejokk window the Rautas Complex is repeatedly overthrust upon itself, whereby a great thickness is achieved for the whole complex.

The Middle Allochthon consists of the Abisko Nappe. The dominant rock of this unit is the so-called Abisko "hardschist". This is a quartz-rich, finely laminated, mylonitic rock of probably sedimentary origin. The cleavage planes are finely striated, mostly in a northwesterly direction. The striation is due to stretching and scratching that were active when the nappes moved from northwest to southeast and the cleavage functioned as planes of movement. Interbedded with the hardschist are layers and lenses of black, graphitic schist and of light grey dolomite.

In easterly areas, such as Luopakte and Stordalen, there are extensive lenses of greenish grey, massive and very fine-grained, hard rock that may be as much as 300 m thick. Because they evidently consist of very finely ground crush material they are mentioned in the literature under the denomination "mylonite". Furthermore, their composition is referred to as granitic to syenitic, with the result that they are equated with the mylonitized basement rocks occurring farther to the west. However, their composition rather corresponds to a combination of magmatic and sedimentary, quartzose rocks, and the structure suggests formation from a mixture of very fine-grained crush material with a pore water solution saturated in silica, which is not the mode of formation of true mylonite. True mylonites of basement origin occur extensively in the lowermost portion of the Abisko Nappe in areas farther to the west, for instance at Abisko village.

The Seve Nappe Complex is represented to the south of Torneträsk by the augen gneisses of Kålkuktjåkka and the several hundred metres thick amphibolite of the South Abisko Mountains with their steep, dark precipices and barren expanses of detached flags of amphibolite at all orientations. On top of these succession there follows the Baddus (or Paddos) Breccia, in which fragments of metamorphosed volcanic rocks occur in profusion in a matrix of calcite marble.

On the north side of Torneträsk (Fig. 4) we find a similar Seve succession. On the western slopes of Vaivantjåkka, where the rocks have been spared from orogenic deformation, their original structure is preserved. Instead of schistose amphibolite we there find a swarm of dolerite dykes that cut through a succession of sandstones and shale, most likely formed in the late Precambrian in relatively shallow water, and definitely in a continental rather than an oceanic setting. Instead of a Baddus Breccia we find a succession of interbedded volcanic tuffs, nodular and bedded limestones, shales, and black chert, all intruded by further dolerite dykes.

Fig. 5. Abisko "hardschist" with striations striking NW–SE and representing the movement direction during a phase of overthrusting. Abiskojokka, near the bridge of the Kårsavagge track. Photo: Benno Kathol.

On the Baddus Breccia and equivalent beds there rests a quartzitic "hard schist" with inclusions of metamorphic magmatics of basic composition. This rock is very similar to some of the hardschists of the Abisko Nappe, except that the latter does not contain the inclusions. Indeed, the interpretation presented in earlier geologic maps is complicated by the circumstance that the "hardschist" in question has been erroneously believed to represent an outcrop of the Abisko Nappe. The schist with greenstone inclusions is regarded as the basal unit of the Köli Nappe, because it is overlain by an apparently continuous, sedimentary succession, the upper part of which certainly belongs to the Köli, and because it rests on a continuous succession of typical Seve rocks. The "hardschist" itself is as strongly mylonitized as one might expect for a rock involved in a major thrust zone. The lower part of the Köli is best preserved in the hills to the west of Vakkejokk (Orddajohka) on the north side of Torneträsk. Interbedded between metamorphosed shale units there is a thick complex of light grey to black and partly sandy dolomite that apparently formed in a basin at the foot of a shallow carbon-

ate bank. This complex is repeated owing to small thrusts of merely local importance. It is overlain by grey and black schists that are the products of metamorphic alteration of clays and siltstones. On top of this unit, a conglomerate is exposed in the upper western part of Vakketjåkka. It contains big, quartzitic pebbles that are stretched and flattened as if they had been made of putty. This conglomerate might be equivalent to the one occurring in the Vaddas Nappe of northern Norway. If this correlation is true, the underlying dolomite was deposited before or during the Finnmarkian orogenic phase and could be Cambrian but probably not younger, the conglomerate itself represents erosion following upon the Finnmarkian phase, and the overlying rocks could be Middle-Late Ordovician, and Early Silurian.

The youngest mapped portion of the Köli Nappe Complex is extensively exposed on both sides of Torneträsk but is thickest and most easily accessible on the south side, in particular on the flanks of Mt Nuolja (Njulla). It begins with quartz-rich micaschists, partly with graded bedding, that originated as sandy siltstones. Their sedimentation probably was nourished by the erosion of a not too distant continent (with Finnmarkian orogenic structure?). Subsidence of the seafloor, and all but stopped delivery of continent-derived sediment, led to the formation of thick succession of dark, bituminous, laminated limestones. The deformation and metamorphism of the Scandian orogenic phase converted these limestones into the Nuolja Marble. The Nuolja Marble is repeated by isoclinal recumbent folding. The latest cycles of weathering has led to karstification, with development of cave systems. On top of the Nuolja Marble there follow further micaschists. The possibility of a tectonic discontinuity (subordinate nappe boundary) between these schists and the underlying marble is suggested by what appears to be a sudden increase in metamorphic grade in the schists.

One of the lessons to be learned from this succession is that no part of it consists of truly oceanic sediments; even the Köli consists of sediments that formed in the vicinity of land that most likely was continuous with the North European continental crust. If this was the case the North European crust extended at least a couple of hundred to a few hundred kilometers to the west of the present Scandinavian coast during the Caledonian orogeny.

Owing to the scale and technique chosen for the mapping it is possible to tell the approximate lithology of an outcrop identifiable, for instance, on a satellite photo. Therefore the maps can be used for the calibration of regional geological mapping based on remote sensing that will probably be used extensively in geological mapping in the future. Furthermore, the base maps can give precise information to ecologists and pedologists.

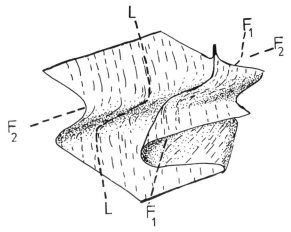

Fig. 6. Principle of repeated deformation about different axes, and establishing chronology of structures. The striation, L, is the oldest structure. It was deformed by the fold, F_1, after which both were deformed by the fold F_2.

Structural geology of the Torneträsk area

The language in which the history of the Earth is written consists of structures in the rocks. The geologist's task is to learn and read it. The first structures formed in a rock contain informations about sedimentation or volcanism, or the solidification of magma. The later recorded history may involve the chemical results of temperature and pressure changes (metamorphism) or deformation related to crustal movements (tectonism). One category of tectonically induced structures consists of fractures that may be simple (joints), or widened, with a filling of some kind (dikes), or combined with movement on the fracture plane (faults). Other structures are due to plastic deformation. Such structures express folding or flattening or elongation, or else a combination of two or all three of these. The shistosity occurring in many deformed rocks most frequently is an expression of flattening by constriction normal to the schistose cleavage in combination with gliding on the cleavage planes.

Any structure may be deformed a number of times, frequently with different stress axes. A fold refolded about intersecting axes presents a most intriguing structure. In the overthrust nappes the schistosity can be folded and refolded. Owing to the gently inclined to nearly flat-lying attitude of the nappes and schistosity of the Torneträsk area (and the Swedish nappe terrain in general, but with important exceptions) the analysis of the latest formed folds is a relatively simple affair. On the other hand, it can be very difficult to reconstruct the older fold generations that formed when the geometry of the nappes may have been greatly different from what we can observe now.

A deformation structure typically occurring in the schists of the nappes at Torneträsk is a fine and perva-

sive striation on the cleavage planes (Fig. 5). The striae were formed apparently by extreme elongation of certain particles and by the formation of trails after particles that were dragged along the cleavage. Therefore the striae indicate a movement direction within the rock and most probably a direction of movement of the nappes during some stage of the overthrusting. The function of the striae for the unravelling of the movement history of the nappes can therefore be similar to that of glacial striations in the reconstruction of ice movements, except that later nappe transport may have rotated the schists with included striae into orientations that differ considerably from the original ones.

Quite frequently the striae have been deformed by folding of the surfaces on which they occur (Fig. 6). In such cases it is evident that the folds are younger structures. If such folds can be shown to belong to a particular family of folds, for instance with similar cross sections, orientations, and geographic location, the age inference can apply to the entire family and is corroborated if further instances of the same family are observed to deform the striations in the same manner. Thus, it gets interesting to assemble structural observations in numbers, in order to establish the age relations statistically and thereby perhaps also the local history of nappe movement. A study of this kind can be very complex but it can also be organized in a simple manner

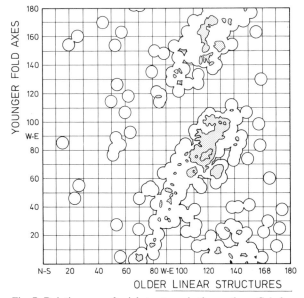

Fig. 7. Relative ages of axial structures in the northern Caledonides of Sweden. Each point plotted in the diagram represents a pair of linear structures that bodily intersect one another on an outcrop surface, with one structure ("younger fold axis") demonstrably the younger, because it deforms the other one ("older linear structure"). Isolines for point density have been constructed by letting each point be surrounded by a circle; areas where several circles overlap have the highest density and are shaded. The diagram shows that younger folds with strikes about 75° (N75°E) and 165° (N15°W) are particularly common, whereas many older lineations strike at about 120°. From Lindström 1961.

by keeping the number or parameters to a minimum, such as orientations and age relations within a few broadly defined categories of structure, such as fold axes, striations and other linear elements, and orientations of schistosity and bedding-planes.

Under certain assumptions, the validity of which can be tested, one can use the interrelations between surface orientations for the reconstruction of axes of major folds even in cases in which the latter are not evident. In order to test the method a great number of structural data were compiled in the field from a large sector of the Swedish flat-lying nappe terrain, including the Torneträsk area (Lindström 1961). The result showed consistent relationships for age and orientation of certain sets of structures. The relations can be expressed in bivariate diagrams like Fig. 7 that shows for instance linear structures with strikes about WNW-ESE (110–130°) to be consistently older than other striking at E–W (90°), N–S (180°), and NE (40–50°). The WNW–ESE-striking structures are approximately at right angles to the mountain chain and roughly parallel to the main Scandian nappe transport.

One consequence of this conclusion is that nappe movement changed its direction during the course of the orogeny, and another is that in a major sector of the mountain chain movement tended to occur in one and the same direction.

Neither of these consequences is at odds with plate tectonic theory. However, arc shaped structures with either divergent or convergent movement are also commonplace in the better investigated, younger orogens, and the concept of geometrically defined movement phases must be tested by other methods.

Radiometric dating of metamorphic and magmatic rocks is a powerful tool to this end. Radiometric dating has made it possible to differentiate between older, Finnmarkian, and younger, Scandian structures in northern Norway. Stratigraphic dating of the rocks is another method, either by fossils or otherwise. Clearly, a set of coeval structures cannot be older than the youngest rocks in which they are contained. By this criterion all the linear structures referred to above, must be either Scandian or younger, because the ESE-striking set is the oldest, and this set occurs in Ordovician rocks that formed after the end of the Finnmarkian phase. If this conclusion is correct the Torneträsk area might contain few sets of structures that are older than Scandian. The Abisko Nappe of the northwestern Torneträsk areas contains penetrative striations that strike at NW–SE and appear to be consistently older than the aforementioned WNW–ESE-striking structures. This possibility is worth considering because the rocks involved in the Abisko Nappe are older than the Scandian phase.

The relations between structures and metamorphism provide further criteria for differentiating the stuctures. Metamorphic minerals can for instance be deformed, in which case metamorphism precedes deformation, or

they can grow across the deformation structures, in which case the deformation tends to be the older of the two. In the Köli of the Abisko area porphyroblasts of biotite and garnet formed by moderate metamorphism are strongly affected by stretching along the WNW–ESE axis that marks a locally predominant transport direction of Scandian nappes. In this case the nappe transport documented by stretching is younger than the metamorphism, and both are Scandian (or, conceivably at least, younger than Scandian).

Further criteria are afforded by the relations between major, mappable structures. Detailed geological mapping is indeed essential for an understanding of the history of crustal movement. Thus, Köli of the Abisko area is not nearly so much affected by thrusting within the underlying basement as one would expect it to be if the basement thrusting had been younger than the emplacement of the Köli Nappe Complex (the relationship is schematically illustrated in Fig. 3). Although the thrusts in the basement appear to have been reactivated on later occasions, they apparently originated before the main documented phase of overthrusting of the Upper Allochton.

Another age relation that is even better documented is that of the basal thrust of the Abisko Nappe and the structure of the underlying Rautas Complex in the eastern Torneträsk area. The Abisko thrust plane cuts clean and straight through all structures of the Rautas; thereafter both were folded together about NEE-striking fold axes, with push from WNW.

In Kålkuktjåkka and its neighbour mountain Kaisepakte a subordinate local unit has been split off from the Abisko Nappe. It has been described as Pånje Unit (Lindström et al. 1985) and consists of a basal sheet of mylonite that has been folded with an overlying, thick sheet of "hardschist". The Pånje Unit carries the same penetrative fabric of NW-striking striations as the underlying, "normal hardschists" of Abisko type, but unlike these it was subjected to metamorphism after deformation. This sequence of events fits the pattern of the overlying Seve rocks, and evidently the Pånje Unit moved together with these.

A major difficulty of interpretation arises from the two circumstances that the nappes experienced great movement on different occasions, and that the latest great movement was not necessarily the one that left the most penetrative structural fabric within the nappes. Nappes could move as blocks without internal deformation as well as plastically, with much rearrangement of the inner structure. The Pånje Unit provides an instance of this principle. It carries exactly the same fabric of linear structures as the underlying Abisko "hardschists" with the only difference that metamorphic minerals formed later than the striations. If the Pånje Unit got its metamorphism while resting on the same Abisko schists that occur beneath it now, the latter schists ought not to have escaped metamorphism, either. Consequently the Pånje Unit moved in after it was metamorphosed, and

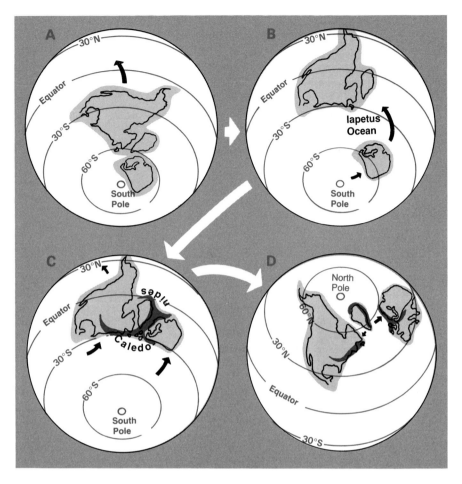

Fig. 8. Different stages in the plate tectonic movement of Scandinavia relative to North America and the latitudes. A: 750 Myr ago; B: 500 Myr ago; C: 370 Myr ago; and D: 60 Myr ago.

the still older striations have nothing to do with this movement.

Geologic development after the Siluran

Northernmost Scandinavia does not contain any rocks of Devonian to Triassic age; the oldest preserved sediments deposited after the Caledonian orogeny are Jurassic and occur on Andøya on the north flank of the Lofoten archipelago. Hydrocarbon exploration in the sea off Troms has revealed the existence of Devonian to Lower Carboniferous sediments, followed in time by carbonate deposition and the precipitation of thick evaporites in Late Carboniferous and Early Permian time (Rønnevik and Jacobsen 1984). Evaporites are salt deposits, formed in an arid climate and mostly in a marine basin. In this case they bear evidence that northernmost Scandinavia in mid-Paleozoic times was situated in the warm and arid zone.

Late Permian and Triassic sedimentation in the offshore of Troms consisted mainly of sand and clay derived from the erosion of the Caledonian mountain

chain. The sediments were deposited on subsiding crust in a relatively shallow bay or strait of the sea that was laid dry on rare occasions. Similar conditions persisted into the Early Jurassic. Beginning in the Early Jurassic and continuing into Middle Jurassic time, the offshore of Troms was the site of a coastal landscape with mudflats, sandy barrier islands, and tidal inlets (Olaussen et al. 1984). The sands deposited during this interval now form the reservoir rock of hydrocarbons occurring in the so-called Hammerfest Basin of offshore Troms.

The hydrocarbon reservoirs are sealed upwards by a compact succession of marine marls deposited from the Late Jurassic to the Early Tertiary, with a couple of interruptions in the Cretaceous.

The Mesozoic rocks of Andøya rest on Caledonian and older basement. The basement formed a deeply weathered land surface before deposition began. The sedimentary succession is over 600 m thick (Dalland 1975). It normally begins with coarse, fluviatile sandstone and mud, with a few minor coal seams. The age is Middle Jurassic. The following sandstones of Late Jurassic age were deposited in a shallow sea and contain ammonites, belemnites, and marine bivalves, as well as occasional remains of land plants. At the top of the

Jurassic, we find dark and bituminous, marine clays. The remaining succession consists of Lower Cretaceous marine siltstones with ironstone nodules.

The latest geological events of northernmost Scandinavia belong to the Quaternary Ice Ages with their interglacial ages that include the Holocene. The results of these events as well as their documentation are part and parcel of the present environment of northernmost Baltoscandia. Because the study of Quaternary deposits and processes depends on material and methods that are radically different from those available for the older Periods, the account has to stop at this point.

The plate tectonic history

Plate tectonics is a method of reconstruction of the movements of continental and oceanic crust. It depends to a great extent on the interpretations of tectonics, structural geology, paleontological data, stratigraphy, sedimentology, etc., but even more on the apparent polar wander paths for the different lithospheric plates, determined by paleomagnetic techniques. Because good paleomagnetic data are scanty in the geological literature on Scandinavia, the plate tectonic history is not known in great detail, and hardly at all for the Precambrian.

In the Early Ordovician we find Baltoscandia at probably about 60° S (Noltimier and Bergström 1976). Because other data make it certain that Baltoscandia was well to the south of North America, and North America's position on the Equator is well established, this reconstruction is plausible (Fig. 8). Because structures found in Lower Cambrian sandstones indicate a cool climate, it is probable that the position of Baltoscandia was in the cool to temperate zones of the southern hemisphere in the Cambrian, as well.

During the Middle Ordovician to Silurian Baltoscandia moved northward; collision with North America occurred in the Silurian. This movement and collision are part of the Caledonian orogeny that has been treated above.

During the 300 Myr that followed, northern Europe and North America remained welded together as a single continental mass that moved slowly northwards. Thus the region with which we are concerned moved across the equator into the northern hemisphere probably in the Devonian and moved out of the northern tropical zone in the late Permian to Triassic. When the Jurassic-Cretaceous sediments of Andøya were deposited the area may have been at about 60° N.

Throughout this time with continuous continental crust and slow northwards drifting there appears to have existed an extensive terrain with lowlands and shallow seas on the continental crust between Norway and Greenland. Toward the end of the Mesozoic this depressed terrain was gradually disrupted by rifting that spread northwards from the south Atlantic. The rift widened, with the result that open sea with oceanic crust existed from the early Tertiary (about 60 Myr) onwards. At the same time northernmost Scandinavia approached the Arctic Circle from the south and probably arrived as far north about 30–40 Myr ago.

Data pertaining to this history are summarized for the Paleozoic by Scotese et al. (1979) and Piper (1985), and for the younger ages by Talwani and Eldholm (1977) and Eldholm et al. (1984).

Concluding remarks

This paper has described the broadest features of the bedrock geology of northernmost Scandinavia with particular focus on the Caledonides and the history of their origin. Caledonian geology has been exemplified by the Torneträsk area that can by now be said to be known in fairly great detail. The geological history of northernmost Scandinavia is the history of a once very mobile crust that got thicker and solidified by the accretion of immense volumes of rock during the Svecokarelian and Caledonian Orogenies. Now the region forms part of a rigid crustal block that performs its role in the movement pattern of crustal plates, but without noticeable inner perturbation.

The plate tectonic history has brought about considerable changes of environment. For 200 Myr the region was situated in the tropical and subtropical zones. Much of this part of the geological history is recorded in the offshore sediments of Troms. Even on land the bedrock surface might contain pockets of weathered matter that formed in a warm climate.

From the environmental point of view the most important product of the geological history is a great variety of rocks with different nodes of morphological expression and different chemical compositions. For a good instance of morphological expression, see for instance Mikkola's (1932) eloquent description of the granulite country with its isolated groups of rugged hills sticking up from the tundra. For the Caledonides the morphology informs us that much of the structure must remain intact at depth, although the once impressive suprastructure has been removed by erosion.

Probably the most important heritage of the geological evolution is the chemistry of the rocks and the weathering products derived from them. Whereas quartz-rich rocks tend to be chemically rather inert, those igneous rocks that are derived from deep sources and are poor in quartz weather easily and yield a great deal of trace elements to their soils. To these rocks belong ultrabasites, gabbros, dolerites, and amphibolites that occur in the Precambrian Basement but even more frequently in the Caledonides.

Another important source of trace elements consists of dark marbles and black schists that occur abundantly for instance in the Caledonian Upper Allochton. These rocks originated as slowly deposited sediments in either stagnant or semi-stagnant marine basins. Such basins are characterized by accumulation of organic matter

34

Tab. 1. Coordination between principal events of the early geological history of northernmost Scandinavia and the rock units (nappes, nappe complexes, Groups and Formations of sedimentary rocks represented within the nappes) in which the events are documented.

Period or other geol. time unit (time in Myr)	Age (Myr)	Geological events and processes	Autochthon	Lower Allochthon	Middle Allochthon	Upper Allochthon	Uppermost Allochthon
Carboniferous –360– Devonian –415–							
Silurian	450–410	Closure of Iapetus Ocean; Scandian overthrusting and metamorphism				*North Troms:* Kåfjord Nappe, Vaddas Nappe (Finnmarkian & older; post-Finnmark sediments)	*North Troms:* Lyngen Nappe (Finnmarkian oceanic crust; post-Finnmark sediments)
–435–		Volcanism				*Narvik area:* Rombak Group *Abisko area:* Köli Nappe (quartz-mica schists, black schists carbonates conglomerate)	*Narvik area:* Salangen Group
Ordovician		Carbonates and clastic sediments including conglomerates					Elvenes Conglomerate
–500–	540–490	Finnmarkian overthrusting and metamorphism				Seve Nappe (amphibolites dolerite intruded sed.; on to the Baddus carbonate complex)	Narvik Schists
Cambrian			*Abisko area:* Dividal Group *Finnmark area:* Digermul Group *Barents Sea Block:* Løkkvikfjell Grp Barents Sea Group	*Abisko area:* Rautas Complex *North Troms:* Gaissa Nappe (Proterozoic to Cambrian?)	*Abisko area:* Abisko Nappe (Precambrian basement and sedim.) *Akkajaure area:* Akkajaure Nappes (Precambrian basement & sediments) *Troms & Finnmark:* Kalak Nappe Complex (Precambrian basement & sediments)		
–570– Vendian							
Riphean	800–700	Opening of Iapetus Ocean					
	1,500	Terminal Svecokarelian magmatism					
	1,780–1,770	Several late Svecokarelian granites					
	1,900–1,800	Culmination of Svecokarelian Orogeny					
	2,200–2,000	Jatulian sedimentation					
	Older than 2,600	Formation of pre-Svecokarelian basement					

and sulphides. Organic matter tends to concentrate trace elements from the sea water, and sulphide ions help to fixate them in the sediment. Therefore these deposits can be expected to stock heavy metals and other, less abundant elements. Because they weather easily under arctic climatic and soil conditions, their metal content can be expected to move into soils and ground water and from there to influence the vegetation. This brief conclusion is not without importance, and the geological evolution might have been necessary in order to get us there.

References

Andersen, T. B. 1981. The structure of the Magerøy Nappe, Finnmark, North Norway. – Norges geol. Unders. 363: 1–23.

Asklund, B. 1933. Vemdalskvartsitens ålder. – Sv. geol. Unders. c 377.

Björklund, L. 1985. The Middle and Lower Allochthons in the Akkajaure-Tysfjord area, northern Scandinavian Caledonides. – In: Gee, D. G. and Sturt, B. A. (eds), The Caledonide Orogen – Scandinavia and related areas. John Wiley, Chichester, pp. 515–528.

Bjørklykke, A. and Olaussen, S. 1981. Silurian Sediments, Volcanics and Mineral Deposits in the Sagelvvatn Area, Troms, North Norway. – Norges geol. Unders. 365: 1–38.

Dalland, A. 1975. The Mesozoic rocks of Andøy, Northern Norway. – Norges geol. Unders. 316: 271–287.

Eldholm, O., Sundvor, E., Myhre, A. M. and Faleide, J. I. 1984. Cenozoic evolution of the continental margin off Norway and western Svalbard. – In: Spencer, A. M. et al. (eds), Petroleum geology of the North European margin, Graham and Trotman, London, pp. 3–18.

Eskola, P. 1952. On the granulites of Lapland. – Am. J. Sci., Bowen Volume, pp. 133–171. New Haven.

Foslie, S. 1941. Tysfjords geologi. Beskrivelse til det geologiske gradteigskart Tysfjord. – Norges geol. Unders. 150.

Føyn, S. 1937. The Eo-Cambrian series of the Tana district, northern Norway. – Norsk geol. Tidskr. 17: 65–164.

– 1985. The Late Precambrian in northern Scandinavia. – In: Gee, D. G. and Sturt, B. A. (eds), The Caledonide Orogen – Scandinavia and related areas, John Wiley, Chichester, pp. 233–245.

Frietsch, R. 1979. Petrology of the Kurravaara area northeast of Kiruna, northern Sweden. – Sv. geol. Unders. C 760.

– 1984. Petrochemistry of the iron ore-bearing metavolcanics in Norrbotten County northern Sweden. – Sv. geol. Unders. C 802.

Geijer, P. 1931. Berggrunden inom malmtrakten Kiruna – Gällivare – Pajala. – Sv. geol. Unders. C 366.

– 1960. The Kiruna iron ore field, Swedish Lapland. – In: Kulling, O. and Geijer, P., Guide to Exkursions Nos A25 and C20, 21. Int. geol. Congr. Norden, 3–17. Geological Survey of Sweden.

Gorbatschev, R. 1985. Precambrian basement of the Scandinavian Caledonides. – In: Gee, D. G. and Sturt, B. A. (eds), The Caledonide Orogen – Scandinavia and related areas. John Wiley, Chichester, pp. 197–212.

Henningsmoen, G. 1961. Cambro-Silurian fossils in Finnmark, northern Norway. – Norges geol. Unders. 213: 93–95.

Holmquist, P. J. 1910. Die Hochgebirgsbildungen am Torne Träsk in Lappland. – Geol. Fören. Stockholm Förhandl. 32: 913–983.

Holtedahl, O. 1931. Additional observations on the rock formations of Finnmarken, northern Norway. – Norsk geol. Tidskr. 11: 241–279.

– 1960. Geology of Norway. – Norges geol. Unders. 208.

Hörmann, P. K., Raith, M., Raase, P., Ackermann, D. and

Seifert, F. 1980. The granulite complex of Finnish Lapland: petrology and metamorphic conditions in the Ivalojoki-Inarijärvi area. – Geol. Survey Finland Bull. 308.

Johnson, H. D., Levell, B. K. and Siedlecki, S. 1978. Late Precambrian sedimentary rocks in East Finnmark, North Norway and their relationship to the Trollfjord – Komagelv Fault. – J. geol. Soc. London 135: 517–533.

Kautsky, G. 1953. Det geologische Bau des Sulitjelma – Salojauregebietes in den nordskandinavischen Kaledoniden. – Sv. geol. Unders. C 528.

Kulling, O. 1930. Studier över den kaledonska fjällkedjans stratigrafi och tektonik inom norra delen av svenska Lappland. – Geol. Fören. Stockholm Förhandl. 52: 647–673.

– 1964. Översikt över norra Norrbottensfjällens kaledonbergggrund. Summary: The geology of the Caledonian rocks of northern Norrbotten Mountains. – Sv. geol. Unser. Ba 19.

Kuovo, O. 1958. Radioactive age of some Finnish Pre-Cambrian minerals. – Bull. Comm. géol. Finl. 182.

Lindroos, H. and Henkel, H. 1978. Regional geological and geophysical interpretation of Precambrian structures in northeastern Sweden. – Sv. geol. Unders. C 751.

Lindström, M. 1955. Structural geology of a small area in the Caledonides of arctic Sweden. – Lunds Univ. Årsskr. N. F. Avd. 2, Vol. 15, No. 15.

– 1961. Beziehungen zwischen Kleinfaltenvergenzen und anderen Gefügemerkmalen in den Kaledoniden Skandinaviens. – Geol. Rundschau 51: 144–180.

– M., Bax, G., Dinger, M., Dworatzek, M., Erdtmann, W., Fricke, A., Kathol, B., Klinge, H., v. Pape, P. and Stumpf, U. 1985. Geology of a part of the Torneträsk section of the Caledonian front, northern Sweden. – In: Gee, D. G. and Sturt, B. A. (eds), The Caledonide orogen – Scandinavia and related areas. John Wiley, Chichester, pp. 507–513.

Lundbohm, H. 1910. Sketch of the Geology of the Kiruna district. – Geol. Fören. Stockholm Förhandl. 32: 751–788.

Lundqvist, T. 1979. The Precambrian of Sweden. – Sv. geol. Unders. C 768.

Mikkola, E. 1932. On the physiography and late-glacial deposits in northern Lapland. – Bull. Comm. géol. Finl. 96.

– 1941. Suomen geologinen yleiskartta, lehdet B7–C7–D7 Muonio-Sodanhylä-Tuntsajoki. – Kivilajikartan selitys, Helsinki.

Noltimier, H. C. and Bergström, S. M. 1976. Paleomagnetic studies of Early and Middle Ordovician limestones from the Baltic Shield. – Geol. Soc. Am. Abstr. Progr. 8, 501.

Ödman, O. 1957. Beskrivning till berggrundskarta över urberget i Norrbottens län. – Sv. geol. Unders. Ca 41.

Olaussen, S., Dalland, A., Gloppen, T. G. and Johannessen, E. 1984. Depositional environment and diagenesis of Jurassic reservoir sandstones in the eastern part of Troms I area. – In: Spencer, A. M. et al. (eds), Petroleum geology of the North European Margin. Graham and Trotman, London, pp. 61–79.

Petterssen, K. 1878. Det nordlige Sveriges og Norges geologi. – Archiv Math. Naturvid. 3: 1–38.

– 1887. De geologiske bygningsforholdene langs den nordlige side af Torneträsk. – Geol. Fören. Stockholm Förhandl. 9: 420–433.

Piper, J. D. A. 1985. Paleomagnetism in the Caledonian – Appalachian orogen: a review. – In: Gee, D. G. and Sturt, B. A. (eds), The Caledonide Orogen – Scandinavia and related areas. John Wiley, Chichester, pp. 35–48.

Ramsay, D. M., Sturt, B. A., Zwaan, K. B. and Roberts, D. 1985. Caledonides of northern Norway. – In: Gee, D. G. and Sturt, B. A. (eds), The Caledonide Orogen – Scandinavia and related areas. John Wiley, Chichester, pp. 163–184.

Reusch, H. 1891. Skuringsmærker og morænegrus eftervist i Finmarken fra en periode meget ældre end 'istiden'. – Norges geol. Unders. 1: 78–85, 97–100.

Roberts, D. and Gee, D. G. 1985. An introduction to the structure of the Scandinavian Caledonides. – In: Gee, D.

G. and Sturt, B. A. (eds), The Caledonide Orogen – Scandinavia and related areas. John Wiley, Chichester, pp. 55–68.

Rønnevik, H. and Jacobsen, H.-P. 1984. Structural highs and basins in the western Barents Sea. – In: Spencer, A. M. et al. (eds), Petroleum geology of the North European margins. Graham and Trotman, London, pp. 19–79.

Scotese, C. R., Bambach, R. K., Barton, C., van der Voo, R. and Ziegler, A. M. 1979. Palaeozoic base maps. – J. Geol. 87: 217–277.

Sederholm, J. J. 1897. Über eine archäische Sedimentformation im Südwestlichen Finnland und ihre Bedeutung für die Erklärung der Entstehungsweise des Grundgebirges. – Bull. Comm. géol. Finl. 6.

Siedlecka, A. 1975. Late Precambrian stratigraphy and structures of the north-eastern margin of the Fennoscandian Shield (East Finnmark – Timan Region). – Norges geol. Unders. 316: 313–348.

– and Siedlecki, S. 1967. Some new aspects of the geology of the Varanger Peninsula (North Norway). – Norges geol. Unders. 247: 288–306.

Simonen, A. 1980. The Precambrian in Finland. – Geol. Survey Finland Bull. 304.

Stephens, M. B., Gustavson, M., Ramberg, I. B. and Zachrisson, E. 1985. The Caledonides of central-north Scandinavia – a tectonostratigraphic review. – In: Gee, D. G. and Sturt, B. A. (eds), The Caledonide Orogen – Scandinavia and related areas. John Wiley, Chichester, pp. 135–162.

Stodt, F. 1987. Die wendisch-kambrische Sedimentfolge am Torneträsk (Schwedisch Lappland). – Diss. Marburg, in prep.

Sturt, B. A., Pringle, I. R. and Ramsay, D. M. 1978. The Finnmarkian phase of the Caledonian orogeny. – J. geol. Soc. London 135: 597–610.

Svenonius, F. 1892. Om berggrunden i Norbottens län och utsigterna till brytvärda apatitförekomster derstädes. – Sv. geol. Unders. C 126.

Talwani, M. and Eldholm, O. 1977. Evolution of the Norwegian-Greenland Sea. – Geol. Soc. Am. Bull. 88: 969–999.

Thelander, T. 1982. The Torneträsk formation of the Dividal Group, northern Swedish Caledonides. – Sv. geol. Unders. C 789.

Törnebohm, A. E. 1888. Om fjällproblemet. – Geol. Fören. Stockholm Förhandl. 10: 328–336.

Vidal, G. 1981. Micropalaeontology and biostratigraphy of the Upper Proterozoic and Lower Cambrian sequence in East Finnmark, northern Norway. – Norges geol. Unders. 362.

Vogt, T. 1941. Trekk av Narvik-Ofoten-traktens geologi. – Norsk geol. Tidskr. 21: 198–213.

Welin, E. 1970. Den svekofenniska orogena zonen i norra Sverige – en preliminär diskussion. – Geol. Fören. Stockholm Förhandl. 92: 433–451.

– and Blomqvist, G. 1964. Age measurements on radioactive minerals from Sweden. – Geol. Fören. Stockholm Förhandl. 86: 33–50.

– , Christiansson, K. and Nilsson, Ö. 1970. Rb-Sr age dating of intrusive rocks of the Haparanda suite. – Geol. Fören. Stockholm Förhandl. 92: 336–346.

– , Christiansson, K. and Nilsson, Ö. 1971. Rb-Sr radiometric ages of extrusive and intrusive rocks in northern Sweden. I. – Sv. geol. Unders. C 666.

– , Einarsson, Ö., Gustafsson, B., Lindberg, R., Christiansson, K., Johansson, G. and Nilsson, Ö. 1977. Radiometric ages of intrusive rocks in northern Sweden. II. – Sver. geol. Unders. C 731.

Ecological Bulletins 38: 38–46. Copenhagen 1987

Mountain climatology: status and prospects

Roger Graham Barry

Barry, R. G. 1987. Mountain climatology: status and prospects. – Ecol. Bull. (Copenhagen) 38: 38–46.

Mountain climate research has recently been stimulated by environmental concern over air pollution and acid precipitation, and by practical needs for assessment and prediction of highland water yields. The roles of wind regimes and temperature structure in pollutant transport are examined, and hydrometeorological processes in orographic cloud/precipitation and factors controlling snow accumulation/ablation in mountains are described. The contributions of new instrumentation and of remote sensing techniques to this research are discussed.

R. G. Barry, Cooperative Inst. for Research in Environmental Sciences, Box 449, Univ. of Colorado, Boulder, CO 80309, USA.

Mountain areas of the world are increasingly becoming accessible to large numbers of people. In Europe and North America they have become the foci of year-round recreational activities, bringing in their wake new settlements in the valleys and on mountain-sides. Locally, such settlements, transportation routes, and small-scale industrial plants are creating air pollution problems that are exacerbated by the special climatic characteristics of mountain valleys. More generally, the exploitation of highland areas for water supply and hydropower resources for the lowlands, creates a need for reliable hydro-climatic data.

There is currently a revival of interest by meteorologists in mountain-related atmospheric phenomena. This article briefly reviews our knowledge and understanding of mountain climates and the new opportunities afforded by modern observational tools.

Basic problems of mountain climatology

Fundamental problems, relating to the diverse scales of atmospheric motion, and practical constraints caused by sparse data, have until recently greatly hindered progress in understanding mountain climates. The physical characteristics of mountainous terrain give rise to a wide spectrum of atmospheric phenomena such as slope and valley winds, mountain lee waves and lee cyclones, which greatly modify the regional and local-scale weather and climate. The paucity of conventional observing station networks, and the fact that few data are available from summit and slope locations, has limited our ability to characterize these atmospheric motion systems and the small-scale, topographically-determined climates ("topoclimates") that occur in a complex mosaic in mountainous terrain.

Study of mountain areas has also been uneven geographically, with research concentrated in mid-latitudes, to the neglect of tropical and high-latitude mountains. Phenomena characteristic of major mountain barriers, such as the Rocky Mountains, Alps, and Tibet-Himalayas, have also received more attention than those occurring over more modest mountain ranges ("Mittelgebirgen"). Nevertheless, the latter account in area for approximately two-thirds of all mountains.

Scale considerations

We can divide mountains, and their effects, into three categories:

(1) isolated mountains; (2) ranges/plateaus of limited extent and vertical relief; (3) massive barriers that significantly block the airflow. Mountains of the third category have pronounced influences on the planetary-scale atmospheric circulation, which have received much attention through theoretical and modelling studies (Smith 1979, Reiter 1982); these are not treated here. More subtle effects are involved for mountain ranges

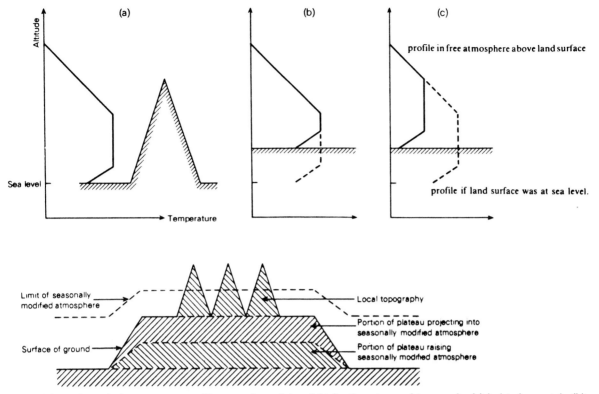

Fig. 1. Schematic vertical temperature profiles on a clear winter night for three types of topography (a) isolated mountain (b) limited plateau and (c) extensive plateau; and a generalized model of the effect of local and mountain topography on the depth of the seasonally modified atmosphere (after Tabony 1985). Reproduced with the permission of the Controller of Her Britannic Majesty's Stationary Office).

1–2 km high. Mountains not exceeding about 500 km in length, if normal to the predominant airflow, allow the air to go both over and around them. More extensive ranges like the Scandinavian Highlands reduce the tendency for air to flow around the ends, unless forced by a strongly stable stratification.

Airstreams and frontal systems that are forced over such mountain ranges are modified in a variety of ways. Small-scale effects include lee waves induced by gravity in stable flows perturbed by topography. Meso-scale effects are downslope winds which include warm, dry föhn (chinook) winds, characteristic of the Alps and east slope of the Rocky Mountains, and the cold dry bora of the northern Adriatic coast. Large-scale effects include the formation of lee cyclones when the flow is blocked by the barrier at low levels, but not above the mountain summits. Such cyclogenesis is common south of the Alps during northwesterly airflow.

Mountains have a number of significant climatic effects. Altitude is a primary factor affecting incoming solar short-wave radiation through the vertical distribution of air density, water vapour content and cloud cover. The reduction of atmospheric extinction with altitude causes global solar radiation to increase about 10% km⁻¹. Altitude similarly modifies the incoming and outgoing infrared radiation from the overlying atmo-

sphere and the earth's surface. Outgoing infrared radiation decreases slightly with altitude due to the colder surfaces but the downward reradiation also generally decreases with altitude, due to lower effective temperature and vapour content of the air, resulting in only small changes in the net balance (Barry 1981: 26–39). Cloud cover over mountains generally reduces the global solar radiation less on summits than at lower elevations due to the shallower depths of cloud overhead. Cloud also increases the downward infrared radiation.

Air temperature and water vapour content are determined more by energy and moisture fluxes from the surface. Fig. 1 illustrates a schematic model of topographic effects on temperature according to the three terrain categories mentioned above (Tabony 1985). An extensive upland area or high plateau creates an atmospheric layer that is seasonally modified by the land, although individual peaks may project through this. Valleys within the uplands have 'enclosed' atmospheres that are diurnally-modified, for example, by nocturnal cold air pools, particularly in winter.

Other climatically important factors relate to the local topographic site. The precipitation – elevation relationship is complex due to the effects of mountain slope and orientation and to the large-scale climatic controls (Barry 1981: 184–199). A recent analytical model (Al-

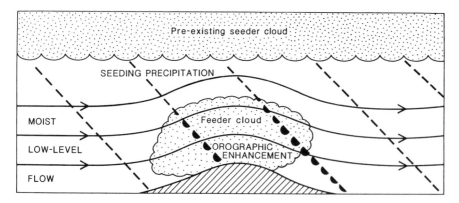

Fig. 2. Model of seeder-feeder orographic cloud and precipitation enhancement (Browning and Hill 1981).

pert 1986) indicates that the principal controls of altitudinal precipitation distribution are the slope-induced moisture convergence and the usual decrease of moisture availability with height. However, for low mountains, cloud microphysical processes and mesoscale air motion play a significant role, as discussed below.

Aspect (orientation angle) and slope angle, also drastically modify the energy budget and temperature regime. These effects can now be modelled to a first approximation given digital terrain elevation data. Models for estimating incoming clear-sky solar radiation on slopes are available (Williams et al. 1972) and this approach has been extended to atmospheric infrared radiation and energy fluxes (Dozier and Outcalt 1979). However, diurnal cloudiness regimes may give rise to significant departures of radiation receipts from the clear-sky potential amounts in mountain terrain. Buildup of convective cloud during summer afternoons causes east-facing slopes and basins to have the largest daily radiation totals as a result of morning sunshine in both mid-latitude and equatorial mountains (Barry 1978, Olyphant 1984). Such results are of significance for climate-ecological relationships and snow hydrology.

Topography also substantially modifies the airflow, setting up eddies and rotors as well as creating thermodynamically-forced mountain/valley and slope winds. These airflow modifications affect the amount and distribution of clouds and of precipitation, especially that falling as snow, with consequent effects on summer ablation and winter accumulation of snowfields and glaciers. It is this net mass balance which in turn controls the existence and location of mountain glaciers. Olyphant demonstrates how the orientation and topographic enhancement ("snow fence") effect on snowfall can be determined empirically for mountain glaciers and the relationships used to assess glacier sensitivity to climatic changes (Olyphant 1985). This topic is of potentially wide significance in areas where seasonal melt and long-term net retreat of glaciers is critical for water supply consideration (Young 1982). On a global scale, Meier (1984) argues that meltwater from the retreat of moun-

tain glaciers may be a major component of the observed twentieth century rise in a sea level. Careful long term monitoring of glacier volume changes is required to test this hypothesis.

Representativeness

According to Brooks (1947), a network density in level terrain of one station/25 000 km² is required to analyze temperature and wind fields, one station/12 500 km² for rainfall and one station/6 000 km² for snowfall. In mountain terrain, closer networks are required: one station/1 250 km² for temperature, wind and rainfall, and one station/500 km² for snowfall. However such densities are almost never achieved in standard climatic observing networks. To overcome this problem for Switzerland, a supplementary network of automatic weather stations (ANETZ) in both the lowlands and mountains has been developed. In 1980, the total Swiss network provided an average of approximately one station/200 km², but with gaps still remaining in the 2000–3000 m altitude range and on slopes (Anon. 1981).

In the absence of such special programs, sparse data cause severe problems of interpretation. This is illustrated by results from the Front Range of Colorado (Barry in press). A comparison of monthly mean temperatures at Niwot Ridge (3743 m) just east of the Continental Divide and at Berthoud Pass (3448 m) some 30 km to the southwest and just west of the Divide, shows correlations of around 0.7–0.8 in most months but these fall to only 0.5 in July and November. Consequently, even monthly temperature fields cannot be defined reliably in this area.

A further difficulty arises with the actual measurement of certain climatic elements. The accuracy of precipitation data is affected markedly by wind eddies around the gauge, especially in mountains, where wind speeds are frequently high. Annual precipitation, most of which falls as snow, may be underestimated at exposed sites by up to 20–50%. In windy, dry environments like the Colorado Rocky Mountains there is sub-

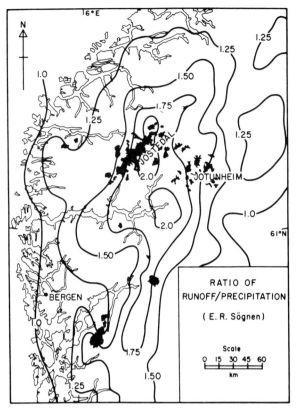

Fig. 3. The ratio of measured runoff to mean annual precipitation in central Norway (Østrem and Ziegler 1969; by courtesy of the authors, the Norwegian Water Resources and Electricity Board, and the American Association for the Advancement of Science).

stantial redistribution of snow by the wind and significant mass loss of this blowing snow occurs through sublimation (Barry 1981: 217–221).

The representativeness of precipitation data is also affected by its meso-scale variability. Radar studies have demonstrated the organization of cyclonic precipitation into a complex pattern of mesoscale precipitation areas (MPAs) (Hobbs 1978). These are produced within the synoptic-scale circulation even over level, homogeneous surfaces; over orographic barriers they may play a significant role in precipitation enhancement. The role of low hills in causing enhanced rates of precipitation was first studied by the Swedish scientist Tor Bergeron (1965). He noted that especially during winter in mid-latitudes high clouds contain ice crystals which can serve as natural seeding agents for lower cloud layers. As moist airstreams moving eastward from the Atlantic encounter the uplands of the British Isles or Scandinavia, low-level stratiform clouds commonly form over the higher ground. These may be too shallow to cause more than light precipitation and, given the typical speed of the airflow across the range (say 20 m s[-1]), there is often insufficient time for cloud drops to grow sufficiently large to fall out over the mountains.

However, if ice crystals are falling from higher cloud layers they can grow rapidly by vapour accretion in the saturated air of the lower cloud. Snowflakes may fall out if the freezing level is close to the surface, or if the snowflakes melt, the raindrops may grow further by sweeping up additional liquid water droplets in the lower cloud. Fig. 2 illustrates this "seeder-feeder" cloud model (Browning and Hill 1981) which is highly significant for precipitation over low mountains and hills. Studies in South Wales show that with strong winds and high relative humidity in the airflow, nearly all of the orographic enhancement takes place in the lowest 1500 m (Hill et al. 1981). In individual storms, the spatial distribution of this enhanced precipitation will be affected by the spacing of MPAs and their interaction with the terrain.

The seeder-feeder process has significance for precipitation chemistry. For example, initially 'clean' raindrops falling from middle level cloud layers may collect cloud droplets in mountain top clouds that have formed in low level polluted air. Observations at mountain sites in northern England (Carruthers and Choularton 1984)

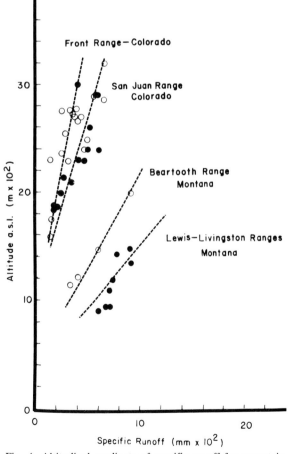

Fig. 4. Altitudinal gradients of specific runoff for mountain ranges in the Rocky Mountain chain from 37° to 50°N. The dashed lines are from linear regression (Alford 1985).

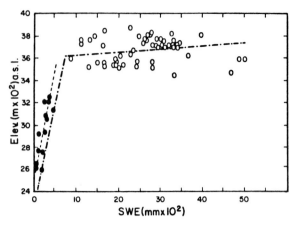

Fig. 5. The altitudinal gradient of winter precipitation (●) determined from snow course data (– – – 1969; –·– mean) and accumulation (○) measured on glaciers in the Front Range, Colorado in 1970 (Alford 1985). Values expressed as Snow Water Equivalent (SWE).

indicate pH values as low as 3.5 and high rates of acid deposition in very localized areas. This is a further illustration of the spatial sampling problem created by mountain terrain and terrain-induced atmospheric processes.

Recent findings with practical implications

Hydroclimatology

As a result of the shortage of truly representative and meaningful precipitation data in mountain areas, and the even greater lack of information on evaporation, the water balance and its altitudinal variation are poorly known. The Alps are perhaps an exception (Barry 1981: 228). More typical is the situation for Norway (Fig. 3) where the ratio of annual runoff measured at stream gauges to measured annual precipitation (Østrem and Ziegler 1969) exceeds unity, with values of 2 occurring over most of the highlands. These ratios should not exceed about 0.8–0.9 assuming 10–20% of the precipitation is lost through evapotranspiration.

A study for western North America (Alford 1985) attempts to separate macroscale patterns of water exchange parameters, determined by the altitudinal interval occupied by a mountain range and its geographical location, from mesoscale patterns of water exchange related to terrain aspect and wind redistribution of snow. Fig. 4 is an example of the gradients of specific runoff with altitude for mountain ranges in Montana and Colorado. The strength of the gradients appears to decrease as the altitudinal interval (between the foot of the mountains and mean ridge crest) increases.

Differences in west- versus east-slopes, not taken into account in Fig. 4, cause additional variations in altitudinal gradients of water exchange parameters. These

altitudinal gradients also show breaks at or near the forest-tundra ecotone. Fig. 5 illustrates this situation for snowfall measured at snow courses below tree line and accumulation on cirque glaciers in Colorado. This may represent an extreme case due to the strong winds, averaging about 12–15 m s^{-1} during winter months, near the mean ridge crest elevation which set up rotors on the lee side that carry snow back into the cirque basins greatly augmenting the accumulation.

Pollutants

Remoteness has not protected mountain areas of the world from the impact of acid precipitation and other pollutants. Pollution may arrive as a result of transport from long-distance or regional sources. Gjessing finds that nitrate, ammonium and sulphate ions of non-marine origin deposited on a 600 m-high ice cap in Nordaustlandet, Svalbard, can be traced to sources in the central USSR or Baltic region that the air had passed over 24 h earlier (Gjessing 1977). There has been extensive research on long-distance pollutant transport from Great Britain and continental Europe to Scandinavia and from Eurasia into the Arctic Basin, where it causes "arctic haze" (Rahn 1985). In Colorado, gas phase measurements of NO_x at 3000 m on the east slope of the Front Range, show that occasional easterly airflows crossing the Denver metropolis 30 km away, can cause increases of up to three orders of magnitude over pristine air levels in northwesterly circulations (Bollinger et al. 1984). Easterly flows occur in this area with cyclonic systems passing to the south in winter and with diurnal upslope circulations on summer afternoons.

Pollutants reach the surface by dry deposition and washout. In a study for western Norway, washout/rainout rates for Mg, SO_4 and Ca relative to dry deposition rates were found to be 5–15 times higher in the 600 m mountains around Bergen than in the city itself (Forland and Gjessing 1975), reflecting the effects of orographic enhancement of precipitation rates. Because much of the precipitation in middle and high-latitude mountains falls as snow, which may accumulate on the ground for up to 6–8 months before melting, acid precipitation in mountain areas requires special consideration. Gjessing et al. (1976) show that the first 30% of the snow meltwater contains 70–80% of the total amount of H$^+$, NO$_3$ and SO$_4$. The episodic nature of ion concentrations in runoff may have implications for fisheries and other components of alpine aquatic ecosystems (Hagen and Langeland 1973).

In many mountain areas, pollutants associated with local sources are redistributed by diurnal wind systems in the absence of a strong regional pressure gradient. Up to now, meteorological research has concentrated mainly on elucidating the controls of mountain/valley wind regimes. Up valley flow during the day (valley wind) and down valley flow by night (mountain wind) is primarily a result of the effect of terrain geometry on

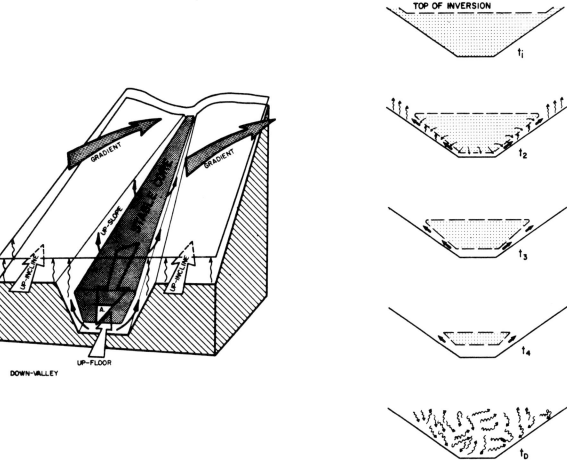

Fig. 6. Valley temperature inversion breakdown by diurnal heating (Whiteman 1982). The right side shows successive temperature cross-sections. At sunrise (t_1) an inversion is present in the valley. At t_2, after sunlight has illumined the valley floor and slopes, a growing convective boundary layer (CBL) is present over the valley surfaces. Mass and heat are entrained into the CBLs from the stable core above and carried up the sidewalls in the upslope flows. This results in a sinking of the stable core and growth of the CBLs $(t_3$ and $t_4)$ until the inversion is broken (t_D) and a turbulent well-mixed, neutral atmosphere prevails through the valley depth. The longitudinal view on the left shows the circulation about mid-morning (t_2/t_3).

the diurnal heating; the volume of air in the valley atmosphere compared with that over a lowland area equivalent to the 'orographic catchment' (defined at the mean crest height) is between 1:2 and 1:3 for the Alps and elsewhere (Steinacker 1984). This ratio closely matches the diurnal amplitude of barometric mean temperature of air in the Inn valley compared with an air column over Munich, for example. The heating effect on air in the valley is amplified by reversals of the vertical temperature profile, due to inversions formed as a result of nocturnal cooling at the surface (Nickus and Vergeiner 1984).

Considerable attention has focused on the structure of the boundary layer in mountain valleys and basins and on the break-down of nocturnal temperature inversions by diurnal heating. Inversions in deep mountain valleys (Fig. 6) are destroyed by the combined action of the descent of the top of the inversions as cold air is removed from the slopes, and of the growth up-

ward from the surface of a convectively mixed boundary layer (Whiteman 1982, Bader and McKee 1983). The process typically takes about three hours after sunrise. Slope heating forms a superadiabatic layer from which convective plumes penetrate into the cold stable air above the inversion and entrain valley air. These processes can have important effects on pollutant dispersal. Thus, pollutants from an elevated source above the valley inversion may be transported down to the valley floor by "fumigation" through the convective mixing. Observations in a broad mountain basin (South Park, Colorado) suggest that there are some differences in such topographic situations. Banta and Cotton (1981) report a downslope nocturnal wind switching over to a shallow upslope flow in the convective boundary layer. No inversion layer lowering is observed and, by late morning or early afternoon, turbulent mixing in the boundary layer causes winds in the basin to resemble those over the ridgetops.

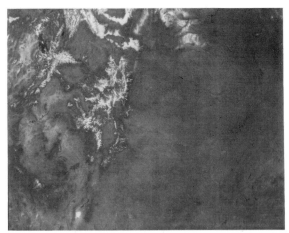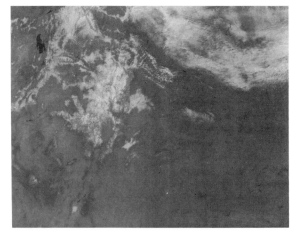

Fig. 7. Defence Meteorological Satellite Program visible band images of snow cover over Colorado in early April 1977 (left) and April 1979 (right) (National Snow and Ice Data Center, Boulder) showing contrasting spring snow packs.

In the absence of measurements of valley winds and temperature structure, preliminary estimates of air pollution potential can be based on topoclimatic inferences. Simple field observations of botanical distributions and temperature can be used to assess the vertical extent of cold air ponding; observations of the drift of smoke (or other tracers) can provide direct indications of local air movement (Radok 1982). Moreover, the breakdown of the cold air pool can be traced by increased short-term variability in the temperature record at a site, as a result of the onset of turbulent mixing.

New opportunities

In recent years new opportunities for mountain meteorological research have opened up, fostered by technological developments in instrumentation systems. This is illustrated by the Alpine Experiment (ALPEX) of the Global Atmospheric Research Programme (GARP), which involved an augmented network of upper-air balloon sounding stations, aircraft with dropsondes (to measure wind and temperature profiles), series of microbarographs (for precise pressure measurements) across passes in the Alps, and specialized local arrays of acoustic sounders and tethered balloons to determine low level temperature and wind structure (Kuettner and O'Neill 1981). Another intensive programme of basic observations has been carried out through the Qinghai-Xizang (Tibet) Plateau Meteorology Experiment (QXPMEX). Results from this study include an energy balance atlas for the Tibetan plateau (First Research Group of the QXPMEX 1984) which is a major elevated heat source for the atmosphere over south-central Asia in summer and greatly influences the monsoon regime of South Asia (Ye 1982).

Other research advances have been facilitated by satellite remote sensing data and digital terrain analysis. Landsat provides data with a resolution of approximately 100 m (30 m for the Thematic Mapper on Landsat 5), permitting basin-scale mapping of snow cover (Castruccio et al. 1981).

Fig. 7 illustrates lower (0.6 km) resolution Defense Meteorological Satellite Program imagery for Colorado in April 1977 and 1979, showing the contrasting seasonal snow covers. The potential value of such information for determining the recession of basin snow cover in spring and improving forecasts of meltwater runoff has already been demonstrated. For the western United States a benefit-cost ratio of 72:1 is estimated, based on models of irrigation and hydroenergy (Bowley et al. 1981), provided that the repetitive coverage of a Landsat-type system were improved from the present 18-day cycle.

A basic obstacle to the application of satellite snow-cover mapping for meltwater yield estimates is the difficulty of discriminating between snow cover and orographic cloud. One solution is to combine multiband data from visible and near-infrared wavelengths (Scharfen and Anderson 1982). A 1.5–1.6 micrometre wavelength sensor is of especial value because water-droplet clouds have a high albedo in these wavelengths, whereas snow appears dark. Such observations can potentially be combined with those from microwawe sensors which enable snow cover extent, snow water content, and wet versus dry snow to be mapped (Foster et al. 1984). Microwave emission from the surface is largely unaffected by clouds, unless they have a high liquid water content or there is precipitation. Satellite microwave data have a ground resolution of only about 30–60 km, but aircraft measurements over mountains may provide an interim solution, until improved sensor resolution can be obtained. Such data need to be calibrated by "ground-truth" observations, but they can greatly augment the spatial coverage of information.

In spite of new technology, many aspects of mountain climate remain little explored. Of interest to biologists would be better energy and moisture balance information; for hydrologists and glaciologists, improved knowledge of snow redistribution (James and Brendecke 1985), evaporation and rime deposition (Hindman, 1986) is needed. Because standard automatic stations will not necessarily meet these needs, a continued role for special field programmes is identified.

Summary

Recent advances in mountain climatology are partly a result of practical concerns. Renewed attention to problems of airflow and pollution dispersal in mountain valleys, as well as to highland water resources, have been two such topics. Theoretical interest in airflow over and around topographic barriers and in orographic cloud and precipitation has provided another stimulus. In addition, both theoretical and practical studies have fostered, and have been aided by, technological developments in instrumentation, in remote sensing and other data collection techniques, and in communications. Strengthened scientific interest in mountain weather conditions, comparable with the late nineteenth century phase of mountain observatory construction (Diaz et al. 1982), can be anticipated for the near future.

Acknowledgements – I am indebted to Dr. U. Radok for his comments on a draft of this article and to Margaret Strauch for word-processing support.

References

Alford, D. 1985. Mountain hydrologic systems. – Mountain Res. Development 5: 349–363.

Alpert. P. 1986. Mesoscale indexing of the distribution of orographic precipitation over high mountains. – J. Climate Appl. Meteorol. 25: 532–545.

Anon. 1981. 100 Jahre Schweizerische Meteorologische Anstalt, 1881–1981, Schweizerische Meteorologische Anstalt, Zurich: 32–38.

Bader, D. C. and McKee, T. B. 1983. Dynamic model simulation of the nocturnal boundary layer development in deep mountain valleys. – J. Climate Appl. Meteorol. 22: 341–351.

Banta, R. and Cotton, W. R. 1981. An analysis of local wind structure in a broad mountain basin. – J. Appl. Meteorol. 20, 1255–1266.

Barry, R. G. 1978. Diurnal effects on topoclimate in equatorial mountains. – Arb. Zentralanst. Meteorologie und Geodynamik, Publ. 32, Vienna: 72/1–72/8.

– 1981. Mountain Weather and Climate. – Methuen, London.

– in press. Mountain climate data for long-term ecological research. – In: Proc. Int. Conf. Meteorology of the Qinghai-Xizang Plateau and Mountain Meteorology. State Meteorological Administration, Beijing.

Bergeron, T. 1965. On the low level redistribution of atmospheric water caused by orography. – In: Suppl., Proc. Int. Conf. Cloud Physics (Tokyo 1965), pp. 96–100.

Bollinger, M. J., Hahn, C. J., Parrish, D. D., Murphy, P. C., Albritton, D. L. and Fehsenfeld, F. C. 1984. NO_2 meas

urements in clean continental air and analysis of the contributing meteorology. – J. Geophys. Res. 89(D6): 9623–9631.

Bowley, C. J., Barnes, J. D. and Rango, A. 1981. Applications Systems Verification and Transfer Project, Volume VIII: Satellite Snow Mapping and Runoff Prediction Handbook. – NASA Techn. Paper 1829, Greenbelt, MD.

Brooks, C. F. 1949. Recommended climatological networks based on the representativeness of climatic stations for different elements. – Trans., Am. Geophys. Union 28: 845–846.

Browning, K. A. and Hill, F. F. 1981. Orographic rain. – Weather 36: 326–329.

Carruthers, D. J. and Choularton, T. W. 1984. Acid deposition in rain over hills. – Atmospheric Environment 18: 1905–1908.

Castruccio, P. A., Loats, H. L., Lloyd, D. and Newman, P. A. B. 1981. Applications Systems Verification and Transfer Project. Vol. VII: Cost Benefit ASVT on Operational Applications of Satellite Snowcover Observations. – NASA Technical Paper 1826, Greenbelt, MD.

Diaz, H. R., Barry, R. G. and Kiladis, G. 1982. Climatic characteristics of Pike's Peak, Colorado (1874–1888) and comparisons with other Colorado stations. – Mountain Res. Development: 2: 359–371.

Dozier, J. and Outcalt, S. I. 1979. An approach toward energy balance simulation over rugged terrain. – Geographical Analysis 11: 65–85.

First Research Group of the QXPMEX, 1984. Atlas of Surface Radiation Balance and Heat Balance over the Qinghai-Xizang Plateau, May-August 1979 (in Chinese; Notes in English). – Meteorological Press, Bejing.

Forland, E. J. and Gjessing, Y. T. 1975. Snow contamination from washout/rainout and dry deposition. – Atmospheric Environment 9: 339–352.

Foster, J. L., Hall, D. K., and Chang, A. T. C. 1984. An overview of passive microwave snow research and results. – Rev. Geophysics and Space Physics 22: 195–208.

Gjessing, E., Henriksen, A., Johannessen, M. and Wright, R. E. 1976. Effect of acid precipitation on freshwater chemistry. – In: Braeke, F. D. (Ed.), Impact of Acid Precipitation on Forest and Freshwater Ecosystems in Norway, (SNSF-Project FR6/76, 1976): 64–85.

Gjessing, Y. T. 1977. Episodic variations of snow contamination of an Arctic snowfield. – Atmospheric Environment 11: 643–647.

Hagen, A. and Langeland, A. 1973. Polluted snow in southern Norway and the effect of the meltwater on freshwater and aquatic organisms. – Environ. Poll. 5: 45–57.

Hill, F. F., Browning, K. A. and Bader, M. J. 1981. Radar and raingauge observations of orographic rains over South Wales. – Quart. J. R. Meteorol. Soc. 107: 643–670.

Hindman, E. E. 1986. Characteristics of supercooled liquid water in clouds at mountaintop sites in the Colorado Rockies. – J. Climate Appl. Meteorol. 25: 1271–1279.

Hobbs, P. V. 1978. Organization and structure of clouds and precipitation on the mesoscale and microscale in cyclonic storms. – Rev. Geophysics and Space Physics 16: 741–755.

James, E. D. and Brendecke, C. M. 1985. The redistribution and sublimation losses of snowpack in the alpine watershed. – Proc. 53rd Annual Western Snow Conference, Boulder, CO, pp. 147–151.

Kuettner, J. P. and O'Neill, T. H. R. 1981. The GARP mountain subprogram. – Bull. Am. Meteorol. Soc. 62: 793–805.

Meier, M. F. 1984. Contribution of small glaciers to global sea level. – Science 226: 1418–1421.

Nickus, U. and Vergeiner, I. 1984. The thermal structure of the Inn valley atmosphere. – Arch. Meteorology, Geophysics and Bioclimatology A33: 199–215.

Olyphant, G. A. 1984. Insolation topoclimates and potential ablation in alpine snow accumulation basins: Front Range, Colorado. – Water Resources Research 20: 491–498.

– 1985. Topoclimate and the distribution of neoglacial facies in the Indian Peaks section of the Front Range, Colorado, USA. – Arct. Alp. Res. 17: 69–78.

Østrem, G. and Ziegler, T. 1969. Atlas over Breer i Sør-Norge (Atlas of Glaciers in southern Norway). – Medd. 20, Hydrologisk Avdeling, Norges Vassdrags- og Elektrisitetsven, Oslo.

Radok, U. 1982. Air pollution in the mountains. – Mountain Res. Development, 2: 385–389.

Rahn, K. A. (ed.) 1985. Arctic air chemistry. – Atmospheric Environment 19 (12): 1987–2207.

Reiter, E. R. 1982. Where are we and where are we going in mountain meteorology. – Bull. Am. Meteorol. Soc. 62: 1466–1472.

Scharfen, G. R. and Anderson, M. R. 1982. Climatological application of a satellite snow/cloud discrimination sensor. – Proc. 50th Western Snow Conference (Reno, Nevada 1982): 92–101.

Smith, R. B. 1979. The influence of mountains on the atmosphere. – Adv. Geophysics 21: 87–230.

Steinacker, R. 1984. Area-height distribution of a valley in relation to the valley wind. – Contr. Atmospheric Physics 57: 64–71.

Tabony, R. C. 1985. The variation of surface temperature with altitude. – Meteorol. Mag. 114: 37–48.

Whiteman, C. D. 1982. Breakup of temperature inversion in Colorado mountain valleys. – J. Appl. Meteorol. 21, 270–289.

Williams, L. D., Barry, R. G., and Andrews, J. T. 1972. Application of computed global radiation for areas of high relief. – J. Appl. Meteorol. 11: 526–533.

Ye, D-Z 1982. Some aspects of the thermal influences of the Qinghai-Tibetan plateau on the atmospheric circulation. – Arch. Meteorology, Geophysics and Bioclimatology A31: 205–220.

Young, G. J. 1982. Hydrological relationships in a glacierized mountain basin. – In: Glen, J. W. (Ed.), Hydrological Aspects of the Alpine and High Mountain Areas. Int. Ass. Hydrol. Sci., Publ. 138, Paris: 51–59.

Ecological Bulletins 38: 47–57. Copenhagen 1987

Soil biological processes in the North – and South

O. W. Heal and W. Block

Heal, O. W. and Block, W. 1987. Soil biological processes in the North – and South. – Ecol. Bull. (Copenhagen) 38: 47–57.

Soil biological processes which have been studied in the north are extended and compared with those of the south polar region. Much can be learned from exploiting the biological similarities and differences of the Arctic and the Antarctic. Firstly, the environmental conditions which control these biological processes are identified, and secondly, the ecology and physiology of the soil organisms are examined as a basis for understanding the functional processes. Soil processes can then be placed in the natural context of the terrestrial ecosystem from their interaction with other components of the system.

O. W. Heal, Inst. of Terrestrial Ecology, Merlewood Research Station, Grange-over-Sands, Cumbria LA11 6JU, U.K. W. Block, British Antarctic Survey, High Cross, Madingley Road, Cambridge CB3 OET, U.K.

Introduction

The traditional fascination of the North has led many biologists to examine the flora and fauna of tundra and polar deserts, but they have rarely studied the below-ground components. That has been the province of the pedologists and glaciologists who have provided considerable insight into the physical processes which determine the present wide variation in soil conditions. Soil biology in the North is a relatively young area of research and, of necessity, has tended to concentrate in the initial stages on description, particularly on the composition of the soil fauna and microflora. Apart from the responses of soil organisms to temperature, other functional aspects have received relatively little attention despite their importance to the understanding of soil development, plant growth and vertebrate populations. Organic matter decomposition, one of the main functions of soil organisms, influences soil temperature and moisture regimes, nutrient supply to the vegetation and the decomposer organisms themselves are the basis for food chains to many birds.

Soil biological research has been concentrated on a small number of sites in the context of the vast expanses of the North and particularly on places, such as Abisko, where the foresight of the scientific community has provided the essential facilities which encourage good soil biological research. The focus on specific sites, whilst having certain limitations, was the approach adopted during the International Biological Programme (IBP) and which stimulated soil biological research, with the important benefit of association between disciplines – the organisms do not function in isolation, neither should the scientists. We draw heavily and unashamedly from those IBP efforts, but it is significant that the momentum in Arctic soil biology developed during the IBP has not been sustained.

We also extend our view of soil biological processes from the North to the South. The reason is that the fundamental controls of soil biology, i.e. climate and geology (lithology) are similar, therefore results from one are applicable to the other – with due precautions, but with the benefit of increasing the value of research results. Further, there is a major difference between the two polar regions in that the flora, fauna and, to a lesser extent, the microflora in the South, have a much smaller range of species, probably through geographic isolation. Thus, a natural bi-polar experiment has been established through which it is possible to explore the effect of species diversity on soil and ecosystem processes.

In considering soil biological processes, we first identify the environmental conditions which control these processes, and secondly examine the ecology of soil organisms as a basis for understanding the processes. Following discussion of soil processes, we place these in the natural context of the ecosystem because of their interaction with other components of that system. Whilst concentrating on polar environments, we include some cold temperate sites in the discussion recognizing that environmental conditions form gradients rather than having sharp discontinuities.

The physico-chemical environment

Although age since exposure from the sea or ice within the Arctic and Antarctic varies widely, the soils tend to be young compared with many temperate and tropical latitudes. Carbon dating of organic deposits indicates that it is unlikely that the oldest soils pre-date the last 12,000 years (Everett et al. 1981). Many soils are obviously younger where there is recent glacial retreat and this provides opportunity for analysis of chronosequences to distinguish successional changes in processes as in the classic studies of Crocker and Major (1955), the raised beach sequences on Devon Island (Bliss 1975), the deglaciated headland on Anvers Island off the Antarctic Peninsula (Smith 1982) and the fellfield studies in the maritime Antarctic (Block et al. 1980). An alternative approach to analysis of the effects of changing environments uses the accumulated peats (pergelic cryofibrists) of the Stordalen mire in Abisko

(Sonesson 1980), at Signy Island in the South Orkney Islands (Davis 1981) and the "temperate tundra" at Moor House, UK and Glenamoy, Ireland (Rosswall and Heal 1975). This evidence within a system of the changes in vegetation and environment since initiation of the peat-forming process, usually 5–10,000 years ago, is of great value to the soil ecologist. A further opportunity for the study of terrestrial ecological processes such as colonisation and succession lies in areas which have been subject to recent volcanic activity; e.g. Surtsey in the Arctic (Brock 1972), Deception Island in the South Shetland Islands, Antarctica (Smith 1984a, 1985).

A wide variety of soils have developed in the tundra – or rather, are developing. Pedogenesis is still in progress and many soils are subject to short term cryoturbation and longer term cyclical processes such as the thaw lake cycle (Brown et al. 1980). Detailed descriptions and classifications are available for soils and for climate, but to bring these together to provide a definition of the environmental conditions of relevance to soil biological processes, French (1981) used selected climatic and soil variables in a multivariate classification of the IBP sites (Fig. 1). The classification identifies that the main axes of variation include both climate and soil factors, implying their functional inter-relationship. The

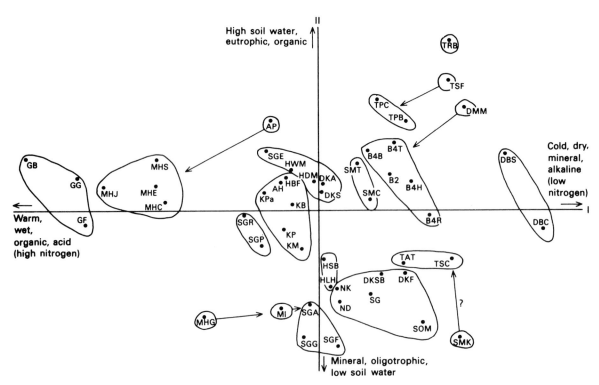

Fig. 1. Abiotic analysis of tundra sites (from French 1981), showing the distribution of sites along components I and II, indicating primary clusters. The analysis used 7 climatic variables, 4 soil temperature variables, 2 soil moisture variables and 8 chemical variables. Arrows show the nearest linkages of 'outlier' sites. Main site codes: – G: Glenamoy, Ireland; MH: Moor House, U.K.; H: Hardangervidda, Norway; K: Kevo, Finland; A: Abisko, Sweden; D: Devon Island, Canada; B: Point Barrow, Alaska, U.S.A.; T: Tareya, Taimyr, U.S.S.R.; M: Macquarie Island, Australia; SG: South Georgia, Antarctica; S: Signy Island, Antarctica; DK: Disko Island, Greenland; N: Niwot Ridge, Colorado, U.S.A. Other letters and numbers in codes refer to sub-sites.

analysis indicates that in some cases the environmental conditions from a number of sub-sites within a small geographic area form a distinctive cluster, e.g. *Acaena* (SGA), *Festuca* grassland (SGG) and fellfield (SGF) at South Georgia. In other cases the conditions in adjacent habitats are similar not to one another, but to geographically distant areas, e.g. the wet depressions of the Stordalen (AP) mire are most similar to the oceanic peat bogs whilst the drier elevated parts at Stordalen (AH) are most closely related, in terms of climate and soil, to sites at Kevo in Finland and Hardangervidda in Norway. Further, the grassland and marble moraine soils of the Antarctic Signy Island (SG, SOM) are most closely related to sites at Disko Island, Greenland (DKSB,

DKF) and the alpine Niwot Ridge, Colorado (NK, ND).

Thus, the soil, climatic and physico-chemical attributes, North and South, show environmental gradients which, whilst partly related to latitude and altitude, show considerable variation within short distances, often over metres. These gradients relate as much to variations in soil moisture, nutrients and acidity as to the more frequently studied temperature parameter. Thus, trends in soil biological processes across polar areas are likely to be influenced as much by local environmental conditions as by the overall temperature regime.

One feature which is inadequately expressed in Fig. 1 is the microclimate variation within a soil. Seasonal air

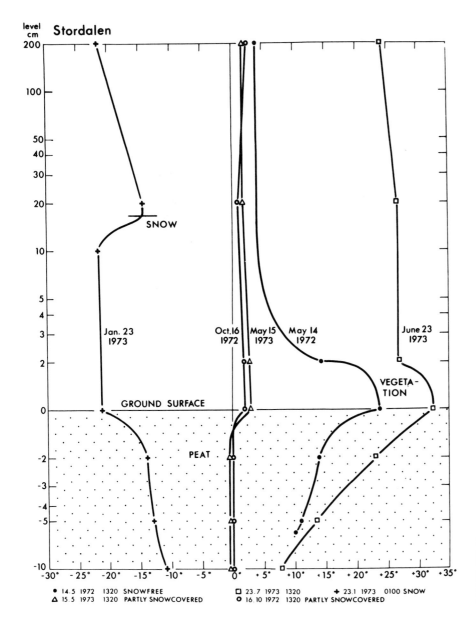

Fig. 2. Typical temperature gradients in air, snow, vegetation and soil at Stordalen, Abisko, Sweden (after Rosswall et al. 1975). Key at bottom of figure.

temperature variations are considerably modified with depth in the soil (Fig. 2); surface temperatures can fluctuate greatly and attain 30°C for short periods as a result of aspect and reflectance; short term surface desiccation of litters occurs on wet sites as well as in polar deserts; severely reducing conditions can occur within a profile where local drainage is impeded. These variations highlight the importance of microhabitat definition and the potential for using microhabitat gradients in biological research. They also emphasise that biological processes respond to an extreme range of conditions on a small scale – sometimes millimetres. There is the added possibility that organisms which are more mobile (arthropods) or can extend over several microhabitats (fungal mycelium) have the potential to utilize such microhabitat variation in time and space.

Physiology and autecology

To what extent have the soil fauna and microflora adapted to or been selected by the prevailing polar environments? An understanding of the response of organisms to their environments provides a mechanistic basis for many soil biological processes, which are measured directly, e.g. soil respiration, organic matter decomposition, nutrient mineralisation.

On present evidence there is no reason to believe that northern and southern fauna and microflora have any significant differences in their physiology, other than those attributable to specific taxonomic differences. There is no obvious dominance of psychrophiles in either Arctic or Antarctic soil communities relative to temperate ecosystems. Fundamental processes such as protein synthesis proceed in a similar fashion in cold adapted organisms from North and South, although different enzymes may be at work. In all organisms which experience freezing temperatures, the maintenance of membrane fluidity appears to be crucial in their survival and this we know little about in many of the polar soil biota.

Metabolic adaptations to low temperatures in soils are similar in temperate and polar species. Cold adaptation has been documented by Block and Young (1978) in soil micro-arthropods, where the metabolism-temperature curve is shifted to a lower temperature range but with no alteration of its slope compared with temperate species (Fig. 3). Such micro-arthropods have Q_{10}s varying from 1.3 to 3.4 over an environmental temperature range of 0 to 10°C. Higher insects in the Arctic (e.g. the tipulids *Pedicia hannai* and *Tipula carinifrons*) have a Q_{10} of 2.3 over 0.5 to 20°C, but the adults show a faster response to increasing temperature than the larvae (MacLean 1980). The soil microflora, on the other hand, tend to exhibit an elevated Q_{10} (average ca. 3.6) for different fungi and substrates with higher values in surface litters (Flanagan and Bunnell 1980). This is reflected in a more responsive microbial respiration in the surface litter compared with that below ground. Bacte-

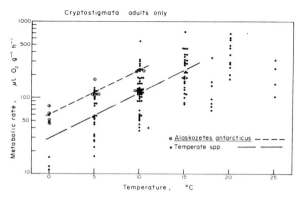

Fig. 3. Metabolic activity of cryptostigmatid mites from Antarctic and temperate systems in relation to temperature (from Block and Young 1978).

ria utilise lower molecular weight substrates at cold temperatures, whereas fungi metabolise complex substances down to −5°C (Flanagan and Bunnell 1980). In general, the soil microbial components seem to have a faster reaction to small temperature increments than the soil fauna.

Resistance to freezing is widespread in polar soil faunal communities, and is achieved in two ways: organisms either tolerate the formation of extra-cellular ice or avoid nucleation by extensive supercooling (the maintenance of body fluids in the liquid phase below their normal freezing point) (Block 1982). The latter, supercooling, strategy is by far the most common in the soil fauna of both northern and southern tundra systems, whereas freezing tolerance is restricted to relatively few higher insects (e.g. beetles, dipterans, etc.) and some plants. Supercooling may be more efficient energetically and metabolically in cold environments with a high frequency of freeze-thaw cycles. Almost nothing is known about freezing resistance in soil microorganisms. The extent of supercooling is determined largely by the absence or masking of potential ice nucleating agents and the action of low molecular weight compounds such as sugar alcohols and sugars. In invertebrates ice nucleators may occur in the gut contents or in the haemolymph. High body water content may encourage lethal freezing. In plant sap, polysaccharides may initiate nucleation at temperatures just below 0°C and thereby protect freeze tolerant species (Krog et al. 1979). Survival at freezing temperatures, especially in overwintering sites, appears to be mainly by avoiding freezing via supercooling in a wide range of soil organisms. Again, such a phenomenon is not restricted merely to cold adapted species, but is known to occur in temperate and sub-tropical soil biota.

The availability of soil moisture to soil organisms is considerably restricted in polar habitats relative to temperate ones because liquid water is not biologically available, being locked up as ice, at least for part of the year. Therefore, much of the biological activity and, in

50

turn, life cycles may be largely regulated by the supply of moisture (e.g. areas of continental Antarctica such as Ross Island and southern Victoria Land). In such habitats, dehydration resistance is as important as cold resistance for the survival of soil organisms (especially invertebrates). Such cold deserts may be regarded as having seasonally-pulsed environments, in which biological activity is regularly triggered by physical events such as freezing/thawing, wetting/drying cycles. At the level of the individual invertebrate, there may be a trade-off between the need for water required for metabolism and growth, and the increased potential for ice nucleation when the animal is fully hydrated during periods of subzero temperatures.

Most of the growth of many soil invertebrates is achieved in summer periods at temperatures around 3–5°C, provided moisture and other environmental conditions are optimal. Antarctic springtails have their highest energy assimilation efficiency around 0°C, and their young stages maintain a positive net production at similar temperatures (Burn 1984). Some Arctic tipulids exhibit similar features, and these species are clearly facultative as distinct from obligate polar forms. Growth rates, although adapted to low temperatures, are necessarily slow in such soil animals, and life cycles of between 7 and 13 years have been shown for particular species (MacLean 1980, Burn 1981). Hence the period of exposure to potentially lethal conditions, and to predation, is prolonged in the life cycle of many species.

Overwinter survival, therefore, becomes a key factor in the success or failure of the inhabitants of polar and tundra soils. In mites and springtails most life stages overwinter, whereas in the higher insects, larvae and pupae are more important. Several soil invertebrates reproduce asexually; the enchytraeids being the best example. The ability to reproduce asexually may be an advantage in the short active summer period in tundra environments by obviating the need to find a mate. It may also increase the colonizing potential of a species especially in remote areas such as the Antarctic (Block et al. 1984). Such features may be pre-adaptive. On the other hand, many soil arthropods employ sexual reproduction, and several species establish 'pools' of immature stages in the soil with maturation occurring as the environment and the climate allow (Goddard 1979, Block 1980). In this way, the production of sexually mature individuals is synchronised.

Populations and communities

Polar soil communities show a general reduction in numbers of species and in their taxonomic range compared with other soils. Such reduction in diversity is more pronounced due to the geographical isolation of the Antarctic, where many of the higher insect groups are absent from the soil fauna (Block 1984). The striking difference with the Arctic is in the almost com-

plete absence of Diptera in the south polar region (only the apterous midge *Belgica antarctica* existing in sheltered localities along the Antarctic Peninsula). However, some invertebrates introduced into the Antarctic by human agency have survived and established small populations (e.g. Block et al. 1984). The general lack of large decomposers in polar terrestrial communities leads to reduced comminution of litter and organic material, which may be partly overcome by the effects of cryoturbation. In the microbial component, yeasts often dominate and exhibit substantial population growth during spring melt (Wynn-Williams 1982). The patchy information on populations of polar soil organisms show that densities are variable (by season and site), but nevertheless they are broadly similar to those of comparable temperate soils (Block 1984). The fauna is often restricted to the top 6 cm of the soil profile by anaerobic conditions below this zone.

Of the population dynamics and their causes, we are largely ignorant. Microbial groups exhibit growth pulses in spring and autumn, but why? Is predation on the microflora restricted only to the surface layers, and what levels of overwintering mortality are sustained by microbes and invertebrates? Predation mortality of invertebrates may be considerable in the Arctic, e.g. 20–25% of adult tipulid production is consumed by insectivorous birds and tipulids may constitute the entire diet of some species (MacLean 1980). However, it is not known whether such predation on invertebrates is opportunistic or not, and whether the population densities of predators and prey are controlled by such interactions (i.e. predation) or by the environment. By way of contrast to the Arctic, the relatively simple terrestrial communities of the maritime Antarctic often have only a single arthropod predator – a mesostigmatid mite (*Gamasellus racovitzai*) – which appears to feed unselectively (Fig. 4) and its population level seems to be controlled by the

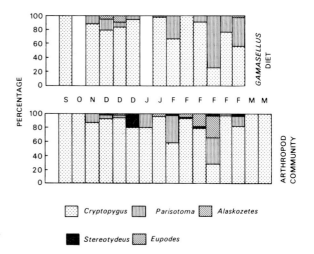

Fig. 4. Field diet and potential prey of a mite predator (*Gamasellus racovitzai*) in an Antarctic terrestrial community during summer months (from Block 1985).

physical environment. It may be that the numbers of obligate polar species are mainly density dependent, whilst populations of facultative species are density independent (e.g. Coulson and Whittaker 1978), but firm evidence is lacking.

In the absence of terrestrial vertebrates and above-ground herbivores of any kind in Antarctica proper, the importance of a below-ground invertebrate-microbial grazing chain is increased compared with northern soil communities. The role of the microflora is enhanced. The full range of metabolic capabilities is possessed by all microbial groups in both North and South polar soil communities, there being no evidence of loss of particular functions. Whilst there is no obvious dominance of psychrophiles in the microbes of polar soils (Ellis-Evans and Wynn-Williams 1985), the functional capabilities of the Antarctic fauna appear to be rather more restricted. This probably reflects the greater age and depauperate nature of the South polar terrestrial biota, compared with the North. However, the functional structure of the simpler communities in the South polar soils suggests fewer biological interactions, where predation and inter-specific competition are at low levels and processes such as grazing are regulated entirely by invertebrates. Niche breadth, especially of free-living forms, may be larger than for comparable Arctic forms. In turn, Antarctic land invertebrates appear less sensitive to variations in primary production due to their catholic diets, and hence more efficient exploiters of cold environments (Block 1980). However, further and more detailed research on both northern and southern soil communities is required to substantiate these hypotheses.

Processes

The combined activities of the microflora and fauna are integrated in the processes of organic matter decomposition and mobilisation of nutrients. The importance of the overall temperature regime and of the localised variations in moisture in the physiology and population characteristics of soil organisms are clearly reflected in the rates of decomposition, analysed under both field and controlled laboratory conditions. In the field, weight loss from confined litter is usually of the order of 5–25% in the first year although much higher rates are recorded from sub-Antarctic sites. Whilst these loss rates are broadly related to site temperature and moisture conditions (Heal et al. 1981, Davis 1986), a more detailed understanding comes from laboratory studies, using respiration as a measure of decomposition, especially when combined with mathematical models (Bunnell et al. 1977 a, b, Flanagan and Bunnell 1980).

Developed to express the decomposition relationships in the tundra of the north slope of Alaska, the model of Bunnell et al. (1977 a, b) is summarised as:

$$R\,(T,\,M) = \frac{M}{a_1 + M} \times \frac{a_2}{a_2 + M} \times a_3 \times a_4^{\frac{T-10}{10}}$$

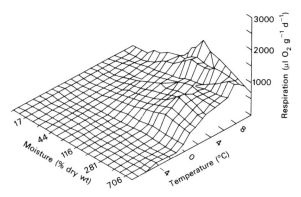

Fig. 5. Respiration rate of litter from Point Barrow, Alaska in relation to temperature and moisture (from Flanagan and Veum 1974).

Where R (T, M) is the respiration rate in $\mu l\,O_2\,g^{-1}\,h^{-1}$ of a resource at temperature T (°C) and moisture M (% dry weight), a_1 is the percentage moisture content at which the resource is half saturated with water; a_2 is the percentage moisture content at which half the pores are saturated or blocked with water; a_3 is the respiration rate at 10°C when neither oxygen nor moisture is limiting; a_4 is the Q_{10} coefficient.

The model represents the hump-shaped surface of respiration response to temperature and moisture in which shortage of moisture limits respiration (a_1), high moisture contents inhibit oxygen diffusion and hence aerobic respiration (a_2). The increased respiration with temperature (a_4) causes oxygen depletion to occur at lower moisture contents as temperature increases, giving an asymmetrical hump. The rate of respiration is also influenced by the quality of the resource, e.g. the concentration of soluble carbohydrates and nutrients. The resource quality influences the overall height of the response surface and is represented by the respiration rate under optimal conditions (a_3).

The model, whilst not unique in general principles, has been developed from laboratory and field data and used to explore the relative importance of environmental factors and quality (Fig. 5). In examining the respiration of a number of resources from different microhabitats and sites Flanagan and Bunnell (1980) concluded that microbial respiration was most sensitive to temperature, then to resource chemistry and least sensitive to moisture, particularly at higher moisture contents. However, low moisture contents may markedly reduce respiration rates in certain microhabitats such as standing dead plant material. Whilst recognising the contribution of many chemical components, Bunnell et al. (1977b) showed that definition of the proportions of ethanol-soluble fractions allowed distinction of the decay rates for different resources.

In the present context, the importance of the decomposition study centred on Point Barrow, Alaska (Flanagan and Bunnell 1980) is that a detailed and rigorous

52

Tab. 1. Annual weight losses of various litters measured and predicted from the simulated microbial respiration (from Flanagan and Bunnell 1980).

Research area	Substrate	Weight loss (% of initial weight)		Simulated as a percentage of measured
		Measured	Simulated	
Abisko, Sweden	*Rubus chamaemorus* leaves	32	23.3	73
Barrow, Alaska	*Dupontia fisheri* leaves	15	13.4	89
	Carex aquatilis leaves	14.6	13.4	92*
Moor House, United Kingdom	*Calluna vulgaris* shoots	15–20	–	–
	Calluna vulgaris stems	8	7.1	89*
	Rubus chamaemorus leaves	36–38	20.1	54*

*Recalculated.

analysis of the controls of a process, based at one site, has much more general application. With limited information on the respiration rates of a number of litters and of the site environmental conditions, Bunnell et al. (1977b) predicted the rate of decomposition of litters at Abisko (Sweden) and at Moor House (UK). The predicted annual weight loss rates were 54–92% of the weight-losses measured in independent field studies (Tab. 1). The basic form of the decomposition (respiration) response to temperature, moisture and chemical composition is derived from laboratory and field measurements. The response surface integrates the wide variety of individual species responses from different microhabitats and substrates. Thus there appears to be a general response curve, e.g. temperature, which is characteristic of the tundra microbial community, and which overrides the variety of responses resulting from adaptation to, or selection by, the environmental conditions (Fig. 6).

Thus the rates of organic matter decomposition shown from physiological and field studies reflect the flexibility of the microbial community. Activity is maintained under the severe environmental conditions by the ability of the different constituents of the community to respond to various environmental regimes. Microbial processes continue at sub-zero temperatures, under a variety of moisture conditions, and short periods when temperatures rise are also exploited. Further, there is no evidence that any restrictions in the species composition of the microflora of the Arctic, or more particularly the Antarctic, have a significant effect in modifying the rates of decomposition.

Availability of essential elements and of readily available energy sources in polar systems may limit heterotrophic activity more than at lower latitudes. This hypothesis is based on the characteristics of four main factors. (1) The litter input to polar soils tends to be low in nutrients and high in structural carbohydrates because of the high proportion of net primary production contributed by dwarf shrubs, mosses and lichens (Wielgolaski et al. 1981, Smith 1984b). The high nutrient-use efficiency of tundra plants, including translocation before death exacerbates this effect (Chapin 1987, Callaghan

1987). (2) Accumulation of organic matter is a general feature of polar regions (Heal et al. 1981). The associated acidity and waterlogging (see 3) and low temperatures are important factors which can retard rates of nutrient mobilisation (Flanagan and Bunnell 1980, Everett et al. 1981). (3) Waterlogging of soils, associated with permafrost, tends to retard decomposition and mineralisation and restrict the production of soluble carbohydrates by inhibiting decomposition of cellulose and lignin (Flanagan and Bunnell 1980). Anaerobic processes, reflected in the high output of methane at some sites (Svensson 1980), are inefficient in energy utilisation, relative to aerobic processes, resulting in a slower

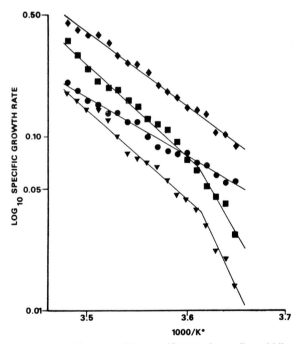

Fig. 6. Arrhenius plots of log specific growth rate (in turbidity units) versus absolute temperature for two aquatic (◆, *Cytophaga* sp. and ●, *Chromobacterium fluviatile*) and two terrestrial (▼, *Corynebacterium* sp. and ■, *Candida* sp.) microorganisms (from Ellis-Evans and Wynn-Williams 1985).

turnover of microbial biomass and hence of nutrients. (4) The incorporation of organic matter into the permafrost results in the permanent removal of potential nutrient sources from recycling through both the heterotrophic and autotrophic systems.

Compensating for some of these restrictions to available nutrient and energy sources, the seasonal and short-term freeze/thaw cycles enhance nutrient and energy turnover, at least partly by disruption of cells (Wynn-Williams 1980). At spring melt, soluble nutrients and carbohydrates held in snow, ice and cryptogams are released over a short period and concentrations of soluble sugars and polyols in excess of 1% soil fresh weight have been reported for Antarctic fellfield fines (Tearle 1987). These sugars are probably derived from disruption of live plant cells, but similar release from microbial biomass may also occur (Wynn-Williams 1982). The high frequency of freeze/thaw cycles in the maritime Antarctic (Fig. 7) indicates that they will be associated with equally frequent and short-term periods of mobilisation and immobilisation, the release of soluble carbohydrates providing the energy source for immobilisation of released nutrients into new microbial biomass. Some evidence for these short-term bouts of microbial activity, linked to freeze/thaw cycles, have been detected by respirometry of field samples from moss-dominated communities (Wynn-Williams 1985a, b).

It is concluded, therefore, that in general the rates of soil processes appear to be controlled primarily by the environment, particularly the prevailing microclimate, and by resource quality. The spectrum of adaptation so far documented for the range of soil organisms found in polar soils, indicates that the physiological characteristics only partly overcome the environmental constraints. On current knowledge, there is no reason to think that the restricted community structure of such soils alters the pattern of biological processes. The main processes occur but often at slower rates and possibly via different factors. For example, the distinctive absence of Antarctic macrofauna may reduce comminution of organic matter and microbial stimulation, but this is compensated by the effects of cryoturbation.

Ecosystems

North and South polar ecosystems have three common features: (1) low temperature limitation of the rates of most biological processes; (2) relatively short annual periods for biological activity; (3) frequent occurrence of freeze/thaw cycles and permafrost. By contrast, there are also important differences: (a) the proportion of primary production contributed by cryptogams is low in the Arctic and high in the Antarctic (Davis 1981); (b) the detritus input into the soil community is utilized in different ways in the North compared with the South; (c) the composition and trophic structure of the invertebrate component varies; (d) levels of herbivory

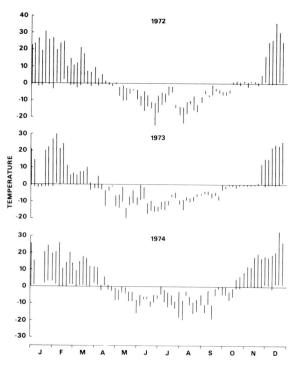

Fig. 7. Maximum diurnal surface temperature range (°C) (within five-day blocks) in a moss bank at Signy Island over three years (from Walton 1982).

and carnivory are well developed in the Arctic and restricted in the Antarctic. French and Smith (1985) detail further similarities and differences.

In the south polar ecosystems which have been analysed, very little of the primary production from mosses (and lichens) is directly eaten by invertebrate consumers as compared with the Arctic. The main energy flux is via the microflora, which assimilate dead organic matter thereby converting it to a form more readily metabolized by invertebrates. The micro-algae play a crucial role in such microfloral energy and nutrient cycling (Davis 1981), which does not seem to have an Arctic functional counterpart. Davis (1981) calculated that an amount equivalent to ca. 58% of the annual net primary production was consumed by the soil fungi in a mossbank in the maritime Antarctic. Comparable Arctic tundra efficiencies have been estimated at < 1.5% (Whitfield 1977). On the other hand, carnivore efficiencies are high (15–33%) in Arctic systems and low (< 1.0%) in the Antarctic. These functional differences between northern and southern terrestrial systems were postulated by Holdgate (1977) from the Heal and MacLean (1975) model on the basis that observed invertebrate production was much less than predicted in the maritime Antarctic environment.

It is instructive to compare land with aquatic systems and their functioning in both the North and South. In the Antarctic, the terrestrial animals appear to be func-

54

tionally analogous to the marine benthic fauna, which is largely composed of suspension feeders of various types. They are similar in that both are unspecialised opportunists with broad ecological niches. The marine benthos, however, is primarily regulated by food supply, whereas the land fauna appears to be controlled more by physical conditions. The marine and terrestrial fauna experience totally different microclimates in which temperature ranges, both seasonally and daily, are in marked constrast. As the temperature of the marine inshore environment is stable throughout the year ($0 \pm 2°C$), so that of land habitats fluctuates widely (-28 to $30°C$). Such thermally different conditions may explain why the physiological phenomenon of cold adaptation has been recognised in certain elements of the terrestrial fauna (Block and Young 1978) but not in the benthic forms which have been studied (Clarke 1980).

It may be concluded that although there are large differences in species composition between northern and southern ecosystems, these have not resulted in significant functional changes. The functioning of tundra ecosystems appears to be a scaled-down version of that operating in temperate ecosystems with environmental temperature as a major constraint. Finally, within particular tundra ecosystems there are many possible variations brought about by microhabitat differences.

Conclusions and future

Despite marked differences in the structure of the heterotrophic communities through the simplifying effect of geographical isolation in the Antarctic, the available information does not indicate significant differences in functioning of polar communities. Controls on heterotrophic activity are predominantly through temperature and moisture, and their interaction. The physiological and behavioural adaptations of the microflora and fauna allow them to exploit the harsh environment, particularly through use of both spatial and temporal variation. The importance of freeze/thaw cycles, clearly recognised in pedological research, has probably been underestimated in soil biological research as a control on energy and nutrient mobilisation. Such cycles may also be an important substitute for the absence of the larger soil fauna which, in temperate soils, enhance microbial activity through organic matter comminution, soil mixing and dispersal of the microflora (Visser 1985).

There is evidence that physico-chemical quality of the litter input, high in structural carbohydrates and low in nutrient concentration, retards heterotrophic activity. The resultant low rate of nutrient mobilisation will have a feed-back effect, the plants responding to reduced nutrient availability through increased nutrient-use efficiency. However, one major variant in this situation is activated through lemmings in which high populations result in an input of relatively high quality plant litter which, combined with input of urine and faeces and a modified microclimate, results in enhanced heterotrophic activity (Flanagan and Bunnell 1980, Chapin et al. 1980). In the Antarctic, sea mammals and introduced land mammals may induce increased microbial activity through nutrient enrichment and change in vegetation composition.

The polar (and alpine) environments provide a series of out-door laboratories for comparative studies. Such research can capitalise on the variations in simplified community structure, as well as the extreme climatic conditions, to clarify basic principles of community and ecosystem function which are more difficult to determine in complex temperate and tropical systems. These opportunities do not support the view of Remmert (1980), when discussing Antarctic terrestrial ecosystems, that "Such systems are mainly of interest to physiologists, since they provide valuable examples of organisms clearly indicating the cold limits of existence. The systems are of no significance for the Antarctic ecosystem as a whole...". The value of understanding the relationships between system structure and function is of particular importance in the Antarctic, where increased human activity is likely to result in further species introductions and potential disruption of communities of major interest to nature conservation (Holdgate 1984).

The success or failure of an introduced organism, whether plant, animal or microorganism, depends upon a combination of physical, physiological, behavioural and reproductive characteristics. As indicated earlier, some species may be pre-adapted to polar environments and therefore likely to become established if introduced. Identification of the characteristics of successful colonists has relevance to ecological theory as well as to conservation. The traditional ideas of r-K selection have been expanded with the recognition of adversity or stress selection in environments which are consistently and predictably severe (Southwood 1977, Grime 1979). Adversity selection is obviously applicable to tundra environments and to soil organisms (Greenslade 1983, Heal and Ineson 1984, Block 1985), but frequent disturbance, the determinant for r-selection, is also a feature in tundra systems. Further analysis of the characteristics of tundra organisms, with physiology as only one component, is necessary to clarify the extent to which there are features selected by severe environments which are distinct from those selected by frequency and intensity of disturbance. This is a fruitful area for future research in polar regions, which can contribute to the general development of ecology.

Acknowledgements – OWH is grateful to the organisers and sponsors of the Abisko Symposium in 1985 for the opportunity to participate and present a version of this paper.

References

Bliss, L. C. 1975. Devon Island, Canada. – In: Rosswall, T. and Heal, O. W. (eds.), Structure and function of tundra ecosystems. Ecological Bulletins 20: 17–60. Swedish Natural Science Research Council, Stockholm.

Block, W. 1980. Survival strategies in polar terrestrial arthropods – Biol. J. Linn. Soc. 14: 29–38.

– 1982. Cold hardiness in invertebrate poikilotherms. – Comp. Biochem. Physiol. 73A: 581–593.

– 1984. Terrestrial microbiology, invertebrates and ecosystems. – In: Laws, R. M. (ed.), Antarctic ecology, vol. 1: 163–236. Academic Press, London.

– 1985. Arthropod interactions in an Antarctic terrestrial community. – In: Siegfried, W. R., Condy, P. R. and Laws, R. M. (eds.), Antarctic nutrient cycles and food webs. Springer, Berlin, pp. 614–619.

– and Young, S. R. 1978. Metabolic adaptations of Antarctic terrestrial micro-arthropods. – Comp. Biochem. Physiol. 61A: 363–368.

– , Smith, R. I. L., Walton, D. W. H. and Wynn-Williams, D. D. 1980. British Antarctic Survey: Fellfield Ecology Research Programme. – Unpubl. Report. British Antarctic Survey, Cambridge.

– , Burn, A. J. and Richard, K. J. 1984. An insect introduction to the maritime Antarctic. – Biol. J. Linn. Soc. 23: 33–39.

Brock, T. D. 1972. Microbiological observations on Surtsey, 1970. – Surtsey Res. Progr. Rep. 6: 11–13. The Surtsey Research Society, Reykjavik.

Brown, J., Miller, P. C., Tieszen, L. L. and Bunnell, F. L. (eds.) 1980. An Arctic ecosystem, the coastal tundra at Barrow, Alaska. Dowden, Hutchinson & Ross, Pennsylvania, U.S.A. US/IBP Synthesis Series 12.

Bunnell, F. L., Tait, D. E. N., Flanagan, P. W. and Van Cleve, K. 1977a. Microbial respiration and substrate weight loss. I. A general model of the influence of abiotic variables. – Soil Biol. Biochem. 9: 33–40.

– , Tait, D. E. N., Flanagan, P. W. and Van Cleve, K. 1977b. Microbial respiration and substrate weight loss. II. A model of the influence of chemical composition. – Soil Biol. Biochem. 9: 41–47.

Burn, A. J. 1981. Feeding and growth in the Antarctic collembolan *Cryptopygus antarcticus* (Willem). – Oikos 36: 59–64.

– 1984. Energy partitioning in the Antarctic collembolan *Cryptopygus antarcticus*. – Ecol. Ent. 9: 11–21.

Callaghan, T. V. 1987. Plant population processes in arctic and boreal regions. – In: Sonesson, M. (ed.), Research in Arctic life and earth sciences. Ecol. Bull. (Copenhagen) 38: 58–68.

Chapin, F. S. 1987. Environmental controls over growth of tundra plants. – In: Sonesson, M. (ed.), Research in Arctic life and earth sciences. Ecol. Bull. (Copenhagen) 38: 69–76.

– , F. S., Miller, P. C., Billings, W. D. and Coyne, P. I. 1980. Carbon and nutrient budgets and their control in coastal tundra. – In: Brown, J., Miller, P. C., Tieszen, L. L. and Bunnell, F. S. (eds.), An Arctic ecosystem, the coastal tundra at Barrow, Alaska. Dowden, Hutchinson & Ross, Pennsylvania, U.S.A. US/IBP Synthesis Series 12: 458–482.

Clarke, A. 1980. A reappraisal of the concept of metabolic cold adaptation in polar marine invertebrates. – Biol. J. Linn. Soc. 14: 77–92.

Coulson, J. C. and Whittaker, J. B. 1978. Ecology of moorland animals. – In: Heal, O. W. and Perkins, D. F. (eds.), Production ecology of British moors and montane grasslands. Springer, Berlin, pp. 52–93.

Crocker, R. L. and Major, J. 1955. Soil development in relation to vegetation and surface age at Glacier Bay, Alaska. – J. Ecol. 43: 427–448.

Davis, R. C. 1981. Structure and function of two Antarctic terrestrial moss communities. – Ecol. Monogr. 51: 125–143.

– 1986. Environmental factors influencing decomposition rates in two Antarctic moss communities. – Polar Biol. 5: 95–103.

Ellis-Evans, J. C. and Wynn-Williams, D. D. 1985. The interaction of soil and lake microflora at Signy Island. – In: Siegfried, W. R., Condy, P. R. and Laws, R. M. (eds.), Antarctic nutrient cycles and food webs. Springer, Berlin, pp. 662–668.

Everett, K. R., Vassiljevskaya, V. D., Brown, J. and Walker, B. D. 1981. Tundra and analogous soils. – In: Bliss, L. C., Heal, O. W. and Moore, J. J. (eds.), Tundra ecosystems: a comparative analysis. Cambridge Univ. Press, Cambridge. International Biological Programme 25: 139–179.

Flanagan, P. W. and Bunnell, F. L. 1980. Microflora activities and decomposition. – In: Brown, J., Miller, P. C., Tieszen, L. L. and Bunnell, F. L. (eds.), An Arctic ecosystem, the coastal tundra at Barrow, Alaska. Dowden, Hutchinson & Ross, Pennsylvania, U.S.A. US/IBP Synthesis Series 12: 291–334.

– and Veum, A. K. 1974. Relationships between respiration, weight loss, temperature and moisture in organic residues on tundra. – In: Holding, A. J., Heal, O. W., MacLean, S. F. and Flanagan, P. W. (eds.), Soil organisms and decomposition in tundra. Tundra Biome Steering Committee, Stockholm, pp. 249–277.

French, D. D. 1981. Multivariate comparisons of IBP Tundra Biome site characteristics. – In: Bliss, L. C., Heal, O. W. and Moore, J. J. (eds.), Tundra ecosystems: a comparative analysis. Cambridge Univ. Press, Cambridge. International Biological Programme 25: 47–75.

– and Smith, V. R. 1985. A comparison between northern and southern hemisphere tundras and related ecosystems. – Polar Biol. 5: 5–21.

Goddard, D. G. 1979. The Signy Island terrestrial reference sites: XI. Population studies on the terrestrial Acari. – British Antarctic Survey Bull. 48: 71–92.

Greenslade, P. J. M. 1983. Adversity selection and the habitat templet. – Am. Nat. 122: 352–365.

Grime, J. P. 1979. Plant strategies and vegetation processes. – Wiley, Chichester.

Heal, O. W. and MacLean, S. F. 1975. Comparative productivity in ecosystems – secondary productivity. – In: van Dobben, W. H. and Lowe-McConnell, P. H. (eds.), Unifying concepts in ecology. Dr W. Junk, The Hague, pp. 89–108.

– and Ineson, P. 1984. Carbon and energy flow in terrestrial ecosystems: relevance to microflora. – In: Klug, M. J. and Reddy, C. A. (eds.), Current perspectives in microbial ecology. Am. Soc. Microbiol., Washington, pp. 394–404.

– , Flanagan, P. W., French, D. D. and MacLean, S. F. 1981. Decomposition and accumulation of organic matter. – In: Bliss, L. C., Heal, O. W. and Moore, J. J. (eds.), Tundra ecosystems: a comparative analysis. Cambridge Univ. Press, Cambridge. International Biological Programme 25: 587–633.

Holdgate, M. W. 1977. Terrestrial ecosystems in the Antarctic. – Phil. Trans. Roy. Soc. Lond. B 279: 5–25.

– 1984. The use and abuse of polar environmental resources. – Polar Record 22: 25–48.

Krog, J. O., Zachariassen, K. E., Larsen, B. and Smidsrød, O. 1979. Thermal buffering in Afro-alpine plants due to nucleating agent-induced water freezing. – Nature, Lond. 282: 300–301.

MacLean, S. F. 1980. The detritus-based trophic system. – In: Brown, J., Miller, P. C., Tieszen, L. L. and Bunnell, F. L. (eds.), An Arctic ecosystem, the coastal tundra at Barrow, Alaska. Dowden, Hutchinson & Ross, Pennsylvania, U.S.A. US/IBP Synthesis Series 12: 411–457.

Remmert, H. 1980. Arctic animal ecology. – Springer, Berlin.

Rosswall, T. and Heal, O. W. (eds.), 1975. Structure and function of tundra ecosystems. – Ecological Bulletins 20: 1–450. Swedish Natural Science Research Council, Stockholm.

– , Flower-Ellis, J. G. K., Johansson, L. G., Jonsson, S., Rydén, B. E. and Sonesson, M. 1975. Stordalen (Abisko), Sweden. – In: Rosswall, T. and Heal, O. W. (eds.), Structure and function of tundra ecosystems. Ecological Bulletins 20: 265–294. Swedish Natural Science Research Council, Stockholm.

Smith, H. G. 1985. The colonisation of volcanic tephra on Deception Island by Protozoa: long-term trends. – British Antarctic Survey Bull. 66: 19–33.

Smith, R. I. L. 1982. Plant succession and re-exposed moss banks on a deglaciated headland in Arthur Harbour, Anvers Island. – British Antarctic Survey Bull. 51: 193–199.

– 1984a. Colonisation and recovery by cryptogams following recent volcanic activity on Deception Island, South Shetland Islands. – British Antarctic Survey Bull. 62: 25–51.

– 1984b. Terrestrial plant biology of the sub-Antarctic and Antarctic. – In: Laws, R. M. (ed.), Antarctic ecology, Vol. 1: 61–162. Academic Press, London.

Sonesson, M. (ed.) 1980. Ecology of a subarctic mire. – Ecological Bulletins 30: 1–313. Swedish Natural Science Research Council, Stockholm.

Southwood, T. R. E. 1977. Habitat, the templet for ecological strategies? – J. Anim. Ecol. 46: 337–365.

Svensson, B. H. 1980. Carbon dioxide and methane fluxes from the ombrotrophic parts of a subarctic mire. – In: Sonesson, M. (ed.), Ecology of a subarctic mire. Ecological Bulletins 30: 235–250. Swedish Natural Science Research Council, Stockholm.

Tearle, P. V. 1987. Cryptogamic carbohydrate release and microbial response during spring freeze-thaw cycles in Antarctic fellfield fines. – Soil Biol. Biochem. (in press).

Visser, S. 1985. Role of the soil invertebrates in determining the composition of soil microbial communities. – In: Fitter, A. H. (ed.), Ecological interactions in soil. Blackwell Sci. Publ., Oxford, pp. 297–318.

Walton, D. W. H. 1982. The Signy Island terrestrial reference sites: XV. Micro-climate monitoring, 1972–74. – British Antarctic Survey Bull. 55: 111–126.

Whitfield, D. W. A. 1977. Energy budgets and ecological efficiencies on Truelove Lowland. – In: Bliss, L. C. (ed.), Truelove Lowland, Devon Island, Canada: a high Arctic ecosystem. Univ. of Alberta Press, Edmonton, pp. 607–620.

Wielgolaski, F. E., Bliss, L. C., Svoboda, J. and Doyle, G. 1981. Primary production of tundra. – In: Bliss, L. C., Heal, O. W. and Moore, J. L. (eds.), Tundra ecosystems: a comparative analysis. Cambridge Univ. Press, Cambridge. International Biological Programme 25: 187–225.

Wynn-Williams, D. D. 1980. Seasonal fluctuations in microbial activity in Antarctic moss peat. – Biol. J. Linn. Soc. 14: 11–28.

– 1982. Simulation of seasonal changes in microbial activity of maritime Antarctic peat. – Soil Biol. Biochem. 14: 1–12.

– 1985a. The Signy Island terrestrial reference sites: XVI. Peat O_2-uptake in a moss turf relative to edaphic and microbial factors. – British Antarctic Survey Bull. 68: 47–59.

– 1985b. The Signy Island terrestrial reference sites: XVII. Peat O_2-uptake in a moss carpet relative to edaphic and microbial factors. – British Antarctic Survey Bull. 68: 61–69.

Ecological Bulletins 38: 58–68. Copenhagen 1987

Plant population processes in arctic and boreal regions

T. V. Callaghan

Callaghan, T. V. 1987. Plant population studies in arctic and boreal regions. – Ecol. Bull. (Copenhagen) 38: 58–68.

The study of plant population biology in tundra and boreal regions is not new but the number of studies is small. Consequently, population biology theory which has been developed in temperate regions where plant competition, self-thinning and opportunistic growth are of particular importance, largely neglects population processes associated with severe physical environments. In these environments, density dependent survival appears to replace the density dependent mortality of temperate populations while strongly deterministic growth replaces opportunistic growth.

The severe physical environment of the tundra selects species which grow slowly over prolonged life cycles. In open habitats, sexual reproduction or vivipary predominate and deterministic cushion and tussock growth forms are common. In closed vegetation, clonal growth predominates in which foraging branches are subsidised in terms of nutrients, water and carbon by older modules within the clone.

Age class distributions arising from sexual reproduction show high mortality of the youngest age classes in contrast to the high probabilities of survival of the large ramets arising from vegetative reproduction. It must be inferred, therefore, that selection acts on the youngest genets but, unfortunately, most investigations of adaptation consider only mature individuals.

A major priority for future research is to use a strategic approach to form an interface between demography and ecophysiology. This approach allows some assessment to be made of the severity of various components of the physical environment while providing a basis for understanding the mechanisms of co-existence which is so important in the tundra.

T. V. Callaghan, Inst. of Terrestrial Ecology, Merlewood Research Station, Grange-over-Sands, Cumbria LA11 6JU, U.K.

Introduction

The study of plant population dynamics in tundra and boreal regions is not new: indeed, Kihlman in 1890 studied the longevity of arctic plants while Warming (1912–1921) collated studies on the biology of arctic plants at the beginning of the present century. As early as 1938, Wager collected data on the age class distributions of plants from East Greenland. However, far more investigations of population dynamics have been carried out in temperate regions (Harper 1977) and few attempts have been made to collate those from tundra and boreal regions (Bliss 1971, Callaghan and Collins 1981, Jolls 1982, Callaghan and Emanuelsson 1985). The surge in interest in plant population biology in temperate regions over the last two decades (Harper 1967, 1977, Harper et al. 1986) has resulted in our present understanding, but this largely neglects aspects related to severe physical environments.

The purpose of this paper therefore, is to emphasise the importance of population biology studies in northern latitudes both in terms of applications within these regions and potential contributions to population dynamics theory developed in temperate regions. Because studies of plant population biology are so few in tundra and boreal regions, another aim of this paper is to suggest topics requiring research in the future.

Population dynamics and some applications

The population is an entity of individual parts which has two basic time-dependent attributes; it has a size deter-

58

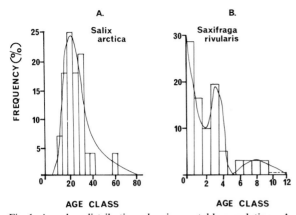

Fig. 1. Age class distributions showing unstable populations. A shows a long period of lack of recruitment and an age class distribution typical of the fragmentation of dwarf shrubs and B shows intermittent recruitment of individuals in East Greenland. It is impossible to calculate survival probabilities from such distributions. (Taken from Wager 1938 and Callaghan and Emanuelsson 1985.)

mined by the number of individuals and it has structure determined by the relative frequencies of individuals of various ages and stages.

The age/stage class structure is driven by the input of new individuals via births and the loss of individuals which die. The balance between these two processes determines whether the population grows in size, remains stable, or decreases. By looking at the dynamics of a population through its component individuals, it is possible to begin to predict what will happen to a relatively large unit of vegetation. Even if the population is stable, it can be seen immediately that this stability is determined by a dynamic but balanced turnover of individuals and it is then possible to predict what will happen if the balance is disturbed.

The dynamic aspects of the individuals within a population – even though the population itself may be stable – is of the utmost importance. It is often too easy to visualise the members of a plant population as stereotypes which are morphologically and functionally uniform and mature individuals; they are not. In natural plant populations, particularly of perennials, in northern latitudes, it is probable that the age/stage class structure will be uneven, with individuals of many ages and stages present. Not only do these individuals look different, they are functionally different too, and may play different ecological roles. In populations with high frequencies of young age classes, the mature stereotype may be a relatively unimportant component in ecological terms.

The study of population dynamics therefore, not only provides an accounting system to predict changes, for example in relation to the environment, but also provides a life-cycle frame-work in which the structure and function of an individual of any age or stage can be interpreted and related to an ecological role.

Another important aspect of studying population dynamics is to develop an interface between population biology and ecophysiology. Too few population studies investigate the physiological or environmental controls on survival and reproduction. On the other hand, few ecophysiological studies measure the difference in survival probability or fecundity due to variations in physiological parameters; yet without assessing the population processes, the adaptive significance of the physiology cannot be determined.

Many plants are constructed of repeated units or modules (Harper 1981, White 1984). In clonal plants, which are particularly common and extensive in the North, the clone may be regarded as a population of modules and the methods of population biology can be applied to estimate the growth and inter-relationships of modules.

The importance of population biology studies in the tundra

The study of population dynamics in the tundra is particularly important for several reasons.

A) Firstly the discipline of plant population biology has developed from studies in mainly temperate and occasionally tropical regions where plant competition is an important ecological factor. This tends to give a biased view of the importance of plant competition and self-thinning in determining population trends. The North offers environments which, in Grime's (1977, 1979) terminology, are stressed or disturbed or combinations of both. In these environments where plant canopies are open, plant competition is probably less important than the physical environment in determining survival, reproduction and plant growth form (Callaghan and Emanuelsson 1985). Studies from the tundra are necessary therefore, to complement the ideas we have about factors determining trends of plant populations from more competitive situations.

B) In contrast to the contributions to theoretical ecology which studies of population dynamics in the tundra can make, there are important applied aspects too. Tundra ecosystems are particularly sensitive to disturbance because of their slow development, and minor perturbations may result in catastrophic and irreversible damage (Bliss and Klein 1981). The study of plant population dynamics and growth strategies should enable us to predict how damage will affect populations, how quickly they will die and how quickly new populations may become established.

C) Another major reason for studying tundra plant populations is that they are amenable to one of the approaches of studying plant populations.

There are basically three ways of studying plant populations. The cohort specific method is that used most commonly in temperate areas and was developed by Tamm (1948), Canfield (1957) and Harper (1967). Members of a cohort are identified and marked in the

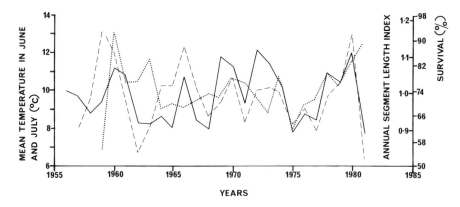

Fig. 2. Application of the retrospective approach to population biology to the correlation (see Callaghan et al. 1986a for statistics) of life-history phenomena of *Lycopodium annotinum* with climate. The solid line is a measure of growing season temperatures, the dotted line represents the survival of plant modules and the broken line represents annual growth increments. (Taken from Callaghan et al. 1986a.)

field and their reproduction, growth and survival is monitored over a number of years. Population events can then be related to time, age, size, environment etc. The method is best suited to short-lived plants such as annuals.

The second method is time-specific and has recently been used by Kawano et al. (1982) and Wijk (1986). Observations at one point in time are used to derive information on population trends. Individuals within a population are classified according to age or size or stage and their distributions are used to derive age-specific probabilities of survival with the major assumption that the population is in a steady state. However, in populations of some species such as *Calluna vulgaris*, it is difficult to identify the youngest age classes (Forrest 1971, Forrest and Smith 1975) and these are under-represented in the age class distributions. Other ericaceous species and dwarf shrubs may reproduce by fractionation, with young individuals absent (Callaghan and Emanuelsson 1985) and these show similar distribu-

tions (Fig. 1A). Also, seed set or recruitment from seed may not occur in particularly severe tundra growing seasons (Wager 1938, Warren Wilson 1964) and disjunct age class distributions will occur (Fig. 1B). In these circumstances, it is impossible to infer survival probabilities from age class distributions. In this method of determining survivorship, past environmental events are masked or bias the assumed survival values.

The third approach, the retrospective approach, involves recovering both living and dead plants from the field and determining mean past and current rates of age-specific survival and reproduction. This method allows past events to be correlated with climate, etc., in a way analogous to dendrochronology (Fig. 2) and mean population trends can be identified for a period extending back as far as the historical records preserved in the plant's past growth (Callaghan et al. 1986a, b). As plants in the tundra live for long periods (clones may survive for hundreds of years – Oinonen 1968) and decomposition rates are low, models of population

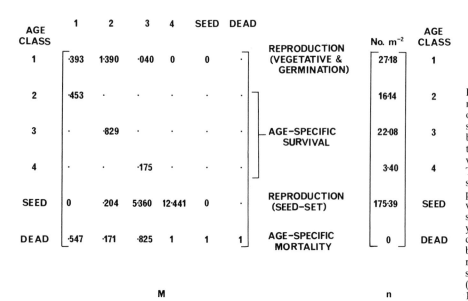

AGE CLASS	1	2	3	4	SEED	DEAD		No. m^{-2}	AGE CLASS
1	·393	1·390	·040	0	0	·	REPRODUCTION (VEGETATIVE & GERMINATION)	27·18	1
2	·453	·	·	·	·	·		16·14	2
3	·	·829	·	·	·	·	AGE-SPECIFIC SURVIVAL	22·08	3
4	·	·	·175	·	·	·		3·40	4
SEED	0	·204	5·360	12·441	0	·	REPRODUCTION (SEED-SET)	175·39	SEED
DEAD	·547	·171	·825	1	1	1	AGE-SPECIFIC MORTALITY	0	DEAD

M   n

Fig. 3. Transition probability matrix (M) and vector of observed age class structure (n). Dots represent biologically impossible transitions and assume the value of zero in calculations. This contrasts with zeros shown in the matrix where probabilities and factors may vary. Age class units (except seed and dead tillers) are years. Future age class distributions are predicted by multiplying n by M and reiterating this with subsequent values of n. (Taken from Callaghan 1976.)

ECOLOGICAL BULLETINS, 38, 1987

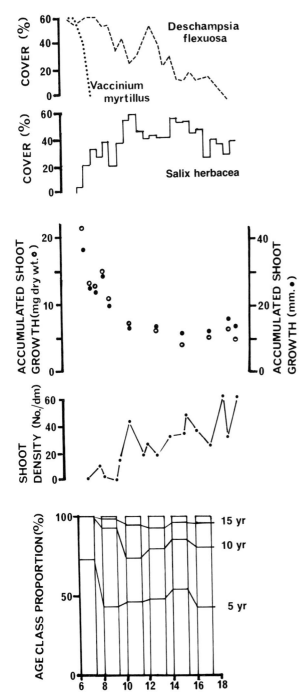

Fig. 4. The reaction of *Salix herbacea* to a snow-bed environment where competition (mainly with *Vaccinium myrtillus*) is associated with that part of the gradient experiencing the longest snow-free period and decreased shoot growth is associated with the shortest growing seasons. Large individual shoots, low shoot density, low cover abundance and a high proportion of young individuals (signifying fast turnover) is associated with the competitive situation and the reverse applies to areas experiencing the longest duration of snow cover. (Taken from Wijk 1986.)

trends may be built for long periods by sampling at only one point in time; the familiar cohort method would be totally inpracticable. By adopting this method, long term trends and processes may be identified and these may be applicable to populations of other areas where studies are not possible because of fast turnover and decomposition.

A convenient way to represent the population trends is to construct transition probability matrices which contain age-specific probabilities of death, survival and reproduction (Callaghan 1976, Fetcher 1983, McGraw and Antonovics 1983a, Callaghan 1984). When multiplied by a vector of current age-class distributions, a predicted age-class distribution can be obtained for the next transition (Fig. 3). This process is iterative, but for more realistic long-term predictions, there must be feed-back so that the values within the matrix can become variable.

Present understanding of plant population biology in arctic and boreal regions

Although the studies of plant population biology in tundra and boreal regions are few, some important implications are already becoming apparent.

Selective forces of the tundra

The environments of the arctic are relatively young and evolution has not proceeded very far according to Savile (1972). The high frequency of vegetative reproduction and vivipary, together with considerable longevity in tundra plants, have probably decreased the rate of evolution there. However, the plants we observe in the northern regions have been selected by a variety of forces. It is perhaps the nature of these forces which contrasts most strongly with the population process of mesic temperate and tropical areas (Callaghan and Emanuelsson 1985).

Biotic selective forces
Plant competition and herbivory are probably only important in increasing the probabilities of plant mortality in areas of closed vegetation in more favourable subarctic climates and soils. Indeed, it is the positive interactions of the biotic environment, such as commensalism and mutualism, which are particularly important in the harsher environments of the tundra. The survival probabilities of individuals are increased by their close association and competitive exclusion and self-thinning seem less important. It is possible, however, to find gradients over short distances, e.g. snow beds, where the physical environment limits the survival of a population at one extreme, but competition with other species limits survival at the other extreme (Wijk 1986) (Fig. 4).

In the most extreme physical environments or at the early stages of colonisation, the vegetation is sparse and

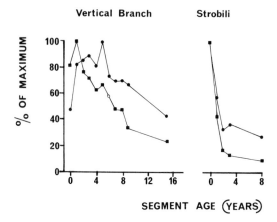

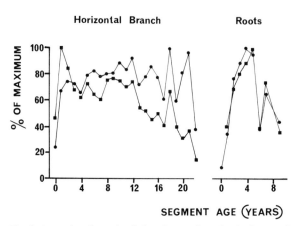

Fig. 5. Age-related trends of phosphorus allocation in tissues of *Lycopodium annotinum* suggesting retranslocation denoted by the difference between tissue dry weight (solid circles) and tissue P content (solid squares). Retranslocation occurs from senescing tissues to growing apices in horizontal branches and particularly vertical branches and strobili. Retranslocation does not appear to take place in the roots. (Taken from Headley et al. 1985.)

aggregated into islands. The benefits of aggregation are mainly shelter from wind exposure, provision of moisture for germination and seed establishment, provision of organic substrates and an increased local temperature.

The importance of these benefits can be estimated by the fact that Griggs (1956) recorded 93 species of vascular plants developing within cushions of five pioneer species, yet the cushions did not sustain damage. Similarly, most seedlings in a high arctic environment become established in moss and lichen mats (Bell and Bliss 1980).

Where controls on water loss from plants are weak, such as in *Hylocomium splendens,* close packing to a density of 6,000 shoots per m² seems essential to maintain an optimum water regime (Callaghan et al. 1978). Plant modules, as well as individual plants, are also

tightly-packed in particularly severe environments. This results from the evolution of strongly deterministic growth (Tomlinson 1982) shown particularly well in the cushion and tussock plant growth forms. This deterministic growth contrasts strongly with the opportunistic growth (Tomlinson 1982) associated with the selection processes of plant competition in temperate regions.

As long ago as 1951, Porsild stated that plants which climb, sting, poison, or possess spines and thorns are absent from the tundra, with the implications that these defences are not necessary and that negative biotic interactions are relatively unimportant. More recently, however, studies of Haukioja (1980) and others suggest that secondary metabolites are present as protection from grazing.

Soil environment

The main selective forces associated with the soil environment are concerned with the primitive nature of the soil, the extremes of water content and temperature and the low levels of plant nutrients. Fell-field soils are often mobile as a result of freeze-thaw cycles and they represent, perhaps, the harshest environment: that with high stress and high disturbance.

Many of the adaptations of tundra plants to soil conditions have been recorded by Chapin and his co-workers (Chapin 1974, Chapin et al. 1979), but here it is important to consider the response of plants in terms of growth form and demography.

It has been recognised since the time of Kihlman in the last century, that northern plants grow slowly and live for long periods (Kihlman 1890). Dwarf shrubs, cushion plants and tussocks of *Eriophorum vaginatum* (Mark et al. 1985) may live for over 100 years while individual graminoid tillers may live for over eight years (Shaver and Billings 1976, Callaghan 1977). Individual roots may live for 17 years (Headley 1986) while some rhizomatous species may have indefinite survival with apical growth and distal senescence (Kujala 1926, Callaghan et al. 1986a, b). This longevity enables an economy of nutrients and carbon such that for an initial investment, the structure has a prolonged period of function.

This strategy is shown well in the tussocks of *Eriophorum vaginatum* researched by Chapin et al. (1979) where there is a successive cannibalism of old tiller generations which are exploited by younger and vertically higher generations. It is also well exemplified in *Lycopodium annotinum* where a deterministic growth pattern allows the re-translocation of nutrients from senescing structures to young growing points (Callaghan 1980, Headley et al. 1985). Here there is a horizontal and vertical cannibalism (Fig. 5). The rhizomatous habit allows a foraging strategy whereby parts of a clone may be subsidised in terms of energy and nutrients while exploring unsafe microsites. Eventually, however, with a branching angle of 60°, a mean annual segment length of 65.5 cm and a generation time of 10–11 years, an individual is capable of re-exploiting the micro-habitat of an ancestor after 60–66 years when the ancestor has decomposed (Callaghan et al. 1986b).

Thus, life history phenomena such as longevity, vegetative reproduction and indefinite growth of many tundra plant species are important mechanisms which increase the survival potential of individuals growing in cold and infertile soils.

The aerial environment

The main selective forces of the aerial environment are low temperatures, desiccating conditions, abrasion of plant parts by wind and ice crystals together with xeric conditions in the fell-field habitats and short-late growing seasons in the snow-bed habitat. Low summer temperatures limit rates of photosynthesis and, more importantly, limit extension growth; they also affect the availability and activity of insect pollinators. Short growing seasons limit the period available for growth and developmental processes such as flowering (Sørensen 1941, Billings and Mooney 1968, Bliss 1971).

The impact of adverse aerial environments on short-term processes are reduced mainly by avoidance strategies whereby dwarf growth forms exploit sheltered micro-habitats (Savile 1972) and the prolongation of the life cycle and its developmental stages (Sørensen 1941).

In more southerly latitudes, and subarctic and low alpine areas, plants exhibit considerable opportunistic growth whereby the controls on growth are loose and the growth form of the plant is extremely flexible so that it can respond opportunistically to favourable conditions such as a gap in the canopy or the death of a competitor. In contrast, in the harsher tundra environments growth is usually strongly deterministic with tight controls. The uniform and closely controlled growth of cushion plants (Salisbury and Spomer 1964,

Spomer 1964) may enable temperature differentials of 32°C to be obtained (Savile 1972, Larcher 1980, Mølgaard 1982) and opportunistic growth could be disastrous.

More elaborate mechanisms to withstand harsh conditions appear to be lacking. The impacts of the aerial environment on long term development such as flowering, are accommodated by increased longevity and prolonged development or alternative forms of reproduction. Early spring growth and flowering are enabled by the presence of perennating storage organs and the pre-formation of flowering buds (Resvoll 1917, Sørensen 1941, Hodgson 1966). In *Puccinellia vaginata* it may take three years from flower bud initiation to seed set (Bell and Bliss 1980).

Forms of reproduction

The selective forces of the aerial environment can act at various stages of the life cycle (McGraw and Antonovics 1983b). Perhaps their greatest effect, however, is by killing young seedlings. It is not surprising therefore, that vegetative reproduction, which allows a period of post-natal care, is common in tundra plants.

Sexual reproduction

Many authors, from Porsild (1951) to Bliss (1971) have discussed the dominance of vegetative reproduction in the tundra. However, seed production is the main form of reproduction in the High Arctic, on fell-fields, on the fore-fields of retreating glaciers and in early successional stages in more favourable sites.

On King Christian Island in the High Arctic, 50% of 27 vascular plant species were observed by Bell and

Tab. 1. The effect on the length of the growing season of the flowering of *Phleum alpinum* (taken from Callaghan 1974). The potential and actual reproductive capacities are the number of florets and number of seeds per tiller respectively.

Site	length of growing season in days	floral initiation ?	internode elongation ?	anther/style exsertion ?	viable seed production ?	potential reproductive capacity	actual reproductive capacity	number of seeds per tiller per 11 yr
South Georgia (fellfield)	>168	yes	yes	yes	yes	77	22	242
Disko Island (quadrat A)	98	yes	yes	yes	no	786	0	241*
Disko Island (quadrat B)	89	yes	yes	yes	no	–	–	–
Disko Island (quadrat C)	70	yes	yes	no	no	–	–	–
Disko Island (snow bed)	42	yes	no	no	no	–	–	–

*assuming 1 favourable growing season and same proportion of florets producing seed as on South Georgia.

Tab. 2. A comparison of propagule size, numbers and the resulting probability of survival of an individual until reproductive maturity. (Summary of details presented in Callaghan and Emanuelsson 1985.)

Variable	Sexual reproduction	Vegetative reproduction Tillering	Vivipary
Propagule dry weight (mg)	0.02 to 7.98	1.1 to 39	0.9 to 3.9
Reproductive capacity (propagules per plant or shoot)	11 to 40 × 10⁶	0.1 to 3.97	11.5 to 40
Probability of survival	0 to 0.07	0.43 to 0.97	0.1 to 0.6

Bliss (1980) to produce viable seed while an additional 25% contained well-developed seed: only 33% of the species showed vegetative reproduction. This form of reproduction is essential for disseminating individuals which are scattered and surrounded predominantly by bare ground. 80–90% of the colonising individuals in the Rocky Mountain National Park were seedlings of *Silene acaulis*.

Some species may produce many seeds in the tundra. The colonising species *Potentilla tridentata, Diapensia lapponica, Juncus trifidus* and *Arenaria groenlandica* produced between 2,500 and 60,000 seed per m² (Griggs 1956).

In other species, there is a trade-off between the number of propagules and the propagule size. The sedges generally have larger seeds but a low reproductive capacity and a tiller can only produce seed once, usually after many years of development. Species at their distributional limit or in severe environments may only set seed infrequently. One of the main limitations to seed set is the shortness of the growing season (Tab. 1) and the potential reproductive capacity of *Phleum alpinum* on Disko Island was related to the frequency of favourable growing seasons (Callaghan 1974): a high potential reproductive capacity occurred, where favourable growing seasons and seed set were infrequent, to allow sufficient seed set in the occasional favourable growing seasons (Tab. 1).

In closed tundra vegetation where both sexual and vegetative reproduction occur, the role of sexual reproduction is often difficult to interpret. This is because the sexual reproduction may be completely unimportant at the site of seed production or at the time of seed production. In the birch forests at Abisko, one tree may produce 40 million seeds (Nordell, pers. comm.) throughout its life span, yet young trees are rare in many areas of the forest. These seeds are probably only important in areas of disturbance or new areas of colonisation outside the forest where plant competition is minimal. On the other hand, clones of *Lycopodium annotinum* may live for 250 years according to Oinonen (1968) and may produce 1.5×10^{14} spores in this period (Callaghan et al. 1986a). Again, young sporophytes are rare and sexual reproduction appears to be geared to infrequent forest fires or other major but infrequent forms of disturbance.

Vegetative reproduction excluding vivipary
In many areas of closed vegetation recruitment from sexual reproduction is negligible, as noted above. Here, vegetative reproduction is dominant and few large propagules are produced representing a trade-off between propagule size and propagule number (Tab. 2). Vegetative reproductive capacities are low but the propagules are large. This large size increases the chance of survival (Tab. 2). Chapin et al. (1980) calculated that the carbon cost of producing a tiller of *Dupontia fischeri* from seed was 10,000 times that of producing one vegetatively due to low survival.

The increased probabilities of survival of vegetative offspring result from a large initial investment of carbon and nutrients but also from a period of post-natal care.

In the rhizomatous sedges a tiller may develop to 40% of its parent's dry weight before initiation of an root and leaf system. During this period all of its growth is subsidised by the parent (Callaghan 1984).

This allows dispersal to distant safe microsites and also allows a competitive advantage over independent individuals. Subsidies of carbon for the growth of vegetative offspring may even come from the inflorescence of a parent tiller (Callaghan 1984).

Many generations of ramets may often remain in physical and physiological contact in tundra and boreal

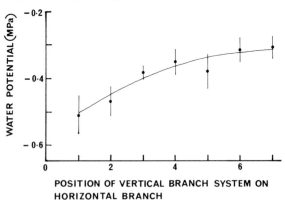

Fig. 6. Water potentials of vertical branches in relation to position along the parent horizontal module. Position numbers represent the age in years of the annual segment on the horizontal branch to which the vertical branches are attached. The trend suggests a dominant flow of water towards the youngest vertical branches which are associated with the dominant "foraging" apex of the parent horizontal module. (Taken from Headley 1986.)

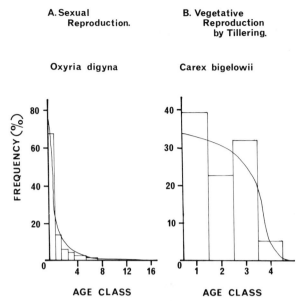

A. Sexual Reproduction.

Oxyria digyna

B. Vegetative Reproduction by Tillering.

Carex bigelowii

Fig. 7. Age class distributions associated with sexual reproduction (A) and vegetative reproduction by tillering (B). The high mortality of young genets contrasts strongly with the high survival of ramets and indicates that evolutionary selection of genets acts primarily on the seedlings and not the mature individuals. (Taken from Humlum 1981 and Callaghan and Emanuelsson 1985.)

areas. This allows the formation of an extensive and complex transport system in which older, apparently dead tillers, form important lines of communication. This transport system allows the movement of nutrients and energy from senescing parts to growing points and allows subsidised growth in unfavourable areas. It also allows transport of hormones to promote the growth of a dominant axis in favourable sites.

Subsidised growth is particularly important for the colonisation of bare rock etc. and the growth of young generations in such situations may depend entirely on the conditions experienced by the subsidising ancestral modules some distance away. In *Lycopodium annotinum,* for example, a dominant apex of a prostrate branch may import water taken up by roots 1 m away (Headley 1986) by having low water potentials (Fig. 6) while nitrogen, phosphorus and potassium are preferentially accumulated at the apex due to high enzyme activity (Headley 1986). In this species, the deterministic growth associated with apical dominance breaks down if the dominant apex dies. "Opportunistic escape" (Tomlinson 1982) then occurs as sub-dominant apices are released from inhibition. They greatly increase the probability of one branch encountering a favourable microsite by increasing the potential zone of exploitation (Callaghan et al. 1986a, b).

Vivipary
Vivipary is intermediate between sexual and vegetative reproduction. The propagules are larger than seed

(Tab. 2), can start to grow immediately on contact with a wet ground surface but are physically and physiologically distinct units which are easier than vegetative ramets to disseminate. Plantlets of *Festuca vivipara* contain between 3 and 4 times the amount of nutrients and carbohydrates as the seed of related species, according to Harmer and Lee (1978a, b), and could germinate in the year of formation, whereas seed of related species germinates in the following year.

This opportunism and increased propagule size makes vivipary particularly successful in harsh and disturbed environments. On King Christian Island in the High Arctic, two out of twenty-seven vascular species were viviparous and in the short season of 1974 only *Saxifraga cernua* reproduced successfully, and this was via bulbils (Bell and Bliss 1980). On the fore-field of the Kårsa glacier near Abisko, 20% of the vascular species were viviparous and were often associated with solifluction areas. Indeed, vivipary may be adapted to high stress and high disturbance – Grime's missing strategy (Grime 1977, 1979).

Age class distributions

Each of the types of reproduction results in a particular type of age class distribution.

Those arising from sexual reproduction show a high frequency of the youngest individuals and then a constant but high rate of decrease in frequency (Fig. 7A). As many as 70% of individuals of *Oxyria digyna* were in the year 0 age class according to Humlum (1981) and other species such as *Ledum palustre, Eriophorum vaginatum* and *Empetrum nigrum* from Alaska (McGraw and Shaver 1982) and *Luzula spicata* (Wager 1938) and *Chionochloa rigida* (Mark 1965) show similar trends. One major implication of this type of age class distribution is that environmental forces selecting for evolution act mainly on the youngest individuals: unfortunately, most investigations of adaptation are carried out on mature plants.

Few age class distributions arising from tillering have been determined (e.g. Flower-Ellis 1971). However, those for sedges suggest low mortality of young individuals and then sudden high mortality of older individuals associated with natural senescence or flowering (Fig. 7B). *Salix herbacea* reproducing in a similar way shows no appreciable mortality in the age classes younger than 6 years (Wijk 1986). This pattern is typical of a well-determined life span.

Distributions arising from bulbils are even fewer but are intermediate between those discussed above (Petersen 1981, Callaghan and Emanuelson 1985).

Many dwarf shrubs, *Lycopodium* and *Juncus* species etc. reproduce by fractionation and layering. Each new unit is old before it can be identified as an independent individual and this leaves a gap in the age class distribution which may be as long as 10 years in *Salix arctica* and *S. pulchra* from arctic North America. A superficial

Tab. 3. A strategic approach, involving demography, to assess the overall response of plants to the physical environment. The example given is that for the response of *Lycopodium annotinum* to soil infertility in Swedish Lapland. (Taken mainly from Callaghan 1980, Callaghan et al. 1986a, Headley et al. 1985, Headley 1986.) NOTE: a) there is no unique combination of options to a particular environmental problem; b) the greater the number of options adopted, the greater the problem; c) the lower the degree of overlap of options between species, the greater the chance of co-existence.

Potential responses to infertility	Adopted by *Lycopodium*?	Evidence
Increased rate of physiological uptake by roots	no	The uptake of P is only 53 nM g^{-1} h^{-1} which is at the lower end of values recorded for tundra plants
Increased root to shoot biomass	no	Root:shoot biomass for *Lycopodium* is 0.075 compared with values around 7:1 for other tundra species e.g. graminoids
Increased surface area of roots relative to weight	no	The youngest unbranched roots are the most efficient at taking up phosphorus
Increased root longevity to exploit soil with reduced cost of C & nutrients	yes	Individual roots may remain active for 17 yr
Presence of foraging habit to locate favourable microsites	yes	The growth of foraging modules is subsidised by older modules
Functioning with low growth rates to reduce nutrient requirements	yes	The Relative Growth Rate of *Lycopodium* is only 0.056 g g^{-1} d^{-1} which is equivalent to 55 mg increment per yr
Increased efficiency of nutrient use	yes	Tissue concentrations of nutrients are lower than those of other vascular species and similar to those of lichens
Conservation of nutrients by recycling	yes	Up to 85% of P in above ground tissues is recycled
Presence of store of non-structural carbohydrates to allow opportunistic growth	?	Soluble carbohydrates are 20 to 45% of the dry weight but opportunistic growth has not been observed

interpretation of these distributions (Fig. 1A) would give a totally wrong interpretation of the likely future of the population and emphasises the caution required when extrapolating from age class distributions to probabilities of survival.

Priorities for population studies in the North

The description of population biology in tundra and boreal regions given above is based on few observations even though Wager initiated modern studies in 1938. A major conclusion must be that much more basic research is required into all aspects of population studies in the North.

Some areas deserve more attention than others, however. We need particularly to redress the biased view of population processes derived from vegetation of more favourable climates and soils by quantifying the importance of negative plant interactions such as self-thinning, i.e. density dependent mortality, and competition compared with positive plant interactions such as commensalism and mutualism and density dependent survival.

In addition to adding to our understanding of theoretical ecology, it is important to understand the interactions between growth and population processes sufficiently to be able to make predictions for environmental

impact assessments and studies of basic vegetation processes such as colonisation.

It is also important to build long term life cycle and population frameworks in which to study physiological processes in a more meaningful way.

As an example of this, it is possible to look at plant responses to infertile soils using a strategic approach. First of all, a hypothesis is formulated to list all of the possible ways in which a plant species may have evolved to combat infertility. This check list can then be used to see which combination of options a particular species has adopted (Tab. 3). It is important to note that there is no unique combination for any particular circumstance but it would be expected that the severity of the environmental stress could be assessed from the number of options adopted by a species.

Species may co-exist if they have evolved different but complementary options to minimise competition. The dwarf shrubs *Vaccinium vitis-idaea* and *V. uliginosum* co-exist over much of the boreal region. They have been extensively researched by Karlsson (1982) at Abisko and it seems that their co-existence is helped by their complementary patterns of leaf canopy depelopment and activity – one is evergreen, the other deciduous – and a separation of rooting zones – one has shallow roots produced along a mobile axis whereas the other has deeper roots which exploit a given soil zone for a longer period.

This strategic approach which includes life cycle and

66

demographic components can, therefore, give an insight into the overall functioning of a species within its microhabitat.

As in other ecosystems, we need to know more about what causes the deaths of individual plants and what controls fecundity. We also need to quantify supposed morphological and physiological adaptations in terms of survival and fecundity benefits.

The ever increasing lines of communication within tundra and boreal regions and the constantly developing facilities for research, will hopefully stimulate research into the problems of the northern latitudes.

Acknowledgements – I would like to express my sincere gratitude to the organisers of the conference where this paper was presented for enabling me to contribute, and to the Director of the Abisko Research Station, Prof. M. Sonesson, and the Swedish Royal Academy of Sciences for the facilities and grants which have enabled much of my research to be carried out at Abisko. I am also grateful to Prof. N. Malmer and the Dept of Plant Ecology at the Univ. of Lund for their support and to the research students B. Svensson, B. Carlsson and A. Headley for their contributions to this work. Dr J.G.K. Flower-Ellis kindly commented on the manuscript.

References

Bell K. L. and Bliss, L. C. 1980. Plant reproduction in a high arctic environment. – Arct. Alp. Res. 12: 1–10.

Billings, W. D. and Mooney, H. A. 1968. The ecology of arctic and alpine plants. – Biol. Rev. 43: 481–529.

Bliss, L. C. 1971. Arctic and alpine plant life cycles. – Ann. Rev. Ecol. Syst. 2: 405–438.

 – and Klein, D. R. 1981. Current extractive industrial development of North America. – In: Bliss, L. C., Heal, O. W. and Moore, J. J. (Eds), Tundra ecosystems: A comparative analysis. Cambridge Univ. Press, Cambridge, pp. 751–771.

Callaghan, T. V. 1974. Intra-specific variation in *Phleum alpinum* L. with specific reference to polar populations. – Arct. Alp. Res. 6: 361–401.

 – 1976. Growth and population dynamics of *Carex bigelowii* in an alpine environment. Strategies of growth and population dynamics of tundra plants 3. – Oikos 27: 402–413.

 – 1977. Adaptive strategies in the life cycles of South Georgian graminoid species. – In: Llano, G. A. (Ed.), Adaptations within Antarctic ecosystems. Gulf Pub. Co., Houston, Texas, pp. 981–1002.

 – 1980. Age-related patterns of nutrient allocation in *Lycopodium annotinum* from Swedish Lapland. Strategies of growth and population dynamics of tundra plants, 5. – Oikos 35: 373–386.

 – 1984. Growth and translocation in a clonal southern hemisphere sedge, *Uncinia meridensis*. – J. Ecol. 72: 529–546.

 – and Collins, N. J. 1981. Life cycles, population dynamics and the growth of tundra plants. – In: Bliss, L. C., Heal, O. W. and Moore, J. J. (Eds), Tundra ecosystems: A comparative analysis. Cambridge Univ. Press, Cambridge, pp. 257–284.

 – and Emanuelsson, U. 1985. Population structure and processes of tundra plants and vegetation. – In: White, J. (Ed.), The population structure of vegetation. Junk, Dordrecht, pp. 399–439.

 – , Collins, N. J. and Callaghan, C. H. 1978. Photosynthesis, growth and reproduction of *Hylocomium splendens* and *Polytrichum commune* in Swedish Lapland. Strategies of growth and population dynamics of tundra plants 4. – Oikos 31: 73–88.

 – , Svensson, B. M. and Headley, A. D. 1986a. The modular growth of *Lycopodium annotinum*. – Fern Gazette: 13(2): 65–76.

 – , Headley, A. D., Svensson, B. M., Lixian, L., Lee, J. A. and Lindley, D. K. 1986b. Modular growth and function in the vascular cryptogam *Lycopodium annotinum*. – Proc. R. Soc. Lond. B 228: 195–206.

Canfield, R. H. 1957. Reproduction and life span of some perennial grasses of Southern Arizona. – J. Range Mgmt 10: 199–203.

Chapin, F. S. III. 1974. Morphological and physiological mechanisms of temperature compensation in phosphate absorbtion along a latitudinal gradient. – Ecology 55: 1180–1198.

 – , Van Cleve, K. and Chapin, M. C. 1979. Soil temperature and nutrient cycling in the tussock growth form of *Eriophorum vaginatum*. – J. Ecol. 67: 169–189.

 – , Tieszen, L. L., Lewis, M. C., Miller, P. C. and McCown, B. H. 1980. Control of tundra plant allocation patterns and growth. – In: Brown, J., Brown, P. C., Miller, P. C., Tieszen, L. L. and Bunnell, F.L. (Eds), An Arctic ecosystem. The coastal tundra at Barrow, Alaska. Dowden, Hutchinson and Ross Inc., Stroudsberg, pp. 140–185.

Fetcher, N. 1983. Optimal life-history characteristics and vegetative demography in *Eriophorum vaginatum*. – J. Ecol. 71: 561–570.

Flower-Ellis, J. G. K. 1971. Age structure and dynamics in stands of bilberry (*Vaccinium myrtillus* L.). – Research Notes No. 9, Dept Forest Ecology and Forest Soils, Royal College of Forestry, Stockholm.

Forrest, G. I. 1971. Structure and production of North Pennine blanket bog vegetation. – J. Ecol. 59: 453–479.

 – and Smith, R. A. H. 1975. The productivity of a range of blanket bog vegetation types in the Northern Pennines. – J. Ecol. 63: 173–202.

Griggs, R. F. 1956. Competition and succession on a rocky mountain fell field. – Ecology 37: 8–20.

Grime, J. P. 1977. Evidence for the existence of three primary strategies in plants and its relevance to ecological and evolutionary theory. – Am. Nat. 111: 1169–1194.

 – 1979. Plant strategies and vegetation processes. – New York, Wiley. Chichester.

Harmer, R. and Lee, J. A. 1978a. The growth and nutrient content of *Festuca vivipara* (L.) S.M. plantlets. – New Phytol. 80: 99–106.

 – and Lee, J. A. 1978b. The germination and viability of *Festuca vivipara* (L.) S.M. plantlets. – New Phytol. 81: 745–751.

Harper, J. L. 1967. A Darwinian approach to plant ecology. – J. Ecol. 55: 247–270.

 – 1977. Population biology of plants. – Academic Press, New York.

 – 1981. The concept of population in modular organisms. – In: May, R. M. (Ed.), Theoretical ecology, 2nd edn. Blackwells, Oxford, pp. 53–77.

 – , Rosen, B. R. and White, J. (Eds) 1986. The growth and form of modular organisms. – Phil. Trans. R. Soc. Lond. B 313.

Haukioja, E. 1980. On the role of plant defences in the fluctuation of herbivore populations. – Oikos 35: 202–213.

Headley, A. D. 1986. The comparative autecology of some European species of *Lycopodium* sensu lato. – Ph.D. thesis, Univ. of Manchester.

 – , Callaghan, T. V. and Lee, J. A. 1985. The phosphorus economy of the evergreen tundra plant *Lycopodium annotinum*. – Oikos 45: 235–245.

 – , Callaghan, T. V. and Lee, J. A. 1985. A field-based demographic approach to nutrient uptake and movement in a clonal perennial plant. – In: Harrison, A. F. and Ineson, P. (eds), Field methods in terrestrial nutrient cycling. Elsevier (in press).

Hodgson, H. J. 1966. Floral initiation in Alaskan Gramineae. – Bot. Gaz. 127: 64–70.

Humlum, C. 1981. Age distribution and fertility of populations of the arctic-alpine species *Oxyria digyna*. – Holarct. Ecol. 4: 238–244.

Jolls, C. L. 1982. Plant population biology above timberline: biotic selective pressures and plant reproductive success. – In: Halfpenny, J. C. (Ed.), Ecological studies in the Colorado Alpine. A Festschrift for John W. Marr. Univ. Colorado, Inst. Arct. Alp. Res. Occ. Pap. no. 37, pp. 83–95.

Karlsson, S. 1982. Ecology of a deciduous and an evergreen dwarf shrub: *Vaccinium uliginosum* and *Vaccinium vitis-idaea* in subarctic Fennoscandia 2. Photosynthesis and carbon economy of leaves. – Ph.D. diss., Univ. Lund, Sweden.

Kawano, S., Hiratsuka, A. and Hayashi, K. 1982. Life history characteristics and survivorship of *Erythronium japonicum*. The productive and reproductive biology of flowering plants. – Oikos 38: 129–149.

Kihlman, A. O. 1890. Pflanzenbiologische Studie aus Russichen Lappland. – Acta Soc. Fauna Flora fenn. 6(3): 263 pp.

Kujala, V. 1926. Forest vegetation in South and Central Finland. II. Limitation of the plant communities (in German). – Communicat. Inst. Quaest. For. Finland. ed. 10(4): 1–29.

Larcher, W. 1980. Physiological plant ecology. – Springer, Berlin.

Mark, A. F. 1965. Flowering, seeding and seedling establishment of narrow-leaves snow tussock, *Chionochloa rigida*. – N. J. Bot. 3: 180–193.

– , Fetcher, N., Shaver, G. R. and Chapin, F. S. III. 1985. Estimated ages of mature tussocks of *Eriophorum vaginatum* along a latitudinal gradient in Central Alaska., U.S.A. – Arct. Alp. Res. 17: 1–5.

McGraw, J. B. and Shaver, G. R. 1982. Seedling density and seedling survival in Alaskan cotton grass tussock tundra. – Holarct. Ecol. 5: 212–217.

– and Antonovics, J. 1983a. Experimental ecology of *Dryas octopetala* ecotypes. 2. A demographic model of growth, branching and fecundity. – J. Ecol. 71: 899–912.

– and Antonovics, J. 1983b. Experimental ecology of *Dryas octopetala* ecotypes. 1. Ecotypic differentiation and life-cycle stages of selection. – J. Ecol. 71: 879–897.

Mølgaard, P. 1982. Temperature observations in high arctic plants in relation to micro-climate in the vegetation of Peary Land, North Greenland. – Arct. Alp. Res. 14: 105–115.

Oinonen, E. 1968. The size of *Lycopodium clavatum* L. and *L. annotinum* L. stands as compared to that of *L. complanatum* L. and *Pteridium aquilinum* (L.) Kuhn. stands, the age of the tree stand and the dates of fire on the site. – Acta. Forest. Fenn. 87: 53 pp.

Petersen, P. M. 1981. Variation of the population structure of *Polygonum viviparum* L. in relation to certain environmental conditions. – Meddr Grønland, Bioscience 4: 1–19.

Porsild, A. E. 1951. Plant life in the Arctic. – Can. Geogr. J. 42: 120–145.

Resvoll, T. R. 1917. Om planter som passer til kort og kold sommer. – Arch. Math. Naturv. 35(6): 1–224.

Salisbury, F. B. and Spomer, G. G. 1964. Leaf temperatures of alpine plants in the field. – Planta 60: 497–505.

Savile, D. B. O. 1972. Arctic adaptations in plants. – Can. Dep. Agric. Monogr. 6: 81 pp.

Shaver, G. R. and Billings, W. D. 1976. Carbohydrate accumulation in tundra graminoid plants as a function of season and tissue age. – Flora 165: 247–267.

Sørensen, T. 1941. Temperature relations and phenology of the North West Greenland flowering plants. – Meddr Grønland 125: 305 pp.

Spomer, G. G. 1964. Physiological ecology studies of alpine cushion plants. – Physiol. Plant. 17: 717–724.

Tamm, C. O. 1948. Observations on reproduction and survival of some perennial herbs. – Bot. Notiser 3: 305–321.

Tomlinson, P. B. 1982. Chance and design in the construction of plants. – Acta biotheor. 31A(1–3): 162–183.

Wager, H. G. 1938. Growth and survival of plants in the Arctic. – J. Ecol. 26: 390–410.

Warming, E. 1912–1921. Structure and biology of Arctic flowering plants. – Meddr Grønland. 36–37.

– 1909. Oecology of Plants. – Clarendon Press, Oxford.

Warren Wilson, J. 1964. Annual growth of *Salix arctica* in the High Arctic. – Ann. Bot. 28: 71–76.

White, J. 1984. Plant metamerism. – In: Dirzo, R. and Sarukhan, J. (Eds), Principles of plant population biology. Sinauer Associates, MA, pp. 15–47.

Wijk, S. 1986. *Salix herbacea* and the alpine snow-bed environment. – Ph.D. diss., Univ. of Lund, Sweden.

Ecological Bulletins 38: 69–76. Copenhagen 1987

Environmental controls over growth of tundra plants

F. Stuart Chapin, III

Chapin, F. S., III 1987. Environmental controls over growth of tundra plants. – Ecol. Bull. (Copenhagen) 38: 69–76.

Arctic tundra plants grow in one of the most extreme of terrestrial environments. It is an environment of low temperature, short growing season, low light intensity, water-logged soils, and low nutrient availability. Most of these environmental features are direct or indirect consequences of the low radiation input and low temperature of polar regions. However, arctic plants exhibit a variety of physiological adaptations that minimize the impact of each of these environmental stresses. Consequently, each species in the community is limited by several factors, and the relative importance of each factor in limiting growth differs among species and between years. Thus it is impossible to identify any single factor as being most important in controlling growth of tundra plants: It depends upon the species, and it changes from one year to another. The fact that species differ slightly in their environmental requirements and therefore in the factors which limit growth means that the productivity of individual species changes in compensatory fashion in response to annual variation in climate. Consequently, community productivity is more stable among years than is the productivity of individual species. This contributes to stability of ecosystem processes such as energy flow and nutrient cycling and enables species with slightly different environmental requirements to coexist in the same community.

F. S. Chapin, III, Inst. of Arctic Biology, Univ. of Alaska, Fairbanks, AK 99775, USA.

Introduction

The effects of temperature upon individual processes of arctic plants have been studied extensively (e.g. Bliss 1962, Warren Wilson 1966, Billings and Mooney 1968, Chapin 1983, Chapin and Shaver 1985a). In general, these studies demonstrate that arctic plants are well adapted to low temperature, i.e. they maintain a high physiological activity at low temperature. Why then does the southern boundary of arctic vegetation correlate so well with summer temperature (Hare 1968), and why is the productivity of tundra communities so consistently low? A second question of equal importance is what causes the variation in productivity among communities within the Arctic? In northern Alaska, for example, heath communities, which have the warmest soils, have lower productivity than any other community type, suggesting that temperature may not determine the variation in productivity among communities within tundra (Chapin and Shaver 1985a). In this paper I consider the effect of various environmental factors on growth of tundra plants and discuss some field experiments which test the relative importance of some of these factors.

Temperature

Tundra plants can grow rapidly at low temperatures, and some species begin growth in spring when air temperatures exceed 0°C for even a few hours each day (Sørensen 1941). Arctic plants have a lower temperature optimum (15–20°C) for shoot growth than do temperate species (25–30°C; Scott 1970, Tieszen 1978b, Kummerow et al. 1980). Similarly, root growth by arctic plants is less temperature-sensitive and in some studies has a lower temperature optimum than that of temperate species (Chapin 1974, Shaver and Billings 1975, Bell and Bliss 1978, Ellis and Kummerow 1982). Leaves and even flowers tolerate temperatures slightly below freezing during the season of active growth, and overwinter-

Tab. 1. Maximum relative growth rate *(RGR)* and annual production of shoots of tundra and temperate graminoids. Rates were calculated from seasonal changes in aboveground biomass. Rates chosen were maximum rates, before water limitation or retranslocation reduced growth rate. The seasonal average relative growth rate showed similar differences among sites (from Chapin 1983).

Species	Site	Latitude	RGR (mg g^{-1} d^{-1})	Annual production (g m^{-2})	References
Arctic					
Carex aquatilis	Barrow, AK	71°18'	67	–	Tieszen 1972
Dupontia fischeri			92	–	
Eriophorum angustifolium			128	–	
Wet meadow tundra			93	101	
Eriophorum vaginatum	Atkasook, AK	70°27'	78	–	Chapin et al. 1980a
Carex meadow	Devon Is., CAN	75°33'	37	38	Muc 1977
Alpine					
Sedge meadow	Mt. Washington, N.H.	44°16'	64	187	Bliss 1966
Heath-rush meadow			110	117	
Sedge-rush meadow			57	104	
Temperate grassland					
Andropogon grassland	Illinois	40°20'	44	240	Baier et al. 1972
Mountain grassland	Bridger, MT	45°47'	60	249	Sims and Singh 1978a, b
Mountain grassland	Bison, MT	47°19'	54	272	
Northwest bunchgrass	ALE, WA	46°24'	16	98	
Mixed grass prairie	Dickenson, ND	46°54'	47	351	
Mixed grass prairie	Cottonwood, SD	43°57'	47	249	
Mixed grass prairie	Hays, KA	38°52'	50	363	
Shortgrass prairie	Pawnee, CO	40°49'	42	172	
Shortgrass prairie	Pantex, TX	35°18'	45	257	
Tallgrass prairie	Osage, OK	36°57'	62	346	
Desert grassland	Jornada, NM	32°36'	32	148	

ing plant parts are cold hardened to temperatures as low as –60°C (Billings and Mooney 1968).

To some extent arctic plants ameliorate their thermal environment. The small size of most arctic plants maximizes the thickness of the layer of still air (boundary layer) between the plant and the bulk air, so that leaf temperatures can be 3–8°C warmer than the bulk air (e.g. Warren Wilson 1957, Mølgaard 1982). Some cushion plants have leaf temperatures up to 20°C higher than air temperature, so that their maximum leaf temperatures are similar to those reported for temperate plants (Gauslaa 1984). Tussocks that protrude above the ground surface are particularly effective in absorbing radiation and warm faster than surrounding vegetation, promoting root growth and nutrient cycling within the tussock (Chapin et al. 1979). Tundra plants have substantial rates of cyanide-resistant respiration. This process produces heat rather than coupling electron transport efficiently to metabolism (A. E. Linkins, unpubl., Mølgaard 1982), although it is still unclear how much this would warm plant tissues except in certain inflorescences. Nonetheless, plant temperatures in the field are generally suboptimal, as indicated by more rapid growth in warm microsites (Sørensen 1941, Warren Wilson 1959) and when plants are transplanted to a warmer climate (Chapin and Chapin 1981). Thus we would expect more rapid growth if temperatures were warmer.

The effect of temperature upon growth of tundra plants is the cumulative result of the effect of temperature upon all physiological processes. Thus tundra plants are characterized by rates of respiration, photosynthesis, and nutrient absorption that are relatively temperature-insensitive and by a low temperature optimum for photosynthesis (Tieszen 1978a, Chapin 1983, Chapin and Shaver 1985a). For example, the 15–20°C temperature optimum of photosynthesis in tundra plants is about 10°C less than in comparable temperate species (Tieszen 1978a); tundra graminoids maintain 20–60% of their 20°C phosphate absorption rate at 1°C, whereas phosphate absorption in temperate plants is strongly inhibited below 10°C (Chapin and Bloom 1976).

The effectiveness of temperature adaptation by tundra plants is seen in a comparison of in situ relative growth rates between tundra and temperate graminoids (Tab. 1). Maximum relative growth rates occur early in spring when growth is supported by rhizome reserves and not yet limited by water or nutrients; thus at this time of year temperature may be the main limitation upon growth. The maximum relative growth rates of tundra plants are at least as high as those of their temperate counterparts, despite a 15–20°C difference in air temperature during the growing season. The 2-fold greater production of temperate compared with arctic graminoid-dominated vegetation must thus be due to their longer growing season and/or greater quantity of overwintering green material rather than to more rapid growth. Tundra plants apparently have their observed growth rates, not because low temperature prevents evolution of a rapid growth rate, but because the pre-

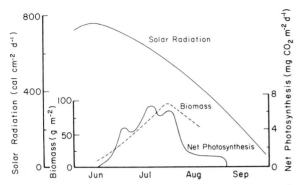

Fig. 1. Seasonal patterns of solar radiation, leaf biomass and net photosynthesis during the growing season at Barrow, Alaska (from Chapin 1983).

sent in situ growth rate is close to the maximum that can be supported by available environmental resources such as light and nutrients. A more rapid growth rate would require more resources.

In summary, tundra plants have at least as high a maximum relative growth rate as do comparable temperate plants, indicating that temperature during the growing season is not the major factor responsible for the low productivity of tundra. The relatively minor effect of temperature on growth of arctic plants is a consequence of very effective temperature adaptation of all physiological processes that have been studied to date.

Length of growing season

During the short arctic growing season plants must produce new leaves and roots. In deciduous species these have only a relatively short time in which to repay the carbon and nutrient costs of synthesis and to provide some net benefit to the rest of the plant. Moreover, snow-melt in the Arctic roughly coincides with the summer solstice, at which time there is little or no photosynthetic tissue displayed except by wintergreen or evergreen species (Fig. 1). By the time there are sufficient leaves produced to photosynthesize effectively, the light regime is rapidly deteriorating. For example, at Barrow, Alaska, at snow-melt there is only 4% of the leaf area that would be required for maximum carbon gain and by the time of peak above-ground biomass there is still only 30% as much leaf material as would be required for maximum carbon gain (calculated from Miller et al. 1976). A 10-d (12%) increase in length of growing season (due to earlier snow-melt) is expected to yield a 55% increase in annual carbon gain (Tieszen 1978b). Thus the short growing season, which is a function of low mean *annual* temperature, is a major factor limiting the productivity of tundra plants and may be more

important than the direct effect of low temperature during the growing season in controlling productivity of tundra.

Tundra plants exhibit many adaptations to the short growing season. Two or more years may be required for an inflorescence to complete development, and such developing flower buds over-winter without damage (Sørensen 1941). Most tundra plants are perennial, presumably because of the difficulty of reliably completing the life cycle in a single short growing season (Bliss 1971). Evergreen shrubs and graminoids with overwintering leaves become increasingly prominant in those communities with very short growing seasons (Bliss 1971, Jonasson and Chapin 1985).

Storage of nutrients and carbohydrates is an essential prerequisite for effective growth in a short growing season. For example, *Eriophorum vaginatum* stores high concentrations of nitrogen as arginine and of phosphorus as soluble organic phosphorus in belowground stems; the concentrations of these substances increase in autumn and then are withdrawn from the stem in spring to support growth of shoots and roots (Fig. 2; Chapin et al. 1986). The effectiveness of these reserves is seen in an experiment in which individual tillers of *Eriophorum* were placed in plastic bags in the natural environment (Jonassson and Chapin 1985). Those tillers in plastic bags showed the same rate of shoot growth and nutrient accumulation above-ground as did tillers with access to soil, indicating that growth was supported entirely from reserves, and that uptake served only to replenish reserves rather than to support growth directly.

The importance of storage depends very much on the growth form of the plant. Deciduous shrubs and forbs and those graminoids without overwintering green leaves must produce leaves very rapidly in spring to exploit the short growing season. Because soils are frozen at this time of year, new growth must be supported entirely by stored nutrient reserves, and active uptake is unlikely to contribute substantially to spring leaf growth (Chapin et al. 1980a, Jonasson and Chapin 1985). In contrast, evergreen shrubs, lichens, mosses, and many

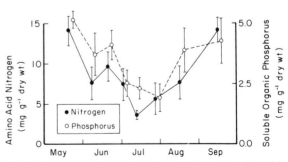

Fig. 2. Seasonal pattern of amino-acid nitrogen and soluble organic phosphorus in belowground stems of *Eriophorum vaginatum* L. from Toolik Lake, Alaska (from Chapin et al. 1986).

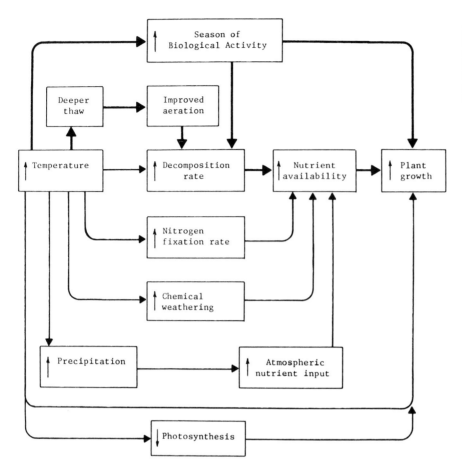

Fig. 3. Predicted direct and indirect effects of temperature upon processes affecting plant growth. Thickness of arrow indicates relative magnitude of effect (from Chapin 1983).

graminoids have considerable leaf biomass displayed at snowmelt and may produce leaves more gradually through the growing season (Chapin et al. 1980a).

shade plants in having high chlorophyll concentrations and low chlorophyll a to b ratio (Mooney and Billings 1961, Tieszen 1978a) and low Hill reaction rates (Tieszen and Helgager 1968, Billings et al. 1971).

Light

Because of low light intensity, photosynthetic rate in arctic vascular plants is rarely light-saturated and more closely parallels daily and seasonal patterns of light intensity than temperature (e.g. Miller et al. 1976, Tieszen 1978a, Chapin and Shaver 1985a). Thus to the extent that photosynthetic carbon gain limits growth, we would expect light intensity to have a substantial effect on growth of arctic plants.

The adaptations of arctic plants to low light intensity are similar to those of temperate plants from low-light (shaded) environments. Photosynthesis becomes light-saturated at a low light intensity, and positive photosynthesis can be maintained down to relatively low light intensities (Tieszen 1978a, Chapin and Shaver 1985a). Similarly, in the light reaction, arctic plants resemble

Water

In northern Alaska productivity increases with increasing soil water content, even at water contents above field capacity (Webber 1978). This is surprising because one would expect soil oxygen to limit many biological processes of roots and of microorganisms in water-logged soils. In most of these coastal tundra communities, water stress is rare and transient (Oberbauer and Miller 1979, Miller et al. 1980) and is unlikely to explain this correlation between productivity and soil water. High water content may promote growth indirectly be enhancing the movement of ground water and thereby the flux of soil solution past roots. This would speed the movement of nutrients to the root surface; because diffusion is usually the rate-limiting step in absorption

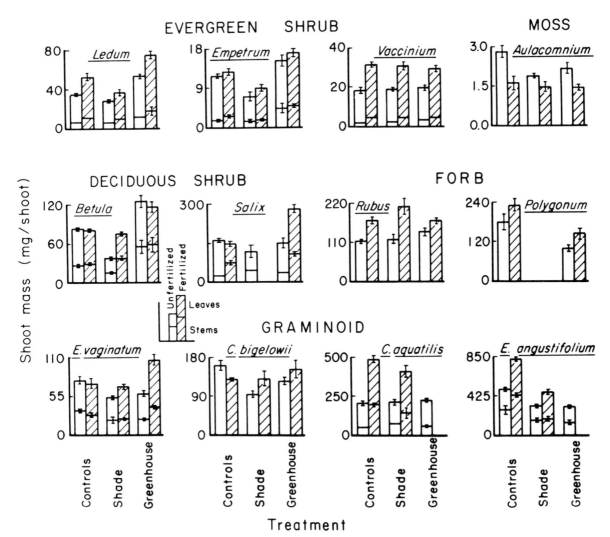

Fig. 4. Response of current year's shoot mass to fertilization in control, shaded, and greenhouse plots for each major species in tussock tundra and wet sedge tundra at Toolik Lake, Alaska. Shrub shoots were divided into leaves and stems and graminoid shoots (except *Carex bigelowii*) into blade and sheath. Mean ± SE, n = 5 replicates of 20 shoots. In some samples, standard errors are too small to be graphically evident (from Chapin and Shaver 1985b).

of nitrogen and phosphorus from low-nutrient soils (Nye 1977), mass flow of ground water should enhance nutrient uptake by plant roots (Chapin et al. 1979).

Nutrients

Addition of nitrogen and/or phosphorus has been found to promote plant growth in every arctic community thus far examined (Haag 1974, McKendrick et al. 1978, Shaver and Chapin 1980, Shaver et al. 1986), indicating that nutrients are important factors limiting plant growth. The low availability of nutrients in arctic soils is an indirect consequence of low temperature (Fig. 3). In contrast to temperate ecosystems, chemical weathering is strongly inhibited by low temperature and provides negligible input to the available pool (Ellis 1980). Consequently, arctic ecosystems receive a larger proportion

of their nutrient input from precipitation and nitrogen fixation than do temperate ecosystems (Chapin et al. 1980b). However, both of these inputs are an order of magnitude lower in the Arctic than in temperate systems, because in the Arctic low temperature limits (1) the quantity of precipitation and the nutrients contained therein and (2) the rate of nitrogen fixation (Barsdate and Alexander 1975, Chapin et al. 1980b). Consequently, arctic ecosystems are more dependent upon recycling of internal nutrient stores than are temperate ecosystems. These rates of organic matter mineralization are extremely slow, primarily as a result of the anaerobic cold nature of Arctic soils (Flanagan and Bunnell 1980, Chapin 1983).

Arctic plants have compensated for low nutrient availability and low temperature by evolving a high capacity for nutrient uptake per unit root biomass (Cha-

73

Tab. 2. Annual vascular aboveground production measured in 5 yr in tussock tundra at Eagle Creek, Alaska. Data are mean ± SE. Data for 1968 to 1970 are from Wein and Bliss (1974). The year of maximum (+) and minimum (−) productivity of each species is shown. Weather data are from the United States Weather Bureau at Central Alaska, 20 km north of Eagle Creek (from Chapin and Shaver 1985b).

	Production (g m^{-2} · yr^{-1})						cv of produc-tion (%)
	1968	1969	1970	1978	1981	Average	
Graminoid							
Eriophorum vaginatum	14.3±3.2	10.7±2.4(−)	27.6±5.3(+)	18.7±15.6	21.6±4.8	18.6±2.9	35
Carex bigelowii	5.0±1.1	1.8±0.4(−)	10.4±2.0(+)	7.2±5.1	9.0±4.1	6.7±1.5	51
Deciduous shrub							
Vaccinium uliginosum	7.3±1.6	12.2±3.3	9.4±1.7	4.3±2.6(−)	13.0±4.2(+)	9.2±1.6	39
Betula nana	1.0±0.5(−)	1.7±1.0	1.8±0.0	8.2±6.0(+)	4.0±4.0	3.3±1.3	88
Evergreen shrub							
Ledum palustre	15.6±2.4	20.3±3.0(+)	9.1±1.2(−)	15.2±5.8	13.4±3.3	14.7±1.8	27
Vaccinium vitis-idaea	16.3±2.7	20.8±3.5(+)	11.6±1.6	3.4±1.4(−)	8.6±2.3	12.1±3.0	55
Empetrum nigrum	3.5±1.3	5.5±2.0(+)	1.1±0.0(−)	1.9±1.3	2.2±0.9	2.8±0.7	61
Andromeda polifolia	0.3±0.2	0.7±0.4(+)	0.2±0.0	0.0±0.0(−)	0.5±0.4	0.3±0.1	79
Forb							
Rubus chamaemorus	2.0±0.1	3.8±1.7(+)	3.4±1.1	0.5±0.5(−)	3.3±1.0	2.6±0.6	52
Total production	65.3±6.2	77.4±8.4	74.6±5.6	59.5±11.5	75.5±5.3	70.5±3.4	11
Number of quadrats	(30)	(30)	(30)	(10)	(10)		
Average temperature (°C)							
June	13.8	16.0	11.4	12.3	...		
July	16.3	13.3	14.3	16.6	...		
Total precipitation (mm)							
June	64	3	61	45	...		
July	26	85	86	16	...		

pin 1974) and a high root:shoot ratio (Dennis et al. 1978), compared with temperate counterparts. In autumn, arctic deciduous plants retranslocate 40–60% of maximum pre-senescent nitrogen and phosphorus contents from senescing leaves (Chapin et al. 1975, 1980a, Muc 1977, Wielgolaski et al. 1975). This proportional retranslocation is similar to that observed in temperate plants (Chapin and Kedrowski 1983). Some species, such as *Eriophorum vaginatum,* are particularly effective in nutrient retranslocation from senescing leaves (Jonasson and Chapin 1985, Shaver et al. 1986) and thereby minimize their annual nutrient demand from the soil.

Single or multiple limiting factors?

From the literature review presented above it appears that growth of arctic plants could be reasonably expected to be limited by temperature, length of growing season, light, or nutrients. However, arctic plants exhibit physiological adaptations which minimize the potential limitation of each of these factors. Which of these factors is actually most important? Is there a single factor such as temperature that most strongly limits growth of tundra plants?

Most plants are extremely effective in compensating for imbalance in the resources required for growth. For

example, plants increase the ratio of shoot biomass to root biomass in response to light limitation and increase their capacity to absorb phosphate in response to phosphate limitation (e.g. Chapin 1980, Bloom et al. 1985). Theoretical considerations suggest that plants should adjust allocation so that their growth is equally limited by all resources (e.g. light, water, nitrogen; Bloom et al. 1985). However, in natural environments this may not be possible because (1) certain environments may be too extreme with respect to resource imbalance and (2) the environment is constantly changing, so that a plant can never be in perfect equilibrium with its environment.

Experiments in northern Alaska and Canada indicated that when light, temperature, and nutrients were manipulated in the field, each species of the community showed a different pattern of response to these manipulations (Fig. 4; Romer et al. 1983, Chapin and Shaver 1985b). This indicates that no single factor limits plant growth in these tundra communities. Consequently, in a single community one species may be most strongly limited by light, another by nitrogen, and others by still different factors or combinations of factors. Moreover, most species responded to change in more than one factor, indicating that growth is not overwhelmingly limited by a single factor such as temperature, i.e. plants have effectively compensated for the resource imbalance in their environment. The lack of strong limitation by any single factor (e.g. temperature) in these

74

field experiments provides independent evidence for the effectiveness of adaptation by tundra plants to their extreme environment.

The fact that each species in the community is limited by a different combination of environmental factors means that natural variation in weather conditions from year to year will have a different effect on each species. For example, *Eriophorum vaginatum* and *Carex bigelowii*, whose growth tended to be reduced by increased air temperature in experimental manipulations (Fig. 4), were most productive in the coolest year at another tussock tundra site (Tab. 2), whereas *Ledum palustre* and *Empetrum nigrum*, which responded positively to increased air temperature, were most productive in warm years (Chapin and Shaver 1985b). Thus although productivity of individual species varied substantially in response to natural variation in climate, this variation in productivity was compensatory in the sense that years that were good for some species were bad for others. Consequently, overall community productivity remained relatively constant, even though productivity of individual species varied substantially. This contributes to stability of ecosystem processes such as energy flow and nutrient cycling (McNaughton 1977) and may also contribute to species diversity of a community by permitting coexistence of species adapted to somewhat different environments (Chapin and Shaver 1985b).

Acknowledgements – Work leading to these generalizations was funded by the National Science Foundation (DPP-7680642, DEB-7905842, DEB-8205344), the Dep of Energy, and the Army Research Office.

References

Baier, J. D., Bazzaz, F. A., Bliss, L. C. and Boggess, W. R. 1972. Primary production and soil relations in an Illinois sand prairie. – Am. Midl. Nat. 88: 200–208.

Barsdate, R. J., and Alexander, V. 1975. The nitrogen balance of arctic tundra: pathways, rates and environmental implications. – J. Environ. Qual. 4: 111–117.

Bell, K. L., and Bliss, L. C. 1978. Root growth in a polar semidesert environment. – Can. J. Bot. 56: 2470–2490.

Billings, W. D., and Mooney, H. A. 1968. The ecology of arctic and alpine plants. – Biol. Rev. 43: 481–529.

– , Godfrey, P. J., Chabot, B. F. and Bourque, D. P. 1971. Metabolic acclimation to temperature in arctic and alpine ecotypes of *Oxyria digyna*. – Arct. Alp. Res. 3: 277–289.

Bliss, L. C. 1962. Adaptations of arctic and alpine plants to environmental conditions. – Arctic 15: 117–144.

– 1966. Plant productivity in alpine microenvironments on Mt. Washington, New Hampshire. – Ecol. Monogr. 36: 125–155.

– 1971. Arctic and alpine plant life cycles. – Ann. Rev. Ecol. Syst. 2: 405–438.

Bloom, A. J., Chapin, F. S. III, and Mooney, H. A. 1985. Resource limitation in plants – an economic analogy. – Ann. Rev. Ecol. Syst. 16: 363–392.

Chapin, F. S., III. 1974. Morphological and physiological mechanisms of temperature compensation in phosphate absorption along a latitudinal gradient. – Ecology 55: 1180–1198.

– 1980. The mineral nutrition of wild plants. – Ann. Rev. Ecol. Syst. 11: 233–260.

– 1983. Direct and indirect effects of temperature on arctic plants. – Polar Biol. 2: 47–52.

– and Bloom, A. J. 1976. Phosphate absorption: adaptation of tundra graminoids to a low temperature, low phosphorus environment. – Oikos 27: 111–121.

– and Chapin, M. C. 1981. Ecotypic differentiation of growth processes in *Carex aquatilis* along latitudinal and local gradients. – Ecology 62: 1000–1009.

– and Kedrowski, R. A. 1983. Seasonal changes in nitrogen and phosphorus fractions and autumn retranslocation in evergreen and deciduous taiga trees. – Ecology 64: 376–391.

– and Shaver, G. R. 1985a. Arctic. – In: Chabot, B. F. and Moneey, H. A. (eds.), Physiological ecology of North American plant communities. Chapman and Hall, New York, pp. 16–40.

– and Shaver, G. R. 1985b. Individualistic growth response of tundra plant species to environmental manipulations in the field. – Ecology 66: 564–576.

– Van Cleve, K. and Tieszen, L. L. 1975. Seasonal nutrient dynamics of tundra vegetation at Barrow, Alaska. – Arct. Alp. Res. 7: 209–226.

– , Van Cleve, K. and Chapin, M. C. 1979. Soil temperature and nutrient cycling in the tussock growth form of *Eriophorum vaginatum*. – J. Ecol. 67: 169–189.

– , Johnson, D. A. and McKendrick, J. D. 1980a. Seasonal movement of nutrients in plants of differing growth form in an Alaskan tundra ecosystem: implications for herbivory. – J. Ecol. 68: 189–209.

– , Miller, P. C., Billings, W. D. and Coyne, P. I. 1980b. Carbon and nutrient budgets and their control in coastal tundra. – In: Brown, J., Miller, P. C., Tieszen, L. L. and Bunnell, F. L. (eds.), An Arctic ecosystem: the coastal tundra at Barrow, Alaska. Dowden, Hutchinson and Ross, Stroudsburg, PA, pp. 458–482.

– , Shaver, G. R. and Kedrowski, R. A. 1986. Environmental controls over carbon, nitrogen and phosphorus fractions in *Eriophorum vaginatum* L. in Alaska tussock tundra. – J. Ecol. 74: 167–195.

Dennis, J. G., Tieszen, L. L. and Vetter, M. A. 1978. Seasonal dynamics of above and belowground production of vascular plants at Barrow, Alaska. – In: Tieszen, L. L. (ed.), Vegetation and production ecology of an Alaskan Arctic tundra. Springer, New York, pp. 113–140.

Ellis, B. A. and Kummerow, J. 1982. Temperature effect on growth rates of *Eriophorum vaginatum* roots. – Oecologia (Berl.) 54: 136–137.

Ellis, S. 1980. An investigation of weathering in some arctic-alpine soils on the northeast flank of Oksskolten, North Norway. – J. Soil Sci. 31: 371–385.

Flanagan, P. W., and Bunnell, F. L. 1980. Microflora activities and decomposition. – In: Brown, J., Miller, P. C., Tieszen, L. L. and Bunnell, F. L. (eds.), An Arctic ecosystem: the coastal tundra at Barrow, Alaska. Dowden, Hutchinson and Ross, Stroudsburg, PA, pp. 291–334.

Gauslaa, Y. 1984. Heat resistance and energy budget in different Scandinavian plants. – Holarct. Ecol. 7: 1–78.

Haag, R. W. 1974. Nutrient limitations to plant production in two tundra communities. – Can. J. Bot. 52: 103–116.

Hare, F. K. 1968. The arctic. – Qart. J. Royal Met. Soc. 58: 439–459.

Jonasson, S., and Chapin, F. S., III. 1985. Seasonal patterns of leaf growth, nutrient uptake, translocation and leaching loss in the cotton sedge, *Eriophorum vaginatum* L. – Oecologia (Berl.) 67: 511–518.

Kummerow, J., McMaster, G. S. and Krause, D. A. 1980. Temperature effects on growth and nutrient contents in *Eriophorum vaginatum* under controlled environmental conditions. – Arct. Alp. Res. 12: 335–341.

McKendrick, J. D., Ott, V. J. and Mitchell, G. A. 1978.

Effects of nitrogen and phosphorus fertilization on carbohydrate and nutrient levels in *Dupontia fisheri* and *Arctagrostis latifolia*. In: Tieszen, L. L. (ed.), Vegetation and production ecology of an Alaskan Arctic tundra. Springer, New York, pp. 509–537.

McNaughton, S. J. 1977. Diversity and stability of ecological communities: A comment on the role of empiricism in ecology. – Am. Nat. 111: 515–525.

Miller, P. C., Stoner, W. A. and Tieszen, L. L. 1976. A model of stand photosynthesis for the wet meadow tundra at Barrow, Alaska. – Ecology 57: 411–430.

– , Webber, P. J., Oechel, W. C. and Tieszen, L. L. 1980. Biophysical processes and primary production. – In: Brown, J. Miller, P. C., Tieszen, L. L. and Bunnell, F. L. (eds.) An Arctic ecosystem: the coastal tundra at Barrow, Alaska. Dowden, Hutchinson and Ross, Stroudsburg, PA, pp. 66–101.

Mølgaard, P. 1982. Temperature observations in high arctic plants in relation to microclimate in the vegetation of Peary Land, North Greenland. – Arct. Alp. Res. 14: 105–115.

Mooney, H. A. and Billings, W. D. 1961. Comparative physiological ecology of arctic and alpine populations of *Oxyria digyna*. – Ecol. Monogr. 31: 1–29.

Muc, M. 1977. Ecology and primary production of sedge-moss meadow communities, Truelove Lowland. – In: Bliss, L. C. (ed.), Truelove Lowland, Devon Island, Canada: A high Arctic ecosystem. Univ. Alberta Press, Edmonton, Canada, pp. 157–180.

Nye, P. H. 1977. The rate-limiting step in plant nutrient absorption from soil. – Soil Sci. 123: 292–297.

Oberbauer, S., and Miller, P. C. 1979. Plant water relations in montane and tussock tundra vegetation types in Alaska. – Arct. Alp. Res. 11: 69–81.

Romer, M. J., Cummins, W. R. and Svoboda, J. 1983. Productivity of native and temperate "crop" plants in the Keewatin District, N.W.T. – Naturaliste Canadienne 110: 85–93.

Scott, D. 1970. Relative growth rates under controlled temperatures of some New Zealand indigenous and introduced grasses. – N. Z. J. Bot. 8: 76–81.

Shaver, G. R., and Billings, W. D. 1975. Root production and root turnover in a wet tundra ecosystem, Barrow, Alaska. – Ecology 56: 401–409.

– and Chapin, F. S., III. 1980. Response to fertilization by various plant growth forms in an Alaskan tundra: Nutrient accumulation and growth. – Ecology 61: 662–675.

– , Chapin, F. S., III, and Gartner, B. L. 1986. Factors limiting growth and peak biomass accumulation of *Eriophorum vaginatum* L. in Alaskan tussock tundra. – J. Ecol. 74: 257–278.

Sims, P. L., and Singh, J. S. 1978a. The structure and function of ten western North American grasslands. II. Intra-seasonal dynamics in primary producer compartments. – J. Ecol. 66: 547–572.

– and Singh, J. S. 1978b. The structure and function of ten western North American grasslands. III. Net primary production, turnover and efficiencies of energy capture and water use. – J. Ecol. 66: 573–597.

Sørensen, T. 1941. Temperature relations and phenology of the northeast Greenland flowering plants. – Meddr Grønland 125: 1–305.

Tieszen, L. L. 1972. The seasonal course of aboveground production and chlorophyll distribution in a wet arctic tundra at Barrow, Alaska. – Arct. Alp. Res. 4: 307–324.

– 1978a. Photosynthesis in the principal Barrow, Alaska, species: A summary of field and laboratory responses. – In: Tieszen, L. L. (ed.), Vegetation and production ecology of an Alaskan Arctic tundra. Springer, New York, pp. 241–268.

– 1978b. Summary. – In: Tieszen, L. L. (ed.), Vegetation and production ecology of an Alaskan Arctic tundra. Springer, New York, pp. 621–645.

– and Helgager, J. A. 1968. Genetic and physiological adaptation in the Hill reaction of *Deschampsia caespitosa*. – Nature, Lond. 219: 1066–1067.

Warren Wilson, J. 1957. Observations on the temperatures of arctic plants and their environment. – J. Ecol. 45: 499–531.

– 1959. Notes on wind and its effects in arctic-alpine vegetation. – J. Ecol. 47: 415–427.

– 1966. An analysis of plant growth and its control in arctic environments. – Ann. Bot. 30: 383–402.

Webber, P. J. 1978. Spatial and temporal variation of the vegetation and its productivity, Barrow, Alaska. – In: Tieszen, L. L. (ed.), Vegetation and production ecology of an Alaskan Arctic tundra. Springer, New York, pp. 37–112.

Wein, R. W, and Bliss, L. C. 1974. Primary production in arctic cottongrass tussock tundra communities. – Arct. Alp. Res. 6: 261–274.

Wielgolaski, F. E., Kjelvik, S. and Kallio, P. 1975. Mineral content of tundra and forest tundra plants in Fennoscandia. – In: Wielgolaski, F. E. (ed.), Fennoscandian tundra ecosystems, Part I: Plants and microorganisms. Springer, Berlin, pp. 316–332.

Ecological Bulletins 38: 77–94. Copenhagen 1987

The nunatak theory reconsidered

Eilif Dahl

Dahl, E. 1987. The nunatak theory reconsidered. – Ecol. Bull. (Copenhagen) 38: 77–94.

The nunatak theory proposes that unglaciated areas existed along the shores of the North Atlantic ocean where plants and animals survived the last or previous glacial ages. This theory is examined in light of recent research.
Reconstructions of summer temperature conditions 18,000 years ago suggest that the lowland flora of Scandinavia could not survive in icefree refuges but immigrated from the south or east when the ice melted. However, numerous species of the alpine flora could not survive in the lowlands south and east of the north European ice sheet 18,000 years ago and must have survived in ice-free refugia. This is confirmed by an analysis of the phytogeographic affinities of the lowland and the alpine floras.
A relatively high amount of endemism, presence of numerous amphiatlantic species lacking in the Alps and similarity between the alpine-subalpine floras of Iceland, the British Isles and Scandinavia indicate that these floras survived in refuges since early Pleistocene times. Recent geological evidence suggest that a land area once connected Scandinavia, Scotland and Iceland up to Late Pliocene – Early Pleistocene. With present topography several areas around the North Atlantic could not be covered by an inland ice because of the plasticity of ice.
New dating methods (amino acid analysis, thermoluminescence) show that some areas in Spitsbergen have remained ice-free during most of the Pleistocene.
Presence of gibbsite and other clay minerals suggest that the mountain top detritus is a remnant of the Tertiary weathering crust which has survived the Pleistocene glacial ages.

E. Dahl, Botanical Inst., P.O. Box 14, N-1432 Ås-NLH, Norway.

Introduction

The *nunatak theory* or hypothesis proposes that some unglaciated refuges existed in Scandinavia or elsewhere north of the southern boundary of the Pleistocene glaciers where plants and animals could survive the last or previous glacial ages. The refuges could either be mountains rising above an inland ice, which in inuit language are called nunataks, or coastal refugia. When the ice melted, plants and animals immigrated into previously ice-covered land from the refugia and from the unglaciated areas south and perhaps east of the inland ice. The alternative hypothesis is called the *tabula rasa* theory or hypothesis which proposes that all highly organized land plants and animals were exterminated north of the southern boundary of the Pleistocene glaciers and that the present biota all have immigrated from the south or east.

The nunatak hypothesis was first formally proposed by Sernander (1896) in a review of a study of Andersson but with reference to the observations by Blytt (1876), about the presence in Scandinavia of an element of species found in Greenland and North America but not elsewhere in Europe; what we now call an amphiatlantic element. However, Warming (1888: 191f.) had already proposed a similar hypothesis pertaining to Greenland. A lively discussion followed around the turn of the centry and in the first decade of the 20th century. After that came a period with little discussion until it was revived by Nordhagen (1931, 1935, 1936). Another period of intense discussions followed around 1960 with contributions published in Svensk Naturvetenskap by Holtedahl og Rosenqvist (1958), Nannfeldt (1958), Lindroth (1958), Hoppe (1959) and Dahl (1961 a) and the NATO symposium in Iceland (Löve and Löve 1963). The purpose of this contribution is to review the evidence brought to light during more recent years, to evaluate whether a solution of previously unanswered questions is in sight and discuss what sort of evidence is likely to help us further.

The first thing to emphasize is that the problem requires a multidisciplinary approach. A solution must be found which is satisfactory both to biogeographers and to geologists. It is not satisfactory to conclude from the biogeographical facts that refuges existed and subsequently explain the present pattern as a result of survival on nunataks; that involves circular reasoning. On the other hand a geological picture permitting no solution on important observable biogeographical facts must also be open to critizism. Both an erratic boulder and a relict plant are witnesses of happenings in the past. The important thing is to interpret their testimony correctly, not that one is a plant and the other a piece of rock.

The geologist would normally approach the problem by studying stratigraphic columns where different layers are superimposed and can be dated. The biogeographer would approach the problem by studying the distribution patterns and the biological properties of plants and animals. In this contribution I shall begin with the biological, especially the botanical approach, and later return to geological evidence. Also the contributions by climatologists and geophysicists are important. But I shall not deal much with the zoological aspects, important as they may be, because I know too little about animals.

Approaching the question from the study of distribution patterns and biological properties of plants, two different approaches are open. One is by intensive studies of a limited group of plants. An excellent example is provided by the studies by Nordhagen (1931) on *Papaver* later followed up by cytological and experimental work by Knaben (1959 a, b). And indeed such studies offer formidable insights. The difficulty rests in the question whether the species or group of species is representative or if we would obtain another picture by studying a different group of plants. The other approach is to search for patterns of distribution where several taxa are considered together. One way of doing this is to take the entire flora of an area e.g. Northern Europe and sort out elements of species sharing distributional or other biological characters. This is mainly the approach I shall use here, but with due regard to the results of detailed investigations. This approach has the advantage that statistical methods can be employed to test the significances of differences.

One danger in this type of studies is that one may be tempted to end up with what has been called "explanations of last resort". Faced with an unexplainable distribution it is tempting to resort to some long distance dispersal hypothesis, that seeds became attached to the foot of a bird or were blown for thousands of kilometres across an arctic ice-covered sea (Savile 1972) or were carried by an iceberg (Nordal 1985 b). The difficulty with such hypotheses is that they may be almost impossible to falsify. According to modern philosophy it is never possible to prove that a scientific theory is right, but it is possible to prove it false. The better the theory

stands up to attemps of falsification, the better the theory. A theory which offers no possibilities of falsification is not a scientific theory.

Maybe the problem appears unsolvable because some of the facts taken for granted are not necessarily true at all. A typical situation is provided by the explanation of the flora and fauna of remote islands, e.g. Hawaii. For long the hypothesis of permanence of the oceans was taken for granted, hence no option was available other than long-distance dispersal to explain the biota of Hawaii. Hence the minimum number of introductions to explain the flora was calculated. It was further assumed that the members of each immigrant group most adapted to long-distance dispersal were similar to the original immigrant taxa and from this evolutionary trees were constructed. Nowadays the hypothesis of the permanence of the oceans is rejected, instead continents move, ridges are created, the sea bottoms subside and perhaps some remote islands, e.g. Jan Mayen, are better explained as being a part of a continent which once broke loose and then sailed away from the parent continent.

In general last resort hypotheses should be avoided. Darwin has given a warning. In his autobiography (Barlow 1958: 84) he tells that he visited the so-called parallel roads at Glen Roy in Scotland and wrote a paper about it: "The paper was a great failure, and I am ashamed of it. Having been deeply impressed with what I had seen of the elevation of land in S. America, I attributed the parallel lines to the action of the sea; but I later had to give up this view when Agassiz propounded the glacier lake theory. Because no other explanation was possible under our then state of knowledge, I argued in favour of seaaction; and my error has been a good lesson to me never to trust in science to the principle of exclusion."

In a case where a hypotesis cannot be verified in some way it seems better to admit that a piece of evidence is unexplainable at present than to propose new, unfalsifiable hypotheses.

The ice age climate

Information about ecological conditions during the period of maximum glaciation of the last or previous glacial ages is important for the judgement of the possibilites of survival of plants on refuges or along the southern border of glaciation in Europe. Many estimates have been made of the climatic conditions by different methods. Among the geophysical ones may be mentioned the oxygen isotope method measuring the ratio between O_{16} and O_{18} in marine shells giving information about the temperature of the ocean water. A geological method is to map the extent of the glaciers during the glacial maximum (Frenzl 1960, Flint 1971) and in this way estimate the depression of the snow line. This method commonly gives a depression of about 1 000 m suggesting a temperature drop of about 6°C. However,

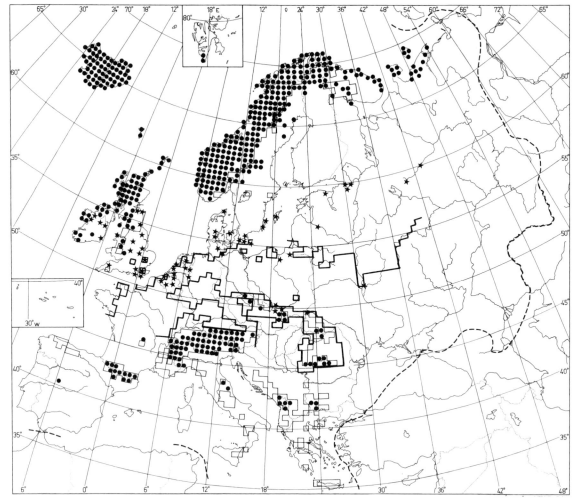

Fig. 1. Present-day distribution of *Salix herbacea* (black dots) (after Atlas Florae Europaeae) with the isotherm (thin line) of 23°C for average annual maximum summer temperatures calculated for the highest summits in each 50×50 km square. In addition Weichselian fossil occurrences (stars) (taken from Tralau 1963 and Conolly in Conolly and Dahl 1970) are given together with the 29°C maximum summer temperature isotherm (thicker line) in Germany and adjacent areas.

the snow-line depends both on temperatures during the snow-melt season and the amount of snow in winter. To estimate summer temperatures by this method information about winter precipitation is needed. A third method has been based on observations of fossil frost phenomena in the soil e.g. polygons or frost wedges in areas with little present-day frost in winter. However, the penetration of frost in the soil depends both on air temperatures and snow cover.

Estimates have also been made based on fossil plants and animals in deposits from the glacial age maximum, pollen or macrofossils. Conditions of treelessness over most of Europe south of the glaciated boundary is suggested by the pollen flora. Finds both of pollen and macrofossils give evidence of presence of alpine and arctic plants outside their present range. Based on all

available evidence Conolly (in Conolly and Dahl 1970) estimated a summer maximum temperature depression during the coldest periods in Britain of 6°C. Fig. 1 shows the present day distribution of *Salix herbacea* correlated with the 23°C maximum summer temperature isotherm, and its subfossil distribution correlated with the 29°C maximum summer temperature isotherm in Europe also suggesting a temperature difference of 6°C. Iversen (1953) estimated a depression of vegetation zones in Greenland during last glacial maximum of about 1 000 m. In general geologists tend to come up with estimates of a colder climate during glacial maxima than botanists do.

But also present-day biota may tell something about climatic conditions in the past. van Steenis (1962) pointed out that a temperature depression of more than

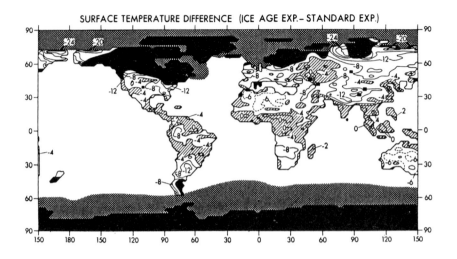

Fig. 2. Geographical distribution of surface temperatures (difference from present conditions in degrees centigrades) for the month of August at maximum last glacial age, 18 000 years ago (after Manabe and Hahn 1977).

2°C would exterminate an endemic lowland flora in Indonesia, a flora which could not have developed during postglacial times.

It is not easy to say whether the different estimates are consistent or not, i.e. if a temperature depression in Indonesia of less than 2°C is consistent with a lowering of the snow line in the area of 1 000 m or a temperature depression in North Europe of 6 or 10°C.

In this situation an important contribution has been made by use of meteorological general circulation models. In weather forecasting models are used simulating the exchange of energy (heat) and matter (e.g. water vapour) in the atmosphere. Such models are also used for analysis of climate. One particular model in order to be specified, requires the following input:

1) Topography including the topography of the ice sheets.
2) The albedo.
3) The surface temperatures of the oceans.

A group of scientists provided the necessary data for conditions during the maximum last glaciation 18 000 years ago (Anon. 1976) and the model was run by Manabe and Hahn (1977). The difference in August temperatures at ground level 18 000 years ago compared with present day conditions is given in Fig. 2. It is seen that the temperature difference increases from the equator to the margins of the northern Pleistocene ice sheets with a temperature difference along the border of about 8°C in Europe, slightly higher than the estimate of Conolly or that suggested by Fig. 1. In Indonesia the difference is zero in the lowlands satisfying the demands of van Steenis.

Assuming the correctness of the climate reconstruction it is obvious that plant species which for physiological reasons could not tolerate a climatic depression of about 6°C could not survive on refuges along the

coast of Norway and must have immigrated from the south or east.

Skre (1979) has made a study of the elements in the Scandinavian flora limited by summer temperature. As a measure he used the respiration sums, i.e. weighted temperature sums with weights according to the effect of temperature on dark respiration. He obtained good correlations between the distribution of numerous plants and respiration sums suggesting that his sums are valid measures of the requirements of the plants to high summer temperatures. An example of such a correlation is given in Fig. 3. In Tab. 1 are given the species correlated with respiration sums of 3 or higher corresponding to the lowland flora with altitudinal limits below 1 000 m in South Norway. In addition the phytogeographic element according to Gjærevoll in Lid (1985) is given. It is seen that this element is dominated by Eurasian and circumpolar plants consistent with the tabula rasa hypothesis. There is in addition an element of amphiatlantic species which also occur in other parts of Europe, and this element consists, with one exception, of species growing in wet habitats. I know of no explanation for this feature.

From the climate reconstruction it would also appear that alpine species restricted to areas with a cold climate could not survive along the southern margins of the inland ice. From Fig. 1 it is seen that species with stricter demands to low summer temperature than *Salix herbacea* could not survive between the Alps and the north European inland ice. If such elements exist in Scandinavia today they must have survived in refugia or have immigrated from the east.

Dahl (1951) correlated the distribution of numerous alpine Scandinavian plants with average annual maximum summer temperature calculated for the highest points in the landscape. An example of such a correlation is given in Fig. 1. In Tab. 2 is given a list of species conforming to this correlation with the limiting isotherm

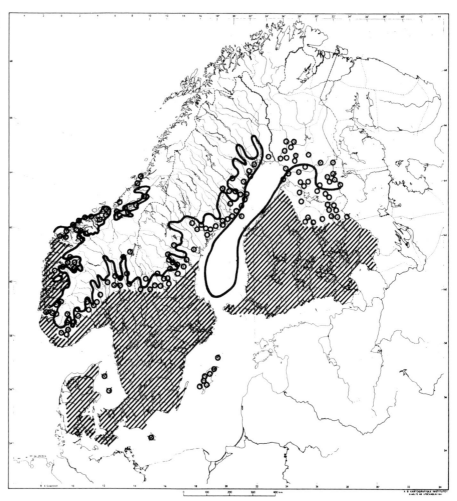

Fig. 3. Distribution of *Alnus glutinosa* in Scandinavia with the 5 respiration units isoline (after Skre 1979).

and the phytogeographic element according to Gjære-voll in Lid (1985) and other sources. It is seen that the element of species, with strict demands as to cool summers, are dominated by northern circumpolar and northern amphiatlantic species not found in the Alps. The element of Eurasian species shared by Scandinavia and the Alps consists of only nine species. This pattern is consistent with the nunatak hypothesis.

It should be noted that an area in Central Asia around Lake Baikal had an estimated temperature depression of only 4°C. Central Asia might have been a refuge for much of the boreal flora, especially more eastern species.

Flora europaea

An important contribution to the study of the European vascular plant flora is the completion of Flora Europaea in five volumes. It is followed by an Atlas Florae Europaeae giving dot-map distribution maps of the European taxa. The total flora of Europe comprises about 12 000 species and about 1 000 dot-maps have been pub-

lished so far. Botanists from many European countries have contributed. For each taxonomic group one author has been responsible for the entire group in all areas of Europe. This facilitates phytogeographical comparisons. Earlier one could not be sure that the same taxonomic standards had been applied e.g. in the Alps and Scandinavia or one might suspect that the same taxon appeared under different names in areas with different taxonomic traditions. Of course in Flora Europaea one can not be sure that similar taxonomic standards have been applied by different authors. Thus, e.g. the genera *Festuca* and *Euphrasia* have many species of local distribution suggesting that the authors to some extent were "splitters" while in other genera, e.g. *Papaver* only few of the described taxa have been recognized. Taxonomists would not be taxonomists if they did not differ in their opinions about the correct treatment of the taxa and new information will certainly bring to light new evidence. In the following comparisons I shall primarily rely on the evaluations in the Flora Europaea and the Atlas Florae Europaeae with some exceptions.

By looking through the flora and the maps it is strik-

Tab. 1. List of thermophilous vascular land plants with distribution limits correlated with respiration units of 3 or more in South Norway (according to Skre 1979) and phytogeographic element according to Gjærevoll in Lid (1985). The elements are: c = circumpolar species (17 species); eu = eurasiatic species (105 species); and aa = amphiatlantic species (12 species).

Pteridium aquilinum	c	3	Myosotis ramosissima	eu	4
Asplenium trichomanes	c	4	Scutellaria galericulata	c	4
Dryopteris dilatata	eu	6	Stachys sylvatica	eu	4
Salix aurita	eu	5	arvensis	c	4
repens	eu	5	Satureja vulgaris	eu	5–
Myrica gale	aa	5	acinos	eu	4–
Betula pendula	eu	4	Thymus pulegioides	eu	5
Alnus glutinosa	eu	5	Lycopus europaeus	eu	6
Corylus avellana	eu	5	Verbascum thapsus	eu	5–
Quercus robur	eu	6	Veronica spicata	eu	7
Ulmus glabra	eu	5–	anagallis-aquatica	aa	5–
Humulus lupulus	eu	5–	Lathraea squamaria	eu	6
Scleranthus perennis	eu	3	Galium odoratum	eu	5
Moeheringia trinervia	c	5–	Viburnum opulus	eu	4
Stellaria alsine	aa	4–	Succisa pratensis	eu	4–
Cerastium semidecandrum	eu	6	Campanula cervicaria	eu	5
Lychnis flos cuculi	eu	3	latifolia	eu	4–5
Silene nutans	eu	6–	persicifolia	eu	5
Ranunculus polyanthemos	eu	5–	trachelium	eu	6
Ranunculus ficaria	eu	6	Jasione montana	eu	6
Hepatica nobilis	eu	5	Eupatorium cannabinum	eu	7
Anemone nemorosa	eu	4	Filago arvensis	eu	5–
Thalictrum flavum	eu	4	Inula salicina	eu	5–
Cardamine impatiens	eu	7	Bidens cernua	aa	5
hirsuta	eu	6	tripartita	eu	5
Dentaria bulbifera	eu	6	Artemisia campestris	c	6
Alliaria petiolata	eu	6+	Arnica montana	eu	5
Sedum telephium	eu	5	Senecio sylvaticus	eu	6
acre	aa	4	Carlina vulgaris	eu	6
Saxifraga tridactylites	eu	6	Centaurea scabiosa	eu	4
Prunus spinosa	eu	6+	jacea	eu	4–
Crataegus monogyna	eu	5	Crepsis praemorsa	eu	6
Fragaria viridis	eu	6	Mycelis muralis	eu	5
Potentilla argentea	c	3	Alisma plantago-aquatica	c	5
tabernaemont.	eu	7	Scheuchzeria palustris	c	4
Geum urbanum	eu	5	Phleum phleoides	eu	6
Filipendula vulgaris	eu	6+	Holcus lanatus	c	5+
Alchemilla glaucescens	eu	5–	mollis	eu	6+
Agrimonia eupatoria	eu	6	Briza media	eu	4–5
Ononis arvensis	eu	6	Bromus benekenii	eu	6
Trifolium medium	eu	5–	mollis	c	4
Astragalus glycyphyllos	eu	5	Brachypodium pinnatum	eu	6–
Vicia sylvatica	eu	4+	Scirpus sylvaticus	aa	5
Lathyrus montanus	eu	5	Eleocharis mamillatus	eu	5
niger	eu	5	palustris	c	4
vernus	eu	5	Rynchospora alba	aa	5
Geranium robertianum	c	5	fusca	aa	5
Linum catharticum	eu	5–	Carex spicata	eu	6
Polygala vulgaris	eu	4	muricata	eu	4–5
Mercurialis perennis	eu	7–	ovalis	eu	4
Acer platanoides	eu	5–	elongata	eu	5–
Impatiens noli tangere	c	5	digitata	eu	3–4
Rhamnus catharticus	eu	7–	caryophyllea	eu	6
Frangula alnus	eu	5–	hartmanii	aa	7
Tilia cordata	eu	5	pseudocyperus	aa	6
Hypericum montanum	eu	7–	hirta	eu	6
perforatum	eu	5	riparia	eu	6
Drosera rotundifolia	c	4–	acutiformis	eu	6
intermedia	aa	6	Iris pseudacorus	eu	6–
Lythrum salicaria	eu	6	Orchis mascula	eu	6
Sanicula europaea	eu	5	Platanthera bifolia	eu	4
Peucedanum palustre	eu	6	Herminium monorchis	eu	6–
Pyrola media	eu	3	Epipactis helleborine	eu	6
Primula veris	eu	4	Cephalanthera rubra	eu	7
Lysimachia vulgaris	eu	6–	Malaxis monophylla	eu	5
Fraxinus excelsior	eu	5	Hammarby paludosa	aa	5
Myosotis scorpioides	c	6			
caespitosa	c	4–			

Tab. 2. List of alpine-subalpine species of South Norway correlated with maximum summer temperature isotherms (acc. to Dahl 1951 and later information) as well as distribution types mainly according to Gjærevoll in Lid (1985). The elements are: nc = northern circumpolar species i.e. circumpolar species absent in the Alps (23 species); c = circumpolar species present in the Alps (32 species); naa = amphiatlantic species absent in the Alps (23 species); aa = amphiatlantic species present in the Alps (19 species); neu = northern eurasiatic species absent in the Alps (6 species); eu = eurasiatic species present in the Alps (9 species) and end = species endemic to Fennoscandia (3 species).

Lycopodium dubium	naa		Pyrola norvegica	end	25
Diphasium alpinum	aa	28	Rhododendron lapponicum	naa	25
Cryptogramma crispa	c	27	Loiseleuria procumbens	aa	27
Athyrium distentifolium	aa	27	Phyllodoce coerulea	aa	27
Salix herbacea	aa	26	Cassiope hypnoides	naa	26
polaris	neu	25	Arctostaphylos alpina	c	27
reticulata	c	26	Diapensia lapponica	nc	26
myrsinites	neu	28–29	Primula scandinavica	end	27
lanata	nc	27	stricta	naa	27
arbuscula	neu	25	Gentiana purpurea	eu	25
Urtica dioica gracilis	naa	26	Gentianella tenella	c	23
Koenigia islandica	nc	24	Myosotis decumbens	eu	25
Oxyria digyna	c	26+	Veronica alpina	aa	25
Sagina intermedia	c	23+	fruticans	aa	25
caespitosa	naa	22	Euphrasia lapponica	end?	27
Minuartia stricta	c	22	Peducularis lapponica	nc	27
biflora	c	26	oederi	eu	24
rubella	nc	22	Rhinanthus groenlandicus	naa	
Arenaria norvegica	neu	23	Campanula uniflora	naa	22
Stellaria calycantha	naa		Erigeron borealis	naa	26
Cerastium cerastioides	aa	26	uniflorus	c	25
glabratum	aa	23	Antennaria alpina	aa	26
arcticum	naa	22	Gnaphalium supinum	aa	26
Silene wahlbergella	nc	24	Artemisia norvegica	neu	22
acaulis	aa	25	Agrostis mertensii	naa	27
Ranunculus glacialis	aa	24	Deschampsia alpina	naa	25
platanifolius	eu	27	Vahlodea atropurpurea	naa	26
pygmaeus	c	25	Trisetum spicatum	c	24–25
nivalis	nc	25	Poa arctica	nc	23
Thalictrum alpinum	c	27	flexuosa	naa	24
Papaver radicatum	neu		Phippsia algida	nc	22
Draba alpina	nc	22+	Festuca vivipara	naa	
daurica	nc	26	Roegneria borealis	eu	26
nivalis	nc	23	Kobresia myosuroides	c	24
fladnisenzis coll	c	23	simpliciuscula	c	23–24
norvegica	naa	26	Carex parallella	naa	23
Arabis alpina	aa	26	arctogena	naa	23–24
Cardamine bellidifolia	nc	26	microglochin	c	24
nymanii	nc		rupestris	c	26
Braya linearis	naa	23	lachenalii	c	26
Sedum rosea ssp. rosea	aa	25	adelostoma	naa	27
villosum	aa	24	atrata	aa	26+
Saxifraga cotyledon	eu	25+	misandra	nc	22
oppositifolia	c	26	atrofusca	c	25
hieraciifolia	c	22	rufina	naa	23
tenuis	ns		bigelowii	c	27
stellaris	aa	25	saxatilis	nc	25
foliolosa	nc	23	Juncus arcticus	nc	24
aizoides	aa	27	castaneus	c	25
cernua	c	25–26	triglumis	c	27–28
rivularis	nc	25	biglumis	c	26
Potentilla nivea coll	c	25	Luzula arcuata coll.	nc	25
Sibbaldia procumbens	c	27	arctica	nc	22
Dryas octopetala	c	27	spicata	c	27
Astragalus frigidus	c	26–27	frigida	nc	27–28
norvegicus	eu	25	Chamaeorchis alpina	eu	23
Oxytropis lapponica	eu	23	Leucorchis straminea	naa	
Epilobium anagallidifolium	c	26			

ing that corresponding taxa may be found in the Alps, Scandinavia, British Isles and Iceland, either vicariant species in polymorphic groups or different subspecies within one species. Tab. 3 summarizes the cases. In Tab. 4 the number of taxa listed in Tab. 1 for each of the areas (diagonal numbers) and the number of taxa

Tab. 3. Corresponding taxa in the Alps, Scandinavia, British Isles and Iceland.

Alps	Scandinavia	British Isles	Iceland
	Lycopodium dubium	Lycopodium dubium	Lycopodium dubium
Woodsia pulchella	Woodsia glabella		Woodsia glabella
Salix breviserrata	S. myrsinites	S. myrsinites	
S. glaucosericea	S. glauca*glauca *stipulifera		S. glauca*callicarpae
S. bicolor	S. phylicifolia	S. phylicifolia hibernica	S. phylicifolia
hegetschweileri			
S. foetida	S. arbuscula	S. arbuscula	
S. helvetica	S. lapponum	S. lapponum	
(S. lapponum)			
Rumex alpestris*alpestris	R. alpestris*lapponica		
Arenaria multicaulis	A. norvegica*norvegica	A. norvegica*norvegica *anglica	A. norvegica*norvegica
A. ciliata*ciliata	A. ciliata*pseudofrigida	A. ciliata*hibernica	
	Cerastium glabratum		C. glabratum
Cerastium latifolium	C. arcticum	C. arcticum	C. arcticum
C. uniflorum			
Cerastium fontanum*fontanum	C. fontanum*scandicum	C. fontanum*scoticum	C. fontanum*scandicum
Ranunculus acris*friesianus	R. acris*borealis	R. acris*borealis	R. acris*borealis
Papaver alpinum group	P. radicatum group		P. radicatum group
Cardamine rivularis	C. nymanii		C. nymanii
Cardamine bellidifolia*alpina	C. bellidifolia*bellidifolia	C. bellidifolia*bellidifolia	
Cardaminopsis hispida	C. petraea	C. petraea	C. petraea
Draba ladina	D. alpina		D. alpina
Draba norica + pacheri	D. daurica		D. daurica
Cochlearia tatrae	C. fenestrata	C. scotica	C. fenestrata
C. pyrenaica		C. pyrenaica	C. pyrenaica
Saxifraga stellaris*alpigena	S. stellaris*stellaris	S. stellaris*stellaris	S. stellaris*stellaris
(S. stellaris*stellaris)			
Alchemilla turkulensis	A. murbeckiana		A. murbeckiana
(A. wichurae)	A. wichurae oxyodonta	A. wichurae	A. wichurae
Oxytropis halleri*halleri *velutina		O. halleri*halleri	
Anthyllis vulneraria*alpestris	A. vulnerara*lapponica	A. vulneraria*lapponica	A. vulneraria*borealis
Linum perenne*perenne		L. perenne*anglicum	
Helianthemum oelandicum*alpestre	H. oelandicum*oelandicum		
Helianthemum canum*canum	H. canum*canescens	H. canum*canum *levigatum	
Pyrola carpathica	P. norvegica		P. grandiflora
Primula halleri	P. scandinavica	P. scotica	
Armeria maritime*alpina	A. maritima*sibirica		
Gentianella amarella*amarella	G. amarella*amarella	G. amarella*septentrionalis	G. amarella*septentrionalis
Thymus praecox*praecox *polytrichus	T. praecox*arcticus	T. praecox*articus	T. praecox*articus
Euphrasia arctica*slovaca	E. artica*borealis	E. artica*borealis	E. artica*tenuis
E. minima	E. frigida	E. frigida	E. frigida
Galium sudeticum	G. normanii		G. normanii
Erigeron neglectus	E. borealis	E. borealis	E. borealis
Juncus alpinus*alpestris	J. alpinus*alpinus *alpestris *nodulosus	J. alpinus*alpinus alpinus	J. alpinus*alpestris *nodulosus
	Festuca rubra*vivipara	F. rubra*vivipara	F. rubra*vivipara
	Festuca vivipara	F. vivipara	F. vivipara
	Poa alpigena		P. alpigena
Poa cenisia	P. arctica		P. arctica
Poa laxa	P. flexuosa	P. flexuosa	P. flexuosa
	Deschampsia caespitosa*alpina	D. caespitosa*alpina	D. caespitosa*alpina
Pseudorchis albida*albida	P. albida*straminea *albida	P. albida*straminea	P. albida*straminea

shared between pairs of areas are given. In the table for the Alps three taxa listed in brackets viz. *Salix lapponicum*, *Saxifraga stellaris* ssp. *stellaris* and *Alchemilla wichurae*. These are found in the Carpathians but not in the Alps and are not included in the comparisons.

Of the 36 taxa listed for Iceland 31 are also found in

Tab. 4. Corresponding taxa in common between the Alps, Scandinavia, British Isles and Iceland (based on Tab. 3).

	Alps	Scandi-navicia	British Isles	Iceland
Alps	47	3	4	2
Scandinavia	3	47	24	31
British Isles	4	24	36	19
Iceland	2	31	19	36

Scandinavia so the floristic similarity on vicariant level is high indeed. Scandinavia shares about an equal number of vicariant taxa with the British Isles and Iceland, while the British Isles share about the same number of taxa with Scandinavia and Iceland. But the striking fact is that very few of the vicariant taxa of the Alps are shared with Scandinavia, the British Isles and Iceland.

The tabula rasa hypothesis proposes that the flora now inhabiting the formerly glaciated areas in the north, in its entirety survived to the south or east of the continental glaciers. If so the flora of North Europe is recruited from a stock surviving in the area between the ice sheets in the Alps and the Carpathians and the ice sheet covering North Europe. Then it is difficult to understand why there are so few vicariant taxa shared between the Alps and North Europe and especially the close similarity between the flora of Iceland and Scandinavia. Although it is dangerous to take anything for granted, one may assume that no land connection existed between Iceland and Scandinavia after the last glacial age; the evidence to be presented later suggests that the connection was broken at the beginning of the Pleistocene. Unless one resorts to some explanation involving extensive long-distance transport of propagules between Iceland and Scandinavia post-glacially and little transport between Scandinavia and the Alps it must be concluded that important segments of the North Atlantic flora survived locally from a time of more close connections between Iceland and Britain and between Iceland and Scandinavia than today. The connections between Britain and Scandinavia could be explained by migrations across land now covered by the North Sea during late-glacial times.

Endemism

The publication of Flora Europaea facilitates a comparison of the degree of endemism in the floras of different parts of Europe. It was noticed early on that the heavily glaciated areas of Europe had few endemics compared with areas less influenced by the glaciations, e.g. the Mediterranean. This is immediately evident by an examination of the "List of rare, threatened and endemic plants in Europe" (1983).

However, it has also been observed that the heavily glaciated areas in North Europe nevertheless have a number of endemics especially in the subalpine-alpine elements of the floras.

A list of endemic taxa in Fennoscandia (excluding Denmark but including the Kola penninsula since the flora of North Scandinavia grades imperceptibly into the flora of Kola) is given (Tab. 5). The list is based on Flora Europaea. Taxa not given formal recognition are given in brackets. In addition some taxa are included where Scandinavian taxonomists have argued strongly for recognition e.g. *Poa stricta*, subspecies of *Papaver radicatum* and *lapponicum* and of *Poa arctica*, subspecies of *Draba cacumium* (Elven and Aarhus 1984) and *Oxytropis deflexa* ssp. *norvegica*. The enumerations do not include taxa of the highly polymorphic, apomictic

Tab. 5. Fennoscandian endemics.

Alpine – subalpine endemics
Alnus incana ssp. *kolaensis*
Rumex acetosa ssp. *serpentinicola*
(*Stellaria crassipes* v. *dovrensis*)
Thalictrum simplex ssp. *boreale*
Papaver laestadianum
P. radicatum several ssp.
P. lapponicum ssp. *scandinavicum*
(*P. chibinense*)
Draba dovrensis
D. cacuminum ssp. *angusticarpum*
           ssp. *cacuminum*
Alchemilla oxyodonta
           borealis
Anthyllis vulneraria ssp. *lapponica*
Oxytropis deflexa ssp. *norvegica*
Viola ruprestris ssp. *relicta*
Pyrola norvegica
Primula scandinavica
Thymus serpyllum ssp. *tanaensis*
Euphrasia hyperborea
E. saamica
(*E. lapponica* ?)
Antennaria nordhageniana
Taraxacum dovrense
(*Poa stricta*)
(*Poa arctica* several ssp.)
Elymus alaskanus ssp. *subalpina*
Dactylorrhiza pseudocordigera
D. traunsterineri ssp. *lapponica*

Öland – Gotland endemics
Helianthemum oelandicum ssp. *oelandicum*
H. canum ssp. *canescens*
Galium oelandicum
Artemisia oelandica
A. maritima v. *humifusa*
Festuca oelandica

Coastal endemics
Euphrasia bottnica
Artemisia campestris ssp. *bottnica*
Alisma wahlenbergii
Deschampsia caespitosa ssp. *bottnica*
Hierochloe odorata v. *baltica*
Carex vacillans

Lowland endemics
Saxifraga osloensis
Arabidopsis suecica

genera *Sorbus, Rubus, Hieracium* and *Taraxacum*. The endemics can readily be subdivided into four groups:

1) The *alpine-subalpine* endemics which should be considered as possible survivors in unglaciated areas. This is by far the largest group. They all belong to polymorphic taxa, since obvious palaeoendemics have not been identified. There might be differences of opinion about the rank of some taxa.

2) The *Öland-Gotland group* which certainly are not inter-glacial survivors. They are suspected of being survivors from the late-glacial period though the islands themselves were below sealevel after the glaciation. This is testified to be the abundant occurrence of pollen of *Helianthemum oelandicum* and *Artemisia* in late-glacial deposits in South Scandinavia and elsewhere in Europe.

3) The *coastal endemics* especially along the shores of the Gulf of Bothnia (Ericsson and Wallentinus 1979). Their present distribution give little information about their tolerance of cold climates. To the list should perhaps be added a new species of *Puccinellia* found on the coast of Finnmark (R. Elven and L. Borgen pers. inf.).

4) The *lowland endemics* which is a small group of two species. *Saxifraga osloensis* is an allopolyploid between *S. adscendens* and *S. tridactylites* (Knaben 1954) and *Arabidopsis suecica* which is probably an allopolyploid with *Arabidopsis thaliana* and *Cardaminopsis arenosa* as parents (Hylander 1947, Löve 1961).

Tab. 6 gives a similar enumeration of endemics in the British Isles, a group discussed by Walters (1978). In the enumerations I have also used information in Perring (1968). The same groups have been excluded as in the Scandinavian enumerations and also *Limonium* which apparently is a highly polymorphic, apomictic genus (Ingrouille and Stace 1985).

The *Scottish endemics*, *Irish endemics* and *Scottish-Irish endemics* are possible interglacial survivors as might also be the case of the *Welsh endemics*. The *Pennines-Lake district endemics* form a British counterpart to the Öland-Gotland endemics in Scandinavia and are probably late-glacial survivors. Then comes a group of *coastal endemics* as a counterpart of a similar group in Scandinavia. Out of these *Spartina anglica* is a recent allopolyploid. The remaining *English endemics*, some of which are also found in Ireland are largely of hybrid or allopolyploid origin. *Fumaria occidentalis* is considered an allopolyploid between *F. capreolata* and *F. bastardii* (Stace 1975). *Fumaria purpurea* is an endemic confined to artificial habitats. *Linum perenne* ssp. *anglicum* is a tetraploid related to the widespread *Linum perenne*. *Euphrasia vigursii* is considered a stabilized hybrid between *E. anglica* and *micrantha* (Yeo in Stace 1975). *Senecio cambrensis* is a recent allopolyploid between *S. squalidus* and *S. vulgaris*. *Bromus interruptus* was doubtful origin, now extinct but appeared as a weed in cultivation of *Onobrychis*. *B. pseudosecalinus* is a diploid closely related to the tetraploid weed *B. secalinus*. It should not be excluded that some of the taxa in this

Tab. 6. British endemics.

Scottish endemics
Athyrium distentifolium v. *flexile*
Cerastium fontanum ssp. *scoticum*
           arcticum ssp. *edmondstonii*
Ranunculus flammula ssp. *scotica*
Gentianella amarella ssp. *druceana*
           ssp. *septentrionalis*
Primula scotia
Euphrasia rhumica
    foulaensis
    (eurycarpa)
    campbelliae
    marschallii
Calamagrostis scotica
Dactylorrhiza maculata ssp. *rhoumensis*

Irish endemics
Salix hibernica
Arenaria ciliata ssp. *hibernica*
Arabis hirsuta ssp. *brownii*
Saxifraga hartii
Gentianella amarella ssp. *hibernica*

Scottish-Irish endemics
Ranunculus flammula ssp. *minimus*
Cochlearia scotica
Dactylorrhiza fuchsii ssp. *okellyi*
      ssp. *hebridensis*
    incarnata ssp. *coccinea* (also in Wales)
(Eriocaulon aquaticum?)

Pennines – Lake District endemics
Helianthemum canum ssp. *levigatum*
Arenaria norvegica ssp. *anglica*
Alchemilla minima

Welsh endemics
Euphrasia cambrica
    rivularis (also in Lake District)

Coastal endemics
Rhynchosinapis wrightii
        monensis
Senecio integrifolius ssp. *maritimus*
Catabrosa aquatica ssp. *minor*
Spartina anglica
Epipactis dunensis

English endemics
Scleranthus perennis ssp. *prostratus*
Fumaria occidentalis
    purpurea (also in Ireland)
    muralis ssp. *neglecta*
Anthyllis vulneraria ssp. *corbieri*
Geranium purpureum ssp. *forsteri*
    robertianum ssp. *celticum*
Gentianella anglica ssp. *anglica*
      ssp. *cornubiensis*
Linum perenne ssp. *anglicum*
Euphrasia vigursii
    pseudokerneri (also in Ireland)
    anglica (?)
Senecio cambrensis
Bromus interruptus
    pseudosecalinus

86

group survived the glacial ages in South England and Ireland.

Let me add that in Eastern North America localized endemics north of the glaciated border are mainly found in the mountains of New England, in Gaspé, in Newfoundland, Labrador and Greenland and that few, if any, are to be found in the lowland flora.

The following conclusion is suggested:

There is no known instance where it can convincingly be demonstrated that a new amphimictic vascular plant species has evolved by purely genetic processes other than alloploidy during the last 18 000 years.

Within apomictic groups localized endemics are common. Thus the relatively high number of endemic taxa within elements which are considered as possible nunatak survivors, must in my opinion be considered as an argument in favour of the nunatak theory. Some of these taxa have, no doubt, arisen as a result of allopolyploidy e.g. *Primula scandinavica* which might be an allopolyploid between *P. scotica* and *P. farinosa* (Knaben 1982). But this leaves the origin of *P. scotica* unexplained.

The amphiatlantic biota

An important part of the discussions in the 1960s was about the amphiatlantic distribution patterns based on the excellent distribution maps by Hultén (1958), the analysis of the zoogeographical aspects by Lindroth (1957) and the discussions during the NATO-symposium in Reykjavik (Löve and Löve 1963). Since then only details of the overall picture have changed. Some new taxa have been added to the list of amphiatlantic plants. First a number of species with European affinities have been found in Greenland (Böcher et al. 1968) viz. *Lycopodium dubium*, *Rumex alpestris* ssp. *lapponica*, *Geranium sylvaticum*, *Epilobium alsinifolium*, *Vaccinium myrtillus*, *Agrostis vinealies*.

To the list are also added (according to Gjærevoll in Lid 1985): *Antennaria villifera* and *Carex stylosa*.

On the other hand Lid's flora (1985) does not list *Puccinellia coarctata* as a proper taxon, and the inclusion of *Poa arctica* ssp. *depauperata* must be a mistake.

In addition a number of European species considered native to Newfoundland and adjacent areas were probably introduced during the early fishing period in ways described by Lindroth (1958). The following species, listed as amphiatlantic by Gjærevoll in Lid (1985), together with some growing in Britain but not in Scandinavia, could for this reason be excluded from the discussion:

Atriplex laciniata, Sagina procumbens, S. nodosa, Ranunuculus hederaceus, Calluna vulgaris, Pedicularis palustris, P. sylvatica, Galium saxatile, Gnaphalium sylvaticum, Potamogeton polygonifolius, Molinia coerulea,

Glyceria fluitans, Juncus conglomeratus, J. acutiflorus, J. capitatus, and J. bulbosus.

On the other hand *Limosella subulata* in Wales is possibly an American species brought back to Europe during the early fishing trade.

But these corrections to the data brought forth by Hultén (1958) do not substantially change the overall picture, apart from a reduction in the number of European species in Newfoundland. The results can be summarized as follows (cf. Dahl 1959, 1961b, 1963):

1) The highest concentrations of amphiatlantic species are on the European side in North Scandinavia, the number decreasing in all directions. There is no single good amphiatlantic species that occurs in the Alps but not in Scandinavia.

2) On the American side the highest number of amphiatlantic taxa occur in South Greenland, the number decreasing in all directions.

3) Most of the amphiatlantic taxa are subalpine-alpine in Scandinavia and generally subarctic-arctic. The percentage of amphiatlantic species increases with altitude and out of the species reaching 2 000 m or more in South Norway half are amphiatlantic species (Dahl 1975).

4) The element of amphiatlantic species not reaching 1 000 m altitude in South Norway is strongly unbalanced, mostly halophilous species, species with light, wind-dispersed diaspores and a high percentage of wet-habitat plants (Dahl 1959). Also the American element in Ireland and Scotland consists of wet-habitat plants (Perring 1962). No explanation is available why wet-habitat plants have different distribution patterns than dry-habitat plants, as discussed before. Very few if any temperate dry land species are amphiatlantic.

5) In the spectrum of dispersal types according to adaptations to long-distance dispersal there is no enrichment of types adapted to such dispersal among the amphiatlants.

6) There is, however, an enrichment of dispersal types adapted to long-distance dispersal among American elements penetrating to South Greenland and Iceland (Lindroth 1960, Dahl 1963). The same applies to insects (Lindroth 1963).

7) Closely related or identical taxa of polymorphic groups occur on both sides of the Atlantic differing from taxa in the Beringian area. This is also borne out by the close taxonomic relationships within the area of Scandinavia–Scotland–Iceland discussed above. Many of the taxa listed for Iceland and Scandinavia in Tab. 3 are also found in South Greenland.

An obvious hypothesis to explain these facts is to propose a land connection across the North Atlantic permitting arctic-subarctic plants to cross but with too cold a climate to permit dispersal of more temperate biota. This indicates a climate somewhat similar to or slightly cooler than the climate of Iceland today. This means that the connection must have existed in late Tertiary time since the climate earlier is supposed to have been too warm. Also the floristic connections where polymorphic taxa are involved indicates a late connection perhaps as late as late Pliocene or Pleistocene.

The spectrum of dispersal types suggest that the connection was first broken between South Greenland and Labrador, then between Greenland and Iceland and last between Iceland and Scandinavia–Scotland.

When this hypothesis was discussed during the Iceland symposium it was not kindly recieved by the geophysicists (Heezen and Tharp 1963). At that time the permanence of the oceans was generally accepted and this and other data did not support a late Tertiary connection between Scotland and Greenland.

However, since then the notion of permanence of the oceans has largely been abandoned. Much information has been obtained from the Ocean Drilling Program providing insight in the stratigraphy of the sediments on the bottom of the oceans. Based on such evidence a NATO symposium was held in Iceland (Bott et al. 1983) and the situation was summarized by Thiede (1983: 315) thus:

"Fossils of terrestrial faunas and floras which have been collected on either side of the Greenland–Scotland ridge or which have been preserved in the intrabasaltic sediments of the subaerial segments of the ridge, suggest that a land bridge once connected Greenland–North America with northwest Europe. However, it is

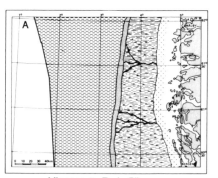

Miocene to Early Pliocene

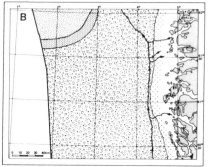

Mid Pliocene

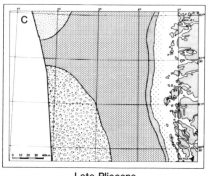

Late Pliocene

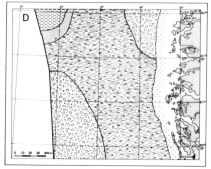

Latest Pliocene/Early Pleistocene

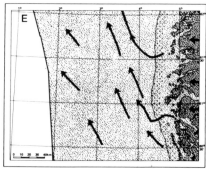

Maximum Quaternary glaciation

LEGEND:

Land areas		Open marine	
River		Marine	
Coastal plain		Basement	
Deltaic		Ice cover	
Shallow marine		Ice Movement	

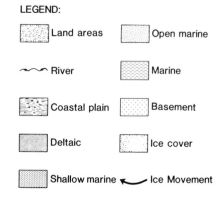

Fig. 4. Generalized palaeogeographic sketches for the Norwegian sector of the North Sea during late Tertiary and Quaternary times (after Rokoengen and Rønningsland 1983).

still unknown when this land bridge first came into existence in late Mesozoic time when probably a shallow seaway connected the the Arctic and the Atlantic oceans, and how long it functioned as a pathway for terrestrial organisms. Estimates of the timing of the break-up range from Eocene to Miocene, others have suggested that it might have existed until Plio-Pleistocene".

Comparisons of fossil faunas (McKenna 1983, Hoch 1983) and floras (Tiffney 1985) suggest the presence of a land connection between North America and Europe in Early Tertiary times which was broken in Mid-Tertiary times, perhaps in the middle Oligocene. Usually it is assumed that the ridge between Iceland and Scotland became submerged in the sea at that time. However, the effect on the land biota could have been the same if it was broken between Greenland and North America or between Greenland and Iceland.

In cores from the ridge, sediments of early Tertiary age, Eocene and Oligocene, are present overlying a weathering crust of Eocene age. Sediments of late Tertiary age, Miocene and early Pliocene, appear to be missing. Then sediments of latest Tertiary age, Upper Pliocene and Pleistocene are present. The crest of the Iceland–Scotland ridge is largely sediment-free (Nielsen and Kerr 1978). To the east of the ridge, in the Norwegian sector of the North Sea, Rokoengen and Rønningsland (1983), based on studies of cores from oil drillings, map a land area during Mid Pliocene times and a coastal plain in Latest Pliocene/Early Pleistocene (see Fig. 4). This is interpreted to have happened because of a subsidence of the ocean floor some 600 m in late Tertiary times.

Quite recent results from the Ocean Drilling Program from the Vøring Plateaux SW of the Lofoten Islands at 1 290 m depth reveals an Eocene volcanic sequence with rocks similar to those found in the Icelandic sector (Eldholm and Thiede 1986, Eldholm et al. 1986). It is divided into a lower part which is subaqueous and an upper part which is partly subaeric. Then follow sediments of Neogene and Quaternary Age. In this area the late Tertiary subsidence must have been more than 1 000 m.

Important data have been provided by Strauch (1970) by comparisons of the mollusc faunas in the Arctic and the North Atlantic Oceans during Tertiary times. Up to Late Tertiary times the faunas in the two basins were separate, suggesting a land barrier to the spread of marine molluscs. This barrier was broken in the early Pleistocene, about 1 Myr ago, when elements from the Polar basin spread to the North Atlantic, and North Atlantic elements began to penetrate into the Polar Basin (Strauch 1983). But a land barrier to marine molluscs is perforce a land bridge to plants.

The last word has certainly not been said about the palaeogeography of the North Atlantic during Late Tertiary times. The new investigations during the Ocean Drilling Program and the study of sediments in the North Sea have opened up possibilities of land connections which could not be imagined 20 years ago.

Glacier dynamics

The standard texbook illustration of the maximum glaciation during the last Ice Age has been one of complete coverage of all land consistent with the tabula rasa hypothesis (see e.g. Denton and Hughes 1981). However, it is not easy to believe in such a picture due to topographic conditions. A land where high mountains exist close to the limit of a continental platform cannot easily be completely covered by ice, a fact already observed by Holtedahl in the Antarctic (Holtedahl 1929, Dahl 1946). In the Antarctic, where climatic conditions are much more severe than they ever were in the North Atlantic area during the Pleistocene glaciations, about 4% of the area is land. This argument can now be specified based on information of glacier dynamics.

An inland ice moves as plastic with most of the differential movement near the bottom. The shear stress, τ, in a plane parallel with the surface of the glacier is given by

$$\tau = \varrho \times g \times h \times \sin \alpha$$

where α is the angle of slope of the ice surface, h is the thickness of the glacier, g acceleration of gravity and ϱ the density of the ice. The shear stress in a plane parallel to the surface is close to the plane of maximum shear stress.

A result of the stress is a strain. The strain increases in ice with stress as a power function with an exponent about 4. This means that when a certain limit is reached, the strain increases very rapidly with stress. For this reason the bottom shear stress in glaciers varies little, between 0.8 and 1.5 bars. Stresses above 1.5 bars can hardly exist in real glaciers.

When an inland ice reaches the deep oceans it floats and breaks into pieces. This means that the ice front can not be very high, about 50 m. This is borne out by the plow-marks on the Norwegian continental shelf which are not found below 500 m suggesting the maximum depth of the icebergs (Lien 1983).

It is now possible to construct a profile of an inland ice from the continental margin towards land with a constant bottom stress of 1.5 bars. Fig. 5 gives an example from South Greenland where the calculated surface does not overtop the highest mountains. With the topography observed today, such a mountain can not be completely covered by an inland ice. Similar conditions pertain also to South Iceland and to Jan Mayen.

Coming to the coast of Norway a reconstruction of profiles from the outer margin of the continental shelf towards Moskenesøy is given in Fig. 6. The highest mountain is Hermansdalstind. It is seen that with a bottom shear stress of 1.5 bars the profile overtops the summit, while the profile with 0.8 bars is below the

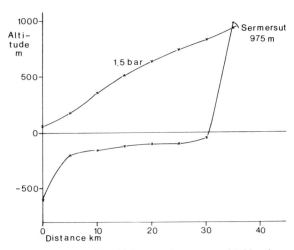

Fig. 5. Glacier profile with bottom shear stress of 1.5 bar from the deep sea to the mountain Sermersut in South Greenland.

summit. Theorethically Hermansdalstind could have been glaciated, but this does not indicate that it was.

With a high bottom stress the flow must be rapid. In order to be stable, the transport of ice has to be balanced by a net accumulation of snow above snow-line. It is tempting to calculate this, but unfortunately calculations on existing glaciers compared with measured flows give very discouraging results. The observed flow is about 10 times faster than that expected from the calculations. There must be something missing in glacier physics and until this is cleared up we cannot do the proper calculations.

It seems reasonable to think that the broad Vestfjord formed a drainage channel for the outflow of ice from the inland ice of Scandinavia preventing the ice from overflowing the Lofoten Islands. This is borne out by the fact that no erratics from the mainland have been found in the outer parts of the Lofoten Islands. A similar situation exists in the eastern parts of the Gaspé

peninsula in Canada, in Newfoundland and in the northern parts of the Outer Hebrides. The geomorphology of Moskenesøy strongly suggest an intense local glaciation.

New dating methods

As is known the radiocarbon assay method covers the period up to 50000 years ago and the potassium-argon method periods in excess of 1 Myr. There has hitherto been no suitable methods to bridge the gap, but here new methods have been found.

One is the method of racemization of amino acids. Mollusc shells contain amino acids which are optically active at their formation. With time the amino acids are racemized and this process has for certain amino acids a constant rate making it possible to date shells 1 Myr back. The process depends on temperature: with 10°C intervals the rate is 2.5 times higher at the higher temperature. But if shells are found e.g. in beach sediments within one area, the degree of racemization gives relative ages. And if something is known about climate an approximate absolute age can be given.

This method has now been used for dating beach deposits in West Spitsbergen (Miller 1982, Forman and Miller 1984). In the area along the coast south of Kingsbay, Miller (1982) found beach terraces containing fossil molluscs at different altitudinal levels. A lowermost group was dated by the racemization method (assuming present-day climate) to 9–12000 years, a figure confirmed by radiocarbon assay. A group at higher elevation was dated to 40–130000 years, another to 90–260000 years, then another at 170–480000 years and the oldest deposits dated come out within the range of 300000–1 Myr. It is hardly conceivable that these terraces could have been preserved under an overriding ice sheet. Also at Brøggerhalvøya beaches of similar ages could be dated (Forman and Miller 1984), and in Greenland in the Disco area Funder and Simonarson (1984) have obtained similar results.

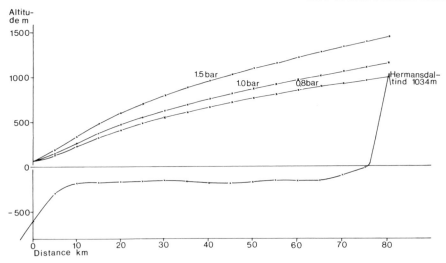

Fig. 6. Glacier profiles with bottom shear stress of 1.5 bar and 0.8 bar from the deep ocean towards Hermansdalstind in Lofoten.

Rønning (1963) argued strongly that a large proportion of the Spitsbergen vascular plant flora had survived on the island, a point previously made by Lynge (1939) concerning lichens. The datings so far available suggest ice-free refugia for a period up to 1 Myr.

The other promising dating method is based on thermoluminescence (Wintle and Huntley 1982). When quartz or feldspar crystals are subjected to radioactive emissions some of the electrons in lattice positions are thrown out of position. If the crystal is heated the electrons jump back and emit a quantum of light. This can be picked up in a photomultiplier. Thus the dosage of radioactive radiation received by the crystal can be measured.

Fortunately, if the crystal is subjected to light, the electrons jump back into position. By taking a sample of a sediment which was deposited in light and then buried and by measuring the radioactive field in the deposit and the thermoluminescence, the age since the deposit was formed can be estimated. This has so far been most successful for loess deposits, but the method is now developed also for beach deposits. This method has been used to date beach terraces in Spitsbergen (Mangerud and Salvigsen 1984) with dates up to 50 000 years consistent with the results of the amino acid assays.

Origin of the mountain-top detritus

The autochthonous mountain top detritus and boulder fields have been invoked as evidence of non-glaciation during the last or previous glacial ages (Dahl 1955, 1963). Especially the weathering products at the outermost part of the Stadt Peninsula, West Norway have attracted attention. The weathering products contain i.a. considerable amounts of gibbsite, a laterite mineral considered typical of tropical weathering (Dahl 1963). These deposits have recently been studied by Roaldset et al. (1982) and Longva et al. (1983) who conclude that they are remnants of a Tertiary weathering profile.

If this point of view prevails, the consequences will be far-reaching. Gibbsite is not confined only to the Stadt Peninsula, it is also present in similar deposits at Stemshesten near Hustad farther north in Norway. The fine-grained mountain-top detritus contains a paragenesis of weathering products which is rather special. The most common mineral is a montmorillonite, and besides there is vermiculite or interstratified vermiculite-biotite (hydrobiotite) derived by weathering of biotite (Dahl 1954). Kaolinite and secondary illite are very rare or absent. These types of material cover extensive areas on higher land along the northwestern coast of South Norway and normally form an easily mappable unit as found also by Longva et al. (1983).

If these deposits are remnants of the preglacial weathering crust the weathering during the glacial ages has not been intense enough to destroy them. Hence we can not be sure that moraines and erratics formed during previous glacial ages could not survive subsequent glacial ages. It has been customary to believe that presence of reliable evidence of glaciation (erratics where the rock could not be of local origin, polished pebbles with striations, striations on unweathered rock surfaces) indicates glaciation during the last glacial age. This standpoint would no longer be tenable.

The fine-grained mountain-top detritus is derived from in situ weathered gneisses which can be found in cuts e.g. along the sea-cliffs. Moving inland such areas are found at higher levels and grade imperceptibly into the autochthonous boulder fields in the mountains. But still remnants of weathered rocks with the same weathering minerals can be found in protected positions up to 1 700 m a.s.l. in the Jotunheimen mountains. The weathering products from the summit of Gjevilvasskammene in Trollheimen described by Sørensen (1949) and Grønlie (1953) contain the same weathering mineral paragenesis (montmorillonite, vermiculite, hydrobiotite).

The obvious hypothesis to explain these features is that the autochtonous boulder fields are derived from the preglacial weathering crust by removal of the finer fractions by solifluction, and leaving the coarse fractions behind. This hypothesis avoids the difficulties inherent in explaining how the bouldery mountain-top detritus could be produced by rapid frost splitting.

By taking proper precautions my experience is that the mountain-top detritus is an easily mappable unit which perhaps marks the upper limit of the Pleistocene ice sheets. Of course, there will be areas where the products of an old weathering come in contact with and mix with glacigenic products from the margins of an inland ice. This is my interpretation of such deposits described by Longva et al. (1983). It is also possible that parts of the old weathering crust are preserved under an overriding ice and overlain by erratics. This seems to be the case for the conditions at Sandviksfjellet near Narvik described by R. Dahl (1963, 1966).

Similar features are widespread. They have been noted by Sollid and Sørbel (1979) from South Norway and they are common along the coast of northernmost Norway, e.g. on the Nordkapp Plateau. The summit of Værøy in the Lofoten Islands is capped by mountain-top detritus and samples of mountain-top detritus from the summit of Hermansdalstind contain flakes of vermiculite. Similar features have been described from Newfoundland and the Atlantic Provinces of Canada by Grant (1977a,b) and from Labrador by Ives et al. (1976). I believe that similar features are present at Tolsta Head on the Island of Lewis in the Outer Hebrides where the gneiss is deeply weathered and the weathering products contain large quaties of montmorillonite (own obs.). The presence of deep weathering in the Outer Hebrides was also noted by Peacock and Ross (1978).

If, and I stress the word if, this hypothesis is correct it would leave ample opportunities to explain the phytogeographic features described previously.

Concluding remarks

During the last 30 years considerable progress has been made towards a solution of the problems raised by the nunatak hypothesis. Progress in plant geography and taxonomy has enlarged the data base from which conclusions can be drawn. Use of meteorological models have given us a better insight into the climate of an Ice Age and the conditions under which plant and animals then lived. Deep sea drillings have opened up possibilities for explaining the close biogeographic connections within the North Atlantic which could not be imagined previously. New dating methods have opened up new possibilities for dating events during the Pleistocene. Development in mineralogical analysis of the mountain top detritus give rise to new interpretations relevant to the nunatak hypothesis.

But many problems remain to be solved. The meteorological model used to simulate the climate of tropical regions of the last Ice Age give less specific information about conditions in the Arctic. It is expected that progress with dating by the new methods can supply positive evidence of nonglaciation. In this direction interesting results on the coast of South Norway have been supplied by Landvik and Mangerud (1985). More work is needed to establish firmly the nature of the mountain top detritus and its origin.

In biology new methods of genetic and morphometric analysis are expected to enlarge our understanding of evolutionary processes (Nordal 1985 a). Good examples are given by the morphometric analysis of the Arctic reindeer by Hakela et al. (1985) and the genetic analyses of Røed (1985) and Røed et al. (1986). The Spitsbergen reindeer is more closely related to populations in Arctic Canada than to Scandinavian reindeer and represents a subspecies distinct from the populations farther south. According to these sources the Spitsbergen reindeer must have been isolated from from its more southern counterparts for at least 200 000 years. Another example is the analysis of Kinloch et al. (1986) on biotypes of Scots pine in Scotland suggesting that some biotype of pine might have survived the last glacial age in northwest Scotland.

References

Anon. 1976. Climap Project Members 1976. The surface of the Ice-Age Earth. – Science 191: 1131–1137.

Barlow, N. 1958. The Autobiography of Charles Darwin 1809–1882. – Collins, London.

Blytt, A. 1886. On the Immigration of the Norwegian Flora during alternating dry and rainy periods. – Cammermeyer, Christiania.

Bott, M. H. P., Saxov, S., Talwani, M. and Thiede, J. (eds) 1983. Structure and development of the Greenland–Scotland ridge. – Plenum Press, N.Y. and London.

Böcher, T. W., Holmen, K. and Jacobsen, K. 1968. The Flora of Greenland. – P. Haase & Son, Copenhagen.

Conolly, A. P. and Dahl, E. 1970. Maximum summer temperatures in relation to modern and quaternary distribution of certain arctic-montane species in the British Isles. – In: Walker, D. and West, R. (eds), Studies in the vegetational history of the British Isles. Cambridge Univ. Press, pp. 159–223.

Dahl, E. 1946. On different types of unglaciated areas during the Ice Ages and their significance to plant geography. – New Phytol. 45: 225–242.

– 1951. On the relation between summer temperature and the distribution of alpine vascular plants in the lowlands of Fennoscandia. – Oikos 14: 22–52.

– 1954. Weathered gneisses at the Island of Runde, Sunmøre, Western Norway, and their geological interpretation. – Nytt Mag. for Bot. 3: 5–23.

– 1955. Biogeographic and geologic indications of unglaciated areas in Scandinavia during the Glacial Ages. – Bull. Geol. Soc. Am. 6: 1499–1519.

– 1959. Amfiatlantiske planter. Problems of amphiatlantic plant distribution. – Blyttia 16: 93–121.

– 1961a. Refugieproblemet og de kvartærgeologiske metode. – Svensk Naturvetenskap 14: 81–96.

– 1961b. Pleistocene history of the flora of the North Atlantic Region with special reference to Scandinavia. – In: Rec. Adv. Bot. University of Toronto Press. pp. 919–925.

– 1963. Plant migrations across the North Atlantic Ocean and their importance for the palaeogeography of the region. – In: Løve and Løve (eds), The North Atlantic Biota and their history, Pergamon Press, Oxford, pp. 173–188.

– 1975. Flora and plant sociology in Fennoscandian Tundra Areas. – In: Wielgolaski, F. E. (ed.), Fennoscandian tundra ecosystems. Part 1. Ecological Studies 16: 62–67.

– 1980. En rekonstruksjon av istidsklimaet. – Naturen 1980 (6): 259–266.

Dahl, R. 1963. Shifting Ice Culmination, Alternating ice covering and ambulant refuge organisms? – Geogr. Ann. 45: 122–138.

– 1966. Block fields, weathering pits and tor-like forms in the Narvik Mountains, Nordland, Norway. – Geogr. Ann. 48 A: 55–85.

Denton, G. H. and Hughes, T. J. 1981. The Last Great Ice Sheets. – John Wiley, New York.

Eldholm, O. and Thiede, J. 1986. Formation of the Norwegian Sea from the Leg 104 shipboard scientific party. – Nature, Lond. 319: 360–361.

Eldholm, O., Thiede, J. et al. 1986. Above the Arctic Circle. Reflector identified, glacial onset seen. – Geotimes, March 1986: 12–15.

Elven, R. and Aarhus, A. 1984. A study of *Draba cacuminum*. – Nord. J. Bot. 4: 425–441.

Ericsson, L. and Wallentinus, H.-G. 1979. Sea-shore vegetation around the Gulf of Bothnia. – Wahlenbergia 5: 1–118.

Flora Europaea, 1964–1980. Vols. 1–5. – Cambridge Univ. Press.

Flint, R. F. 1971. Glacial and Quaternary Geology. – John Wiley, New York.

Forman, S. L. and Miller, G. H. 1984. Time-dependent soil morphologies and pedogenic processes on raised beaches, Brøggerhalvøya, Spitsbergen, Svalbard Archipelago. – Arct. Alp. Res. 16: 381–394.

Frenzl, B. 1960. Die Vegetation und Landschaftzonen Nord-Eurasiens während der letzten Eiszeit und während der postglazialen Warmezeit. – Abh. d. matematisch.-naturwiss. Klasse d. Akad. d. Wiss. u.d. Litt. in Mainz 1959 (13): 934–1099.

Funder, S. and Simonarson, L. A. 1984. Bio- and Aminostratigraphy of some Quaternary marine deposits in West Greenland. – Can. J. Earth. Sci. 21: 843–852.

Grant, D. G. 1977a. Altitudinal weathering zones and glacial limits in Western Newfoundland, with particular reference to Gros Morne National Park. – Geol. Surv. Can. Paper 77-1A: 455–463.

– 1977b. Glacial style and ice limits, the Quaternary stratigraphic record, and changes of land and ocean level in the

Atlantic Provinces, Canada. – Geogr. phys. Quat. 31: 247–260.

Grønlie, A. 1953. Litt om Trollheimen under siste istid. – Norsk Geol. Tidsskr. 32: 168–190.

Hakela, A. V. K., Staaland, H, Pulliainen, E. and Røed, K. H. 1985. Taxonomy and history of arctic island reindeer with special reference to Svalbard reindeer. – Aquilo Ser. Zool 23: 1–11.

Heezen, B. and Tharp, M. 1963. The Atlantic floor. – In: Løve and Løve (eds), North Atlantic Biota and their history, Pergamon Press, Oxford, pp. 21–27.

Hoch, E. 1983. Fossil evidence of early Tertiary North Atlantic events viewed in European context. – In: Bott et al. (eds), Structure and development of the Greenland–Scotland ridge, Plenum Press, N.Y. and London, pp. 401–416.

Holtedahl, O. 1929. On the geology and physiography of some antarctic and subantarctic islands. – Avh. Norske Vid. Akad. 1929 (12): 1–14.

– and Rosenqvist, I. 1958. "Refugie-problemet" på den skandinaviske halvøy fra geologisk synspunkt. – Svensk Naturvetenskap 11: 108–118.

Hoppe, G. 1959. Några kritiska kommentarer till diskussionen om isfria refugier. – Svensk Naturvetenskap 12: 123–134.

Hultén, E. 1958. The Amphi-Atlantic plants and their phytogeographic connections. – Kungl. Svenska Vetenskapsakad. Handl. Ser. 4b.7. 340 pp.

Hylander, N. 1947. Cardaminopsis suecica (Fr.) Hiit., a northern amphiploid species. – Bull. Jard. Bot. Bruxelles 27: 591–604.

Ingrouille, M. J. and Stace, C. A. 1985. Pattern of variation of agamospermous Limonium (Plumbaginaceae) in the British Isles. – Nord. J. Bot. 5: 113–125.

Iversen, J. 1953. Origin of the Flora of Western Greenland in the light of pollen analysis. – Oikos 4: 85–103.

Ives, J. D., Nichols, H. and Short, S. 1976. Glacial history and palaeoecology of northeastern Nouveau-Quebec and northern Labrador. – Arctic 29: 48–51.

Kinloch, B. H., Westfall, R. D. and Forrest, G. I. 1986. Caledonian Scots pine: origins and genetic structure. – New Phytol. 104: 703–729.

Knaben, G. 1954. Saxifraga osloensis n. sp., a tetraploid species of the Tridactylites section. – Nytt. Mag. Bot. 3: 117–128.

– 1959a. On the evolution of the radicatum-group of the Scapiflora Papavers as studied in 70 and 56 chromosome species. Part A. Cytotaxonomical aspects. – Opera Bot. 2 (3).

– 1959b. On the evolution of the radicatum-group of the Scapiflora Papavers as studied in 70 and 56 chromosome species. Part B. Experimental studies. – Opera Bot. 3 (3).

– 1982. Om arts- og rasedannelse i Europa under kvartærtiden. I. Endemiske arter i Nordatlanteren. – Blyttia 40: 229–235.

Landvik, J. Y. and Mangerud, J. 1985. A Pleistocene sandur in western Norway: facies relationships and sedimentological characteristics. – Boreas 14: 161–174.

Lid, J. 1985. Norsk, svensk og finsk flora. – 5 utgåva v. Olav Gjærevoll. Det norske Samlaget, Oslo.

Lien, R. 1983. Pløyemerker etter isfjell på norsk kontinentalsokkel. – Inst. kontinentalsokkelundersøkelser. Publ. 109.

Lindroth, C. H. 1957. The faunal connections between Europe and North America. – Wiley, Stockholm and New York.

– 1958. Istidsövervintrare bland djuren. – Svensk Naturvetenskap 11: 134–151.

– 1960. Is Davis Strait – between Greenland and Baffin Island – a floristic barrier? – Bot. Notiser 113: 130–140.

– 1963. The problem of late land connections in the North Atlantic area. – In: Löve and Löve (eds), North Atlantic Biota and their History. Pergamon Press, Oxford, pp. 73–85.

List of rare, threatened and endemic plants in Europe 1983. Council of Europe. Nature and environment series 327.

Longva, O., Larsen, E. and Mangerud, J. 1983. Beskrivelse til kvartærgeologisk kart 1019 II-M 1:50000. – Norges Geol. Unders. Nr. 393 66 s. Kart.

Lynge, B. 1939. On the survival of plants in the Arctic. – Norsk Geogr. Tidsskr. 7: 225–242.

Löve, A. 1961. Hylandra – a new genus of Cruciferae. – Svensk Bot. Tidskr. 55: 211–217.

– and Löve, D. (eds). 1963. North Atlantic Biota and their history. Pergamon Press, Oxford.

Manabe, S. and Hahn, D. G. 1977. Simulation of the tropical climate of an Ice Age. – J. Geophys. Res. 82: 3899–3911.

Mangerud, J. and Salvigsen, O. 1984. The Kapp Ekholm section, Billefjorden, Spitsbergen: a discussion. – Boreas 13: 155–158.

McKenna, M. C. 1983. Cenozoic paleogeography of North Atlantic land bridges. – In: Bott, H. P., Saxov, B., Talwani, M. and Thiede, J. (eds), Structure and development of the Greenland–Scotland Ridge. Plenum Press, New York, pp. 351–399.

Miller, G. H. 1982. Quaternary depositional episodes, Western Spitsbergen, Norway: Aminostratigraphy and glacial history. – Arct. Alp. Res. 14: 321–340.

Nannfeldt, J. A. 1958. Den skandinaviska fjällfloran och nedisningarna. – Svensk Naturvetenskap 11: 119–133.

– 1963. Taxonomic differentiation as an indicator of the migratory history of the North Atlantic flora with especial regard to the Scandes. – In: Löve and Löve (eds), The North Atlantic Biota and their history. Pergamon Press, Oxford, pp. 87–97.

Nielsen, H. T. and Kerr, R. D. 1978. Paleoclimatic and paleogeographic implications of a lower Tertiary laterite (latosol) on the Iceland-Faroe Ridge, North Atlantic region. – Geol. Mag. 115: 153–236.

Nordal, I. 1985 a. Overvintringsteori og evolusjonshastighet. – Blyttia 43: 33–41.

– 1985 b. Overvintringsteorien og det vestarktiske element i skandinavias flora. – Blyttia 43: 185–193.

Nordhagen, R. 1931. Studien über die skandinavischen Rassen des Papaver radicatum Rottb., sowie einige mit denselben verwechselte neue Arten. – Bergens Mus. Årbok 1931 Naturv. Rekke. 2: 1–50.

– 1935. Om Arenaria humifusa og dens betydning for utforskningen av Skandinavias eldste floraelement. – Bergens Mus. Årbok. Naturv. Rekke 1935: 1–185.

– 1936. De senkvartære klimavekslinger i Nordeuropa og deres betydning for kulturforskningen. – Inst. Sammenliknende Kulturforsk. Oslo.

Peacock, J. D. and Ross, D. L. 1978. Anomalous glacial erratics in the southern part of the Outer Hebrides. – Scot. J. Geol. 14 (3): 262.

Perring, F. H., 1962. The Irish Problem. – Bournemouth Nat. Sci. Soc. Proc. 52: 1–13.

– 1968. Critical supplement to the Atlas of the British flora. Bot. Soc. British isles. London.

Roaldset, E., Pettersen, E., Longva, O. and Mangerud, J. 1982. Remnants of preglacial weathering in western Norway. – Norsk Geol. Tidsskr. 62: 169–178.

Røed, K. H. 1985. Comparison of the Genetic variation in Svalbard and Norwegian reindeer. – Can. J. Zool. 63: 2038–2042.

Røed, K. H., Staaland, H., Broughton, E. and Thomas, D. C. 1968. Transferrin variation in caribou (Rangifer tarandus L.) on Canadian Arctic Islands. – Can. J. Zool. 64: 94–98.

Rokoengen, K. and Rønningsland, T. M. 1983. Shallow bedrock geology and Quaternary thickness in the Norwegian sector of the North Sea between 60°30′N and 62°N. – Norsk Geol. Tidsskr. 63: 83–102.

Rønning, O. I. 1963. Phytogeographical problems in Svalbard. – In: Löve and Löve (eds), North Atlantic biota and their history. Pergamon Press, Oxford, pp. 99–107.

Savile, D. B. O. 1972. Arctic adaptations in plants. – Monogr. 6, Res. Branch, Can. Dept Agr.

Sernander, R. 1896. Några ord med anledning av Gunnar Andersson: Svenska växtvärldens historia. – Bot. Notiser 1896: 114–128.

Skre, O. 1979. The regional distribution of vascular plants in Scandinavia with requirements for high summer temperatures. – Norw. J. Bot. 26: 295–318.

Sollid, J. L. and Sørbel, L. 1979. Deglaciation of western Central Norway. – Boreas 8: 233–239.

Sørensen, N. A. 1949. Gjevilvasskammene-nunatakker i Trollheimens midte. – Naturen 73: 65–81.

Stace, C. A. (ed.) 1975. Hybridization in the flora of the British Isles. – Academic Press, London.

Strauch, F. 1970. Die Thule-Landbrücke als Wanderweg und Faunenscheide zwischen Atlantik und Skandik im Tertiär. – Geol. Rundschau 60: 381–417.

– 1983. Geological history of the Iceland-Faeroe-ridge and its influence on Pleistocene glaciations. – In: Bott et al. (eds), Structure and development of the Greenland–Scotland ridge. Plenum Press, London, pp. 601–606.

Thiede, J. 1983. Outstanding geological problems of the Greenland–Scotland ridge: An introduction. – In: Bott et al. (eds), Structure and development of the Greenland–Scotland ridge. Plenum Press, london, pp. 313–317.

Tiffney, B. H. 1985. The Eocene North Atlantic land bridge: Its importance in tertiary and modern phytogeography of the Northern Hemisphere. – J. Arnold Arboretum 66: 234–273.

Tralau, H. 1963. The recent and fossil distribution of some boreal and arctic montane plants in Europe. – Arkiv Botanik 5 (3): 533–571.

Van Steenis, C. G. G. J. 1962. The mountain flora of the Malaysian tropics. – Endeavour 21: 183–193.

Walters, S. M. 1978: British endemics. – In: Street, H. E. (ed.), Essays in plant taxonomy. Academic Press, London, pp. 263–274.

Warming, E. 1888. Om Grønlands Vegetation. – Medd. Grønland 12: 1–223.

Wintle, A. G. and Huntley, D. J. 1982. Thermoluminescenence dating of sediments. – Quatern. Sci. Rev. 1: 331–353.

Ecological Bulletins 38: 95–111. Copenhagen 1987

Human influence on vegetation in the Torneträsk area during the last three centuries

Urban Emanuelsson

Emanuelsson, U. 1987. Human influence on vegetation in the Torneträsk area during the last three centuries. – Ecol. Bull. (Copenhagen) 38: 95–111.

The Torneträsk area in northern Swedish Lapland is mountainous with birch forest in the valleys and some pine forest in its most eastern parts. Up to the 17th century the human land-use in the area was probably confined mostly to hunting and fishing. From this time on intensive reindeer husbandry spread into the area. Probably the reindeer grazing had a great impact upon the vegtation at the timberline as the Saami-people often stayed close to the timberline with their grazing animals. Severe climatical conditions in combination with this type of grazing probably depressed the timberline. Around 1900, an extensive form of reindeer grazing was introduced into the area. The grazing has since then been more spread out and is not so intense at the timberline. Probably partly as an effect of this change in grazing pattern the timberline has been rising in the area during the 20th century.
Swedish and Finnish farmers also effected the vegetation in the area during the later part of the 19th century and the first decades of the 20th century. The cutting of hay on both mires and on man made meadows in the birch forest was extensive. Also birch leaves were cut on a large scale locally close to some of the settlements.
During the building of the railway from Kiruna to Narvik, which was opened in 1903, extensive cuttings of the forest took place along the railway. Also mining activities during the 18th and 19th centuries could have indirectly affected the structure of the forest in the region. Probably the pine has suffered from such activities.
Subalpine heaths and open mires and tall herb meadows at the timberline could all be successional stages after an earlier human activity on these sites. Also the tree composition in many forest sites in the area could be a result of earlier human inmpact.

U. Emanuelsson, Abisko Scientific Research Station, S-980 24 Abisko, Sweden, and (offprint requests) Dept of Ecology, Plant Ecology, Univ. of Lund, Ecology Building, S-223 62 Lund, Sweden.

Introduction

Wilderness is a word often used when talking about northernmost Sweden. No doubt this area is usually much less affected by man than other parts of Europe, but whether it should be regarded as untouched or only slightly affected is open to discussion. In the present paper, an attempt is made to evaluate the magnitude of the human impact on the Torneträsk area (Figs 1–4), especially during the last three centuries.

Methods and material

This paper is largely based upon historical and ethnographical material already published but this is now evaluated and interpreted from an ecological perspective.

Mårtensson (1956), Sandberg (1963a), Sonesson (1970) and Sonesson and Lundberg (1974) present general information on the investigation area and its ecosystems. It is necessary to give a general historical background of the Torneträsk area to understand the human impact on it during the last centuries.

Since 1970, I have kept notes about traces of earlier human activity during my travels and many walking tours through different parts of the Torneträsk area. From the summer of 1984, I have mapped traces of former meadows, wooden constructions for drying hay, exceptionally young forest, saami (Lappish) camp sites, birch fences etc. in a more systematical way. This has been carried out from the ground, by air (two flights in

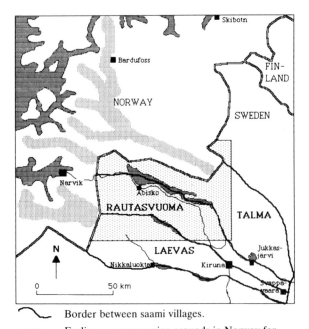

Border between saami villages.

Earlier summer-grazing grounds in Norway for the villages of Talma, Rautasvuoma and Laevas.

Investigation area.

Fig. 1. Territories of the saami villages which had some of their reindeer grazing grounds in the investigation area.

summer 1985 and 1986), and by interviews with the local population. The mapping is still incomplete, however, and the maps presented here should be regarded as preliminary (Figs 6, 8–10). Photographs taken at the beginning of this century in the Torneträsk area, by tourists, scientists and artists, are important sources of data on the general vegetation structure. The large collection of pictures taken by Borg Mesh, which are available at Hjalmar Lundbomsgården in Kiruna, are especially valuable. In many of these pictures it has been possible to identify the geographical location and then compare them with the present day situation. Using this method, it has been possible to obtain qualitative data on the vegetational development of many sites during the past 60–70 years (Figs 11–14).

Bio-historical background

Prehistory

Archaeological findings which are older than 1500 yr have not been positively identified from the Torneträsk area (Janson 1960). Bagge (1937) claims to have found remnants of stone-age culture on the shores of Lake Torneträsk. However, Janson (1960) doubts if these findings have a human origin. Along several lake systems to the south of the investigation area there have

been several finds of fireplaces and broken stones which were used for cooking meat (Lundholm 1973a,b). Most of these were found during special archaeological surveys of areas along lakes which were planned to be used as water reservoirs for hydroelectrical power plants. The age of these remains varies greatly. Lundholm (1973a) states that, 6000 yr ago, hunters and fishermen were already living in the mountain area of Lapland, for at least part of the year. It is, therefore, possible that an investigation around Lake Torneträsk could result in finds similar to those at the Lule river system and other large lakes.

It is not possible, at present, to say if a bronze-age culture existed in the western part of Lapland. The regular use of iron tools (Lundholm 1973a) may have started quite late, i.e. around AD 600 in western Lapland. Based on archaeological and linguistic evidence the existence of Saami-people in Scandinavia can be positively traced back to AD 200 (Fjellström 1985).

Early history

The first historical traces of the Saami-people, that is the "Lappish" people, appear in the first century AD. In AD 98 the Roman author Tacitus wrote about the "fenni" and described them as a hunting people living north of the Germanic tribes (Manker 1947).

The first detailed description of the saami peoples in northern Scandinavia was given by Ottar, an Norwegian chief from the vicinity of Tromsø (north of the Torneträsk area) during his visit to King Alfred the Great in the 9th century. According to Ottar, there were domestic reindeer at this time and he himself owned a herd. Lundmark (1982), argues that reindeer husbandry was not a major occupation among the saami people until after the beginning of the 17th century but Fjellström

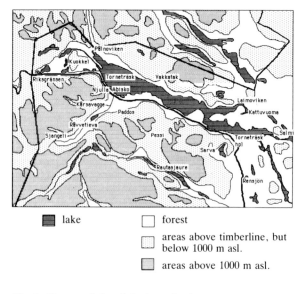

lake

forest

areas above timberline, but below 1000 m asl.

areas above 1000 m asl.

Fig. 2. Characteristics of the investigation area.

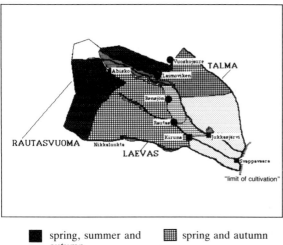

Fig. 3. Seasonal reindeer grazing grounds in the Torneträsk area (from Fjällrenskötsel med binäringar 1974).

(1985) disagrees placing more emphasis on the importance of reindeer husbandry earlier than the 17th century.

Much of Ottar's income came from so called "taxes" that the saami people had to pay him in addition to profits from trading.

It is probable that the saami people in the Torneträsk area were mainly occupied with hunting and fishing at this time. The coin-treasures, found at certain sacred places in Lapland, are evidence of long-distance trading by the saami people. One of the largest treasures was found at Lake Rautasjaure (Fig. 2), in the Torneträsk area (Hallström 1932). Both Norwegian noblemen, and traders from the southeast (Fjellström 1985), probably tried to control the trade and the saami people in this area. This type of control is documented from medieval times when the Birkarls had taxation rights and trading privileges with the Saami (probably including the people living in the Torneträsk area) (Ruong 1975).

The direct control of Lapland was taken over by the Swedish state in the 16th century. Taxation documents from the 17th century indicate more or less circular territories to which only certain saami families had the right (Lundmark 1982). Lundmark suggests that these documents together with others, are evidence that hunting was the major income of the saami people in the 16th century. Although the studies refer mainly to Lule Lappmark, it is probable that the situation was similar in the Torneträsk area during the 17th and 18th centuries (Lundmark 1982).

During the medieval period, and up to the 17th–18th centuries, the saami economy in Swedish Lapland de-

pended considerably on hunting (Lundmark 1982). Fjellström (1985) also stresses other aspects of the early saami economies. Hunting not only provided meat, but also furs which were exported and used as tax payments. The trading economy of the saami involved the import of grain paid for by the export of furs which allowed a fairly large population to be maintained. For example, there are several signs that poverty existed among the saami people around AD 1600. Only small quantities of furs were paid as tax at this time. This was probably a result of overexploitation of the fur-animals, including the wild reindeer. Consequently, the Swedish state tried to expand the reindeer husbandry to establish a new source of tax revenue. The husbandry of reindeer forced the saami population into full nomadism because the income from hunting was insufficient (Lundmark 1982). The development of the domestic reindeer population was, therefore, largely a result of a severe taxation policy levied by the Swedish state in combination with the overexploitation of the population of fur-animals (Lundmark 1982).

Several works (see Lundmark 1982 for a review) have stressed that the husbandry of reindeer can never exist on a large scale in an area that has a large population of wild reindeer. The wild reindeer are regarded as grazing competitors and are heavily culled. The wild reindeer also disturb the domestic herds during the mating season and can split them up.

Ekman (1910) shows that the wild reindeer became extinct in Lule Lappmark (the area of Lundmark's studies) earlier than in the Torneträsk area where the extinction took place in the early 19th century. This indicates that the transition from a hunting society to reindeer

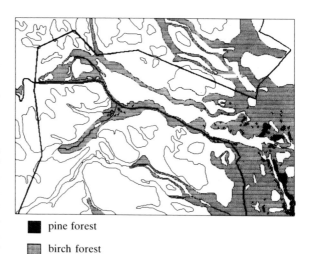

Fig. 4. Birch and pine forest in the Torneträsk area. Map simplified from Vegetationskarta 1979 to 84. The pine forest is very open and to a large extent mixed with birch, particularly in the west.

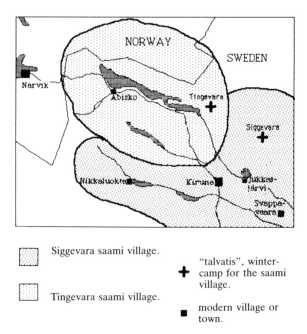

Siggevara saami village.

Tingevara saami village.

+ "talvatis", winter-camp for the saami village.

■ modern village or town.

Fig. 5. The approximate range of the "fishing and hunting" lapp villages occurring in the Torneträsk area during the 16th century. After Ruong 1937.

transhumance occurred later in the Torneträsk area than in Lule Lappmark. The transition in the Torneträsk area took place probably around the year 1700 (Lundmark 1982). In the Pålnoviken area and at Nissonjokk there are two systems of large holes dug for reindeer hunting which are especially well known (Manker 1960). However, their age is unknown, and they may have been in use for a very long time.

Hunting has had a long standing influence on the ecology of Lapland, but it is hard to estimate its indirect affect on the vegetation. At least two species of animals, moose and reindeer, have periodically changed their abundance drastically, as a result of hunting. When these species occur in high numbers, they can affect the vegetation greatly (Steen 1965).

Before the year 1700, two Lapp villages, Siggevare and Tingevare, were the centres of two territories with a round configuration. The round territories had a winter-meeting place in the center. The configuration of the territories indicates an economy built upon hunting of stationary or semi-stationary animals combined with fishing (Fig. 5) (Lundmark 1982). During the 18th century, a new type of taxation territory or "lapp village" appeared and these still exist. Their territories are very long and narrow, around 200 km by 30 km and have a northwest-southeast orientation (Fig. 1). They include high mountains in their western parts, and coniferous

forests in their southeastern extremes. These territories contain all the types of grazing land that the mountain reindeer need during the year. The territories may be regarded as administrative adaptations to the full reindeer nomadism in which the people can follow the migrating reindeer all the year round inside their own territory. Although geographically quite similar to those found here in the 18th century some smaller administrative changes of the saami villages are apparent today.

Saami reindeer husbandry

There are at present three saami villages in the Torneträsk area, Talma, Rautasvuoma and Laevas (Fig. 3). Much of their spring-, summer-, and autumn-grazing land is situated in the Torneträsk area. Some of the summer-grazing land is situated in Norway and all of the winter grazing areas are located eastward, in the coniferous region. More of the summer-grazing occurred in Norway during the 19th century than today. On the other hand, Norwegian saami people grazed reindeer in Sweden but this was during the winter. This movement of the domestic reindeer herds across the border was originally regulated in 1751 in an agreement called "Kodicillen".

The pattern of reindeer grazing varies greatly between the seasons of the year. It has also varied considerably depending upon the type of husbandry. There have been two different types of reindeer husbandry in the Torneträsk area; the old traditional type, with relatively few tame, and intensively milked reindeer and the more recent type introduced by immigrants from Kautokeino/Karesuando with many extensively managed reindeer kept mainly for meat and furs.

Traditional reindeer husbandry in the Torneträsk area between about 1600 and 1910 (mainly after Ruong 1937)

In the winter, the reindeer mainly grazed in the coniferous forests east of the mountain range. The animals from the Talma village were mainly found north and east of Jukkasjärvi, those from Rautasvuoma around Svappavaara and those from Laevas southeast of Svappavaara. In spring time the saami people migrated westwards with the reindeer into so called "springlands". These were areas where the snow melted early and they were important sites for the calving of the reindeer. During this time of the year, the reindeer were tended very carefully. When approximately half of the female reindeer had given birth to calves, the herd was divided into a female herd and into a herd of males and young. Both herds were followed closely by herdsmen throughout the summer except during the incidence of reindeer disease (Ruong 1975). However when reindeer disease occurred they were left "wild" as the herdsmen found that fewer were diseased when they roamed freely.

The reindeer cows were milked from the middle of July up to Christmas. During the whole summer period,

98

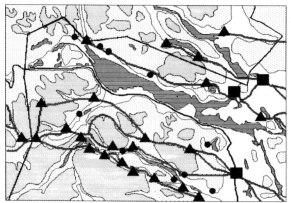

▲   Larger camps "viste" used around 1900.

■   Permanent settlements, still used after 1930.

〜   Earlier migration routes.

●   Traces of "viste" and old clearances in the birch forest.

Fig. 6. Migration routes, camps and settlements used during the intensive reindeer husbandry period. Mainly after Ruong 1937 and Manker 1947 and including field observations made by the author.

and also during parts of the spring and autumn, the people had to slowly follow the reindeer herds continuously as they grazed down area after area. The camps were called "viste" and the saami had to change viste quite often during summer to follow the reindeer. Most of the camps were situated at the timberline where there was access to firewood and where it was not far to the grazing grounds. Often, there were fenced milking areas in the vicinity of the camps.

Ruong (1975) has given a good description of the importance of the timberline for the older method of reindeer husbandry (translated by me): "The role of the timberline in reindeer husbandry can be inferred from the location of the more or less regularly situated spring- and autumn camps immediately below the timberline. Here the camp was protected against strong winds and firewood was at hand. There was also a good view of the grazing grounds from here and it was a short way to the treeless mountain where the reindeer herds grazed during the warm days in the autumn and from which they retreated down into the birchforest during rainy weather. Earlier, when the saami people milked the reindeer cows regularly, the location of the camp at the timberline was important as the herds were collected on the mountain and taken to the area around the camp to be milked."

Fig. 6 shows the more important migration routes during the period of traditional reindeer husbandry. Ruong (1937) also mentions the presence of several milking fences in the area, for example at Kuokkel, in Kårsavagge and at Paddos, east of Abisko, and there were many such fences in the Rautas Valley and in Vakkatak, north of Torneträsk (Fig. 2).

In the Pessi Valley and Laevas Valley, older summer-camps were situated close to great *Salix* thickets, as they were areas with good provisions of both firewood and water.

It is obvious that the number of reindeer was increasing in the investigation area during the 19th century, that is, before the extensive form of reindeer husbandry became prevalent during the late 19th century (Fig. 7). After this, however, there was a further increase in the total number of reindeer. The wild reindeer still existed in the area up to the early 19th century (Ekman 1910) but in low numbers.

The period of extensive reindeer husbandry in the Torneträsk area (mainly 20th century)

From the beginning of the 20th century it became less important for the whole saami family to follow the reindeer herds all the year round as a result of modern extensive reindeer husbandry. The earlier temporary spring camps now became permanent camps, "storvisten", used in spring, summer and autumn (Fig. 6). A "storviste" was already developing at the western end of Lake Torneträsk towards the end of the last century and in 1906, the "storviste" Laimoviken and Vuoskojaure were founded in the northeastern part of the investigation area. The "storviste" at Pålnoviken became less and less used and was finally abandoned during the Second World War.

Many families in the saami village Rautasvuoma were concentrated in the storviste Rensjön, not far from the railway, in 1910. In 1916, all of the families from Rautasvuoma lived in Rensjön from spring to late autumn. Originally, this storviste was situated at the timberline and was moved several times due to lack of fuel (Ruong 1975). No "storviste" from Laevas was founded inside the investigation area but Rautas, just south of the investigation, area was founded in 1928.

The change in way of life in the saami villages at the beginning of this century was partially in response to the railway and the better transport it provided, particularly to the people in Rautasvuoma. However, much of the change was also due to the transition of reindeer husbandry to a system excluding the milking of reindeer; that is a change from intensive to extensive husbandry. An important factor for this change was the immigration of saami people from Finnmarksvidda in Norway into the investigation area during the second half of the 19th century. This was caused by the closure of the Finnish border in 1870. Many saami families in the Kautokeino region, for example, could not survive as reindeer herdsmen after the closure of the border because their annual migration into Finland was prevented. The immigrants practiced extensive reindeer husbandry with fur and meat products, while the "old" reindeer herders in the Torneträsk area were mainly milk-producers (Ruong 1975). Ruong, when discussing the whole of Lapland, also points out that the reindeer owners occupied with meat production from an exten-

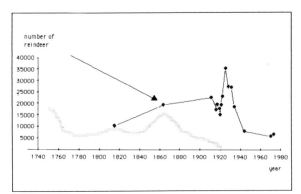

number of reindeer

Estimated number of intensively managed reindeer in Talma, Rautasvuoma and Laevas according to Ruong (1937).

Total number of reindeer in these villages. The arrow marks the date of the introduction of extensive reindeer husbandry into the investigation area.

Fig. 7. The numbers of reindeer in the villages of Talma, Rautasvuoma and Laevas. This probably underestimates the reindeer which have used the investigation area. However, the diagram shows the relative variations in numbers. (After Ruong 1937, Manker 1947 and Fjällrenskötsel med binäringar 1974).

sive area, had large herds, sometimes consisting of up to 10,000 reindeer. Owners of milk-producing reindeer often kept herds of only around 50 to 100 animals (compare Fig. 7).

Today, in the 1980s, the reindeer husbandry is extensive and the reindeer move freely during the summer. The old routes used for moving the herds are seldom used (Fig. 5). The herds more or less decide their own routes, although the topography of the landscape still forces them to choose migration routes similar to those used during the period of intensive reindeer husbandry.

Settlers

During the 17th century, the Swedish authorities showed an increasing interest in Lapland for two main reasons. There were no fixed borders against Norway and Russia and good control of the land and people was regarded as important. Interest in mining activity was also growning. The River Torneälv formed an important trading route between the Baltic Sea and Norway along which a chapel was constructed on the shore of the river in Jukkasjärvi in 1607 (Lundmark 1973) and in 1673, the parish of Jukkasjärvi was created. This comprised the whole Torneträsk area (Arell 1977).

The Swedish authorities encouraged Swedish and Finnish farmers to settle in Lapland. Jukkasjärvi was the only farming village in the vicinity of the Torneträsk area for a long time (Rudberg 1957). However, several settlements were founded in the area during the 19th century, particularly from 1850 onwards. At least five small villages then existed in the northeastern part

(Rudberg 1957, Ruong 1937). During this period, there were also between 10 and 20 attempts to establish other farming sites in the area (Ruong 1937, Rudberg 1957, Sandberg 1963b, Paulaharju 1966, Andersson 1981). These were abandoned after a while, however. None of them were legally registered by the authorities as they were too small and situated above the administrative boundary called "the cultivation limit" ("odlingsgränsen"). This boundary is situated 50 km east of the investigation area (see Fig. 3) and was established to control the expansion of agriculture for the saami people.

The term "farming settlement" is difficult to define since many saami settlements developed gradually in a similar direction during the 19th century and had permanent dairy production, although on a small scale. In addition, mixed farming was common where both farming, cattle raising and reindeer husbandry occurred together. Fishing and hunting were very important, particularly in poorer households (Ruong 1937). For general information on these types of "mixed farming" see Campbell (1947), Ruong (1975) and Sjulsson (1979).

In the eastern parts of the Torneträsk area, fire may have been an important tool used by the settlers to create grazing areas. According to Zackrisson's (1986) investigations, which were carried out in many sites in northern Sweden, approximately 1% of the coniferous forest of northern Sweden burnt annually before the time of modern fire-control. These fires were caused naturally by lightening, or accidents due to Man. Sometimes, the forests were set on fire deliberately to create open areas in the forests as they attracted wild animals or domestic animals could graze there. It may be as-

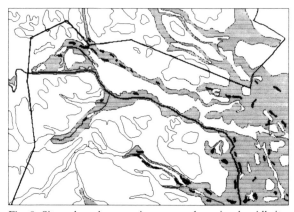

Fig. 8. Sites where hay mowing occurred previously. All sites were visited during the period 1972 to 1985. In nearly all of the black areas, at least one wooden construction for drying hay has been found. Such constructions were also found at some small mires, but these are not included on the map as it was assumed that the mowing area was smaller than 0.1 ha. About 200 wooden constructions have been found in total. The following literature has been used to try to find former hay meadows: Ruong 1937, Sandberg 1963b, Sonesson 1970, Persson 1961, and Lundmark 1937b.

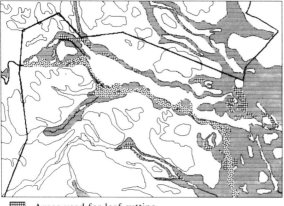

▦ Areas used for leaf cutting.

▨ Birch forest partly cut during the building of the railway, 1898 to 1902.

Fig. 9. Birch forest documented as having been affected by leaf cutting for fodder and cutting for fuel along the railway.

sumed that the frequency of fires was lower in the mountainous forests as a result of the cooler and more humid climate there. Saami reindeer herdsmen burnt birch-forests of the heath-type (Campbell 1947). This killed the birch trees, or at least some stems, allowing new shoots to develop from the base. *Empetrum hermaphroditum,* which is often a dominant dwarf shrub in this vegetation type, was almost completely destroyed, while species such as *Vaccinium vitis-idaea* and *V. myrtillus* survived by regeneration from subterranean rhizomes (Emanuelsson 1984). The grasses (especially *Deschampsia flexuosa* and *Calamagrostis lapponica*) were particularly favoured. As these grasses are more or less green in winter, such burnt sites were preferred by the reindeer, especially during spring. It seems probable that this type of burning occurred in the eastern part of the area and today, there are several recently burnt areas close to the Torneträsk railway station (hpl., Fig. 2) caused by trains.

According to the investigations by Sonesson (1974), only small and scattered quantities of charcoal occurred in the peat and sediment profiles from the Torneträsk area. At Luovare, in the cental-eastern part of the Torneträsk area, however, "An increased quantity was observed in the Luovare profile towards the surface, but obviously comprised only the last decades." (Sonesson 1974).

Swedish settlers moving up to northern Lapland at the end of the 18th century primarily burnt coniferous forest to create summer-grazing grounds for their cattle. They also used fire, to some extent, to create "slash and burn" farmland which was used for hay-making for several years and then for grazing (Campbell 1947, Paulaharju 1966). This type of activity is just vaguely indicated in the easternmost parts of the Torneträsk area (Paulaharju 1966).

It has been said (Laestadius 1831) that the settlers

also used the burnt coniferous forest to expel the saami people from an area. Such fires were serious since the reindeer were largely dependent on epiphytic lichens growing on the coniferous trees as a source of food during severe winters with hard snow.

The statements of Laestadius (1831) were doubted by several authors, but it is certain that Swedish and Finnish farmers were often in conflict with the saami nomads. A direct cause of conflict often arose when the saami reindeer were attracted to the settlers' haystacks during autumn and consumed or destroyed them. The hay was cut on widely scattered sites and control of the stacks was nearly impossible. As many saami also became owners of cows, sheep and goats during the 19th century, there was, in fact, strong competition in many areas for sites where hay could be gathered.

Such a conflict in the Torneträsk area was clearly documented in a recently discovered diary written in the 1930s by the saami author Johan Tuuri (Lundmark 1973) (the passage translated by me): "But around Talma there were no hay meadows. They are further away. The last areas of grassland and mires are lost [to the farmers] as they are leased out [by the state] ... And in the village of Talma, many poor people have settled and they survive by fishing, hunting red grouse, and keeping goats. They live in Kattuvuoma on the shore of Malajärvi. – The hay is dragged from Vuoskovuoma, which is ten kilometers away. This is a difficult task especially when it is considered that the mires are leased by settlers in Kattuvuoma [probably Swedish-Finnish farmers] without asking the Lapps ... When the Lapps mentioned this [i.e., conflicts about hay meadows and fishing] at the meeting with the "lappfogden" [local government representative, earlier responsible for the administration of the saami], the youths of Kattuvuoma used bad language and threatened [the Lapps] with thrashing ... Two widows have lived in Salmi for the past ten years, and they live by dragging the hay or carrying it on their backs for fourteen kilometers. Their [fishing] nets were destroyed a long time ago. Aslak's widow Inga lives in the same way. She has two cows, one bull and five goats and she also looks after six goats owned by [nomadic] Lapps. She must, therefore, carry the hay, as the permanent settlers own the nearby woodland meadows ... And it is strange that the women must carry and drag fuelwood and leaves for themselves from so far away. It is dreadful..."

The cutting of trees

The historical practices of tree-cutting in the investigation area can be referred to five categories:

a. The cutting of firewood by saami people, in combination with the cutting of fence material, during the time of intensive reindeer husbandry, which was often located around the timberline.

b. The cutting of firewood around permanent settlements by later saami people and settlers.

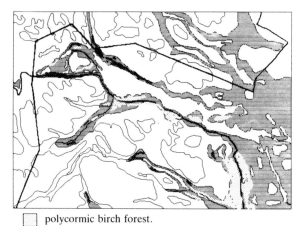

☐ polycormic birch forest.

■ monocormic birch forest.

Fig. 10. Areas with marked dominance of monocormic or polycormic birch forest. The whole investigation area has not been systematically surveyed with respect to this variable.

c. The cutting of firewood associated with the building of the railway around AD 1900.

d. The cutting of wood for making charcoal.

e. The selective cutting of pine trees, often in relation to construction work.

Around AD 1900, when the railway was built between Kiruna and Narvik, the birch forest was cut in a zone varying in width between 100 and 1000 m on both sides of the railway. Sjögren (1905, 1921) describes these clearances. Rosén (1902) also discusses felling for both building purposes and firewood. Grenegård (1958) discusses the area of trees cut during the building of the railway. He does not consider that the pines growing in the Abisko valley were cut on a large scale at this time, as they were too few, too far from the railway and their quality was too poor. On the other hand, both Grenegård and Rosén think that the cutting of fire wood, i.e. birch, was intense at Abisko.

Grenegård (1958) and Emanuelsson and Wijk (1979) have found evidence in official documents showing that pine wood was cut at Laimoviken and at Alajaure at the turn of the century. However, the quality of the logs was not good and much of the cut timber can still be seen on the ground.

Cattle in the Torneträsk area

The grazing of cows and goats in the Torneträsk region probably began in the early 19th century when Swedish/Finnish farmers began to create small farms east of lake Torneträsk, and also to some extent north and west of the lake. Both legal and illegal cultivation occurred. The número of cows and goats was probably at most a few dozen by 1850 (Ruong 1937).

At the end of the 19th century, the number of farmers increased (Rudberg 1957). Also, former railway workers built small farms at some of the railway stations and combined keeping livestock with hunting, fishing and seasonal work on the railway. Such farms occurred, for example, at Torneträsk railway (Björn Blomberg, pers. comm.).

At this time, the saami people also began to keep goats and cattle in great numbers. The number of cattle and goats seems to have increased up to the 1930s. It is, however, difficult to give any exact numbers of cows and goats for the period, as official statistics (Sveriges Officiella Statistik 1860–1940) and other sources widely disagree on the numbers. For example, Ruong 1937 gives the number of goats kept by saami people in the whole Jukkasjärvi parish in 1936 as 415. Ruong writes that he had collected most of the information himself. In 1927 there were, according to the official statistics, a total of 107 goats kept by saami people and Swedish/Finnish farmers in the Jukkasjärvi parish.

An estimate, based on Ruong's figures, shows the following number of goats in the investigation area in 1936: Talma 95, Rautasvuoma 66, Laevas 76. This is half the number given for Laevas, as many of the goat-keeping settlements were outside the investigation area.

According to Tuuri (in Lundmark 1973) and to information from old residents of the area (in the northeastern part of Torneträsk area and along the railway), it can be assumed that there were approximately 50 other goats kept in the investigation area by the Swedish/Finnish settlers alone. A total of around 300 goats should then have been present in the investigation area in 1936. The official statistics show a doubling of the number from 1910 to 1927 in the whole parish. From that it can be assumed that there were significantly fewer goats in the area in 1900 than in 1936. On the other hand, several authors (Asplund 1905, Sjögren 1905) mention "herds of goats" around 1900 at the Rautasjaure delta and at Pålnoviken. Two to three hundred goats probably existed in the area in 1900.

According to the official statistics, there were around 2,000 cattle and 500 horses in the whole of the Jukkasjärvi parish in 1927. Most of these animals must, however, have been found around and in Jukkasjärvi, along the Kalix river system and at Soppero, east of the Torneträsk area. According to Ruong (1937), the saami people owned around 50 cattle and 2 horses in the investigation area in 1936. Settlers northeast of Lake Torneträsk (Kattuvuoma, Salmi, Lattiluokta) are assumed to have had between 100 and 150 cattle and 10–20 horses in 1936 (estimates based on Paulaharju 1966 and the size of the former farms). Other settlers, especially those along the railway, are calculated to have had 20 to 40 cattle and 20–40 horses in 1936 (estimates based on information from B. Blomberg). In total, there were, therefore, 170–240 cattle and 30–60 horses in the investigation area in 1936.

In some areas, such as Pålnoviken, there are no rec-

102

ords of cattle in 1936 according to Ruong, but several authors record cattle from this site in 1900–1910. There were also cattle at the beginning of the 20th century at Rautasjaure and Jieprenjokk. However, there had probably been a total increase in the numbers of cattle and horses between 1900 and 1936. Horses used in relation to the building of the railway are not taken into consideration.

Mining and the railway

In 1698 copper mining started at Sjangeli, about 30 km SW of Abisko (SGU 1877). The ore was transported by reindeer to Kengis via Svappavaara in winter (Lundmark 1973). The mining continued periodically up to the end of the 19th century.

In 1736, Anund Anundsson Mangi revealed the existence of the large iron-ore mountains Kirunavaara and Luossavaara to the authorities after being promised that the Lapps would not be forced to work there (Ahlström 1966). It was not however, until around 1900 that mining really began in Kiruna.

For the purpose of iron ore transportation a railway was built from Gällivare via Kiruna to Narvik during the years 1898 to 1902. The building of the railway through the Torneträsk area brought about many changes (Brunnström 1981). Much birchwood was cut along the railway during the building and later, several small settlements grew up near the railway stations. These settlements were primarily dependent upon the railway as the inhabitants were partly employed for its maintenance. The total number of people living at the stations along the Kiruna-Riksgränsen railway were several hundred around 1930. These settlers used the surrounding countryside to some extent for keeping goats and cows, and also for fishing and hunting. Citizens of the town of Kiruna built, both legally and illegally, small huts in the vicinity of the railway to use for hunting and fishing.

With the opening of the railway in 1902, tourism was also introduced into the region. In Abisko, the Tourist Hotel was built in 1903.

Besides the cultural and economical influences from the mining society, and from tourism, the railway made the saami people more sedentary, especially in Rautasvuoma. Important reasons for this were that the railway crossed the traditional migrating routes and that the railway runs parallel with the migration routes in the western part of the territory of Rautasvuoma (see Fig. 6). After some years, the families stopped moving westwards into the summer grazing areas; only the herdsmen moved. Instead, permanent peat-huts and later on, wooden huts were built in the spring-autumn grazing land along the railway at Rensjön. In the villages of Laevas and Talma also, fewer places were used for living during the warmer part of the year. Only the herdsmen were permanently present in the summer grazing lands. Finally, during the summers of the 1930s, all the families of Rautasvuoma were living in Rensjön,

those of Talma in Laimoviken and Vuoskojaure, and those of Laevas in places outside the Torneträsk area as defined here. In 1936, the numbers of people in the saami villages of the Torneträsk area were: Talma 181, Rautasvuoma 86 and Laevas 203 (Ruong 1937).

During the 1930–1980 period a decreasing number of people were living along the railway, while tourism was steadily increasing. Today, tourism is concentrated in the areas around Abisko, Björkliden and Riksgränsen and is highlighted by chairlifts, a number of signposted tracks and small cabins. A new road was opened between Kiruna and Narvik in 1984. Although this road runs more or less parallel with, and close to, the old railway, it has substantially increased the possibilities for tourist activities in the area. It is now possible to stop on any part of the road and it is easier to gain access to many "new" fishing lakes or hunting grounds throughout the year. In winter time, it is now possible to start with snow mobiles/snow scooters from many places along the road and reach any fishing lake with ease. The snow scooter, which came into use in the 1960s, has shortened the distances radically for the people of the region. It has also totally changed the practices of reindeer husbandry. The introduction of this vehicle ensured the extinction of the wolf in the region.

The different types of land-use and their impacts on the Torneträsk area

Reindeer grazing

The old, traditional reindeer husbandry must have had a very different impact on the vegetation, compared with the modern one. In the older type, grazing was concentrated in the areas closer to the campsites. It was also more localised around the timberline than the modern extensive practice of reindeer husbandry (Ruong 1975: 15–18).

The felling of trees for fuel, and building of milking fences, were also concentrated around the timberline where particularly suitable sites occurred for the spring and autumn camps (Ruong 1975). It is interesting to note that at the beginning of the 20th century, the Norwegian authorities banned the felling of trees by the saami people in the grazing areas that were used by the people from the Swedish villages of Talma, Rautas and Laevas (Holmgren 1912). Obviously, the reindeer nomadism was regarded as a threat to the forest.

The general grazing impact on the area at the beginning of the 19th century seems to have been fairly small, although quite intense in some areas around the treeline (Fig. 7). At the turn of the century, the impact around the treeline should have been reduced, but the change towards a more extensive reindeer husbandry resulted in a greater increase in the impact. There should have been a peak increase in the impact around 1925, before a decreasing trend, which continued more or less up to

1970. This was due to a pronounced reduction in the reindeer population.

The grazing of reindeer must have been quite intense close to several "storviste" also in the 1920s and 1930s when there should have also been a peak in the grazing pressure here from other domestic animals, especially from goats. During the Second World War, there were a number of catastrophic winters that wiped out many of the reindeer herds. From this time, and up to the late 1960s, the grazing pressure from reindeer in the investigation area must have been lower than at any time during the 19th and 20th centuries. After the 1960s, the grazing pressure seems to have increased again (Fig. 7).

Cattle and the grazing of goats

Many of the settlements at which livestock were kept were situated in areas of medium productivity which originally had birch forest (Vegetation maps 1982–86). How great could the grazing pressure have been in such areas? According to information in the literature (Lidman 1963, Paulaharju 1966) and from inhabitants at Kangos 150 km E of the Torneträsk area and from G. Berggård, from areas similar to that under consideration, 3 to 5 ha per year would be the grazing area required for a cow or a horse. The figure for goats is estimated at 2 ha. This gives an estimated total "grazing area" of 1,200 to 2,100 ha for livestock during 1936 and this does not include reindeer grazing in the investigation area. The Torneträsk area is approximately 500,000 ha of which 40,000 to 50,000 ha are below timberline and were potential grazing areas for cows, horses and goats. On these premises, the grazing impact must have been quite substantial on some parts (< 10% of the area below the timberline) of the study area since the goats and cattle were not permitted to roam freely due to predators, and the grazing had to be restricted to particular areas. An example of the impact is the effect on tree saplings which must have been set back consierably. In other areas, however, there must have been very little grazing pressure from cows, horses and goats.

The livestock had also to survive winter. Figures from 1890 for the whole parish of Jukkasjärvi show that one cow or horse needed hay from around 2 ha of natural meadow as winter feed (Sveriges Officiella Statistik, Jordbruksdelen 1890). However Grenander (1937), estimated that a cow needed hay from 10 "hässjor" (wood constructions for drying and storing of hay) corresponding to around 5 ha of natural meadow. Assuming that a goat or a sheep needed half as much hay as a cow, and also that half of their winter fodder was leaves from deciduous trees and bushes, then about 550 to 750 ha in the investigation area should have been used for hay production in 1936. This is using 2 ha as a normal figure for the winter fodder requirement for a cow. Using the figure 5 ha gives us the figures 1375–1875 ha. However, many of the areas in which I have found wooden constructions for drying hay, are relatively unproductive

fens dominated by *Carex, Scirpus* or *Eriophorum*. Here, the productivity may be assumed to be less than a third of that of the "natural meadows" on mineral soil (Elveland 1976). This means that between 6 and 15 ha would be needed in such areas to provide a cow with winter feed. When the area of present "natural meadows" together with traces of former natural meadows, is estimated from the air reconnaissance and field observations, a figure of 200 to 300 ha is obtained. This includes areas where there are no indications of past haymaking. It seems impossible, therefore, that a larger area was harvested from mineral soils. Theoretically between 750 and 4,500 ha of mire must, therefore, have also been used to provide the required quantity of winter fodder. However, the lower figure may be the more accurate as much fodder was probably bought from other regions. In the 1910s and 1920s, there was undoubtedly a shortage of winter fodder, at least in the eastern part of the Torneträsk region (compare Tuuris' dairy, p. 25).

In many places in the Torneträsk region, birches with marked traces of leaf cutting still grow. However, it is known that in other areas in northern Sweden, the whole tree was often cut down, rather than just branches, when birch leaves were collected (Grenander 1937). Leaves probably provided half of the winter fodder for 300 goats in a normal year. Some poor people in Laimoviken, for example, probably fed their goats winter fodder consisting mainly of leaves. It is also probable that cows were fed leaves. It is difficult to estimate the area that was used each year for harvesting leaves. Between 100 and 200 bunches of leaves are said to feed one sheep over the winter (G. Berggård, pers. comm.). Assuming that 100 bunches are half of the fodder for one goat, then 30,000 bunches of leaves should have been harvested. This is estimated to correspond to the production of approximately 600–1500 ha of birch forest per year. However, these figures should be treated with caution as they only roughly illustrate the significance of leaf collecting. Tuuri talked about the long distance (15 km) which the poor people in Salmi had to walk to collect leaf-fodder. This indicates the devastating effect of leaf fodder gathering on the areas of available leaf-fodder in the birch forest around the permanent settlements.

The cutting of trees

The tree-cutting practice which probably has had greatest influence on the forests in the Torneträsk area is the cutting of wood by the saami people for firewood and fences. This cutting was concentrated at the timberline which is probably the most sensitive part of the forest. In the old practice of reindeer husbandry, where milking was important, birch branches were cut for fuel along the old migration routes (Ruong 1975). The regrowth of the birches at such sites would be hampered by the grazing of reindeer concentrated just around

Fig. 11a and b. Photos taken at Pålnoviken in 1906 (a) and 1986 (b) facing southeast. In 1906 the surroundings of the camp, the "viste" was very open. In 1986 the birch forest was dense here.

(Fig. 7) by using the variation in the number of nomads and reindeer during the later part of the 18th century (Ruong 1937). If a stable climate is assumed, the inverse of this diagramme can be said to show the changes in altitude of the forest around the timberline in valleys through which the old migration routes passed. When more permanent saami settlements (Pålnoviken, Vuoskojaure, Laimoviken, Rensjön) were founded around 1900, these were often placed close to the timberline in the same way as the old nomad camps. Ruong (1975) mentions that the settlement of Rensjön was moved three times due to depletion of fuel. In a number of photographs (a selection taken from approximately 30 is published here) taken around 1910, a comparatively open landscape can be seen around Pålnoviken, Abisko and Låktatjåkka (Figs 11, 12, 13, 14). The sites of these photographs are fairly well forested today. Tuuri (Lundmark 1973b) also mentions the lack of fuel around the settlements northeast of Torneträsk.

Several square kilometers around Rensjön, Salmi, Kattuvuoma and Laimoviken (Fig. 2) are today covered by forests which consist of low, highly polycormic open-canopy birch trees. Around Pålnoviken, large areas are now wooded with thick, but probably young monocormic trees (Fig. 10). Some birch wood cutting still

Fig. 12a (1906) and b (1986). Those photos are taken north of Pålnoviken just at the border between Sweden and Norway. In 1986 it was not possible to get any overview over the landscape from the same place were the photo was taken 1906.

these areas by herdsmen. Other parts of the forest, both at lower altitude and between camps were affected to a smaller extent. Today, it is still possible to find areas below the present timberline, down to an altitude of around 150 m below it, where the forest is significantly younger than that surrounding it. There are examples along the Rautas valley and at the timberline on the northern side of Lake Torneträsk. From 10 similar sites, it has been possible to associate 8 of them with old campsites (Fig. 6). Four of these had traces of milking fences. Ruong (1937) described and mapped a number of such sites but this phenomenon has not been fully studied.

What then, was the number of nomads and reindeer that were involved in this type of impact on the forests at the timberline?

In 1850, there were around 20,000 reindeer in Talma, Rautasvuoma and Laevas in total, all managed in the "old" practice (Fig. 7). Even if the total number of reindeer continued to rise during the 19th century, a larger part of them were being gradually managed in the "new" extensive practice. A hypothetical diagramme can be constructed showing the number of reindeer managed in the old practice in the investigation area

Fig. 13a (1910) and b (1986). Abisko Tourist Hotel and surroundings close to the railway.

exists around Rensjön, but the regrowth seems to be faster than the cutting, even in areas quite close to the settlement.

A number of photographs (cf. Fig. 14) taken in the years following the construction of the railway clearly shows that large areas of birch trees had been cut on both sides of the railway. Photographs taken by Sjögren around 1905 give evidence of recent clearance of the whole area between the railway and the present timberline, at the Laktatjåkka railway stop. Stumps were seen on the photographs.

There are a lot of stumps and only a few living birches remaining and it is possible to identify several birches seen on the photographs still today. Some of them grow at an altitude approximately 70 m higher than the upper limit of the younger birches which were established during the 1960s. The same pattern occurs along the railway and road built in 1984 westwards to Riksgränsen although few thick birches remain and the large majority of trees are recently established monocormic birches. There is an exception however: 2 km from Riksgränsen there is evidence of very thick old trees growing at the highest altitudes. This pattern is not so clear east of the Kopparåsen railway station. It is possible to see clear felled areas which are now covered by

quite open polycormic woodlands at sites from which there are photographs, for example Abisko. Further east, there are only a few good photographs illustrating the forest development around the railway.

The pine woods in the Torneträsk area (Fig. 4) are limited to the eastern part of the region, but there are also isolated stands of pine in the Abisko valley mostly on southfacing slopes of eskers. Grenegård (1958) concludes that there was some exploitation of the pine woods during the building of the railway and, perhaps, some pines were felled during the wintertime to feed reindeer with their epiphytic lichens. However, the most intense exploitation of pine trees must have taken place in connection with the mining at Sjangeli, 25 km SW of Abisko (Fig. 2). This copper mine was opened in the 1700s and the peak activity in the mining occurred in 1840 (SGU 1877). Pine logs were needed for the mine, and most of this material seems to have been cut in the eastern part of the region. Probably a still greater impact on the pinewoods in the Abisko valley was the making of charcoal (Grenegård 1958). Grenegård estimates that 1,000 to 1,500 pine trees were cut in the Abisko valley for this purpose in 1844. This was then, possibly, one of the years with the greatest exploitation of pines as the ore production reached a peak of 70 tonnes, while only approximately 20 tonnes were extracted in the previous year (Grenegård 1958). Assuming that charcoal was made in the Abisko valley for the mining of Sjangeli over a 50 yr period and that 500 trees were cut per year, it can be calculated that 25,000 trees would have been felled which, at a density of 200 trees per ha (Grenegård 1958) would be equivalent to 175 ha of pine woods. The area has probably, however, been much larger.

From such a large clearing, a number of stumps should still be left today, and indeed, there are a few. This casts doubt on the existence of a large pine wood in the Abisko valley at the beginning of the 19th century. However so far, there has been no systematical field

Fig. 14 (1903). Photo taken at Låktatjåkka railway stop.

106

investigation of the actual number of pine stumps in the area. Since pine stumps make excellent fuel, many stumps may have been used as firewood by tourists and the local population.

Modern exploitation

Today, Man's impact on the vegetation of the Torneträsk area is slight. No intense reindeer grazing occurs around the timberline, practically no cutting of the forest takes place, and grazing and browsing by cows and goats together with the collecting of leaves and hay has not occurred since the 1940s. The present impact is mostly associated with tourism and amenity activities in addition to an extensive form of reindeer husbandry and some fishing and hunting.

Tourism was introduced to the investigation area after the opening of the railway in 1903. It increased steadily during the following 70 years (Bäck and Hedlund 1982) and there was a large increase in the early 1970s. Since the autumn of 1984, when the road between Kiruna and Narvik was opened for cars, there has been a further increase in the number of people visiting the area. The number of tourists walking a few hundred metres from the road has hardly increased, however. Tourist activities are concentrated at Abisko, Björkliden and Riksgränsen (Fig. 2) from which trails radiate outwards. In these places there are areas of a few square kilometers that are dissected by small roads, tracks, chairlifts etc. The impact outside these intensively used areas is difficult to observe and measure, although there is a great variation in the ability of different vegetation types to withstand trampling (Emanuelsson 1984).

Some preliminary studies (Emanuelsson, unpubl.) indicate that the reindeer tracks cover a larger area than the tracks of humans in the Torneträsk area.

Vegetation

Very little is known about the relative importance of various types of human impact compared with the natural dynamic changes of the ecosystems in the Torneträsk area. It is, for instance, difficult to assess the importance of the former goat grazing in the birch forests in relation to the grazing from the natural, indigenous rodent populations (Emanuelsson 1984). The reindeer is probably a very old component of the ecosystems of the area and inhabited the arctic-subarctic regions long before man. The populations are now largely controlled by man however, both in terms of their sizes and migrations. Today, it is hard to distinguish between the impacts of the reindeer related to man's management and those that should be natural (Sonesson 1970).

Dynamics of the timberline

Several workers have observed that the treeline has risen in altitude significantly in the Scandinavian mountains during the 20th century. It has also been documented that the climate in northern Scandinavia has been warmer during most of the period from 1910 up to the present day, compared with most of the second half of the 19th century (Wallén 1963). This climate change has been proposed as the most important explanation of the increasing altitude of the timberline (Sonesson 1980, Sonesson and Hoogesteger 1983). Also the retreat of the glaciers has been shown to be roughly parallel to the increase in altitude of the timberline (Wallén 1963). The increasing altitude of the timberline has been partially explained by the discontinuation of grazing by cows and goats in Härjedalen (south of Lapland) (Kullman 1976). However this explanation for the altitudinal expansion of the birch forest has never been presented for the Torneträsk area, probably due to the good correlation which exists between climate and dendrochronological data. Also Kullman (1979) stresses the importance of warmer climate as a main factor for the rising of timberline in the south Swedish Scandes.

Kullman (1984) has recently presented some evidence that the mountain birch requires a number of climatically good years to establish from seeds in environments around the timberline in the southern Swedish Scandes. The saplings which survived the first three to five years had an ability to withstand years with bad climatic conditions. Perhaps this may explain the solitary old birches which are often found much higher than the present young trees which are "advancing uphill" in the mountains of the Torneträsk area. Photographs taken by Sjögren in 1907 in the northern part of Kärkevagge (Fig. 14) show that the forest had been cut recently but that some trees had survived. Some of them are still alive and some grow at a much higher altitude (75 m) than the young expanding birch forest. This indicates that the birch forest may be able to expand in altitude only during a few climatically good years, but that it does not retreat during periods of bad years, if these periods are not longer than the life span of the trees. The retreat of the forest is caused by other factors, in this case by the tree cutting during the construction of the railway.

In this part of the Torneträsk area, the birch seems to have a poor ability to form new shoots from the cut stumps, a process which would result in potentially indefinite life spans. There may be a negative correlation between this ability and snow depth.

Only a small fraction of the timberline in the Torneträsk area has been affected by cutting during the building of the railway, however. Other factors may have also caused a depression.

The old traditional practice of reindeer husbandry that existed in the area up to 1920, should have substantially affected the birch forest at the timberline, especially during the second half of the 19th century. The herding of reindeer here, for most of the summer, probably resulted in a high probability of new shoots from the cut birch stumps being eaten by the reindeer.

The saami had to move further down the mountain each decade to follow the retreat of the timberline and to be close to firewood supplies. The destruction of the forest at timberline can be assumed to have been most intensive during 1750, 1810 and especially between 1850 and 1860, as the reindeer numbers at these times were very high (Fig. 7). In 1860, there were about three times as many reindeer in the area as in 1971, and all were more or less grazing around the timberline, which means approximately ±50 m. In 1860, the dramatic change in reindeer husbandry began, and, from this time, the old method of herding the reindeer close to the timberline became less important. During most of the 19th century and especially during the second half, the climate was so severe (Wallén 1963) that the establishment of birch saplings at the treeline was likely to have been low or non-existent.

When the climate became warmer in the 1910s, most of the old practices of keeping the reindeer around the timberline ended and the conditions for the recovery of the forests began to improve. During the 1920s and 1930s, there was again a large increase in the number of reindeer (Fig. 7). Although these reindeer were managed in the "new" extensive husbandry practice, many of them would have still hampered the recovery of the birches at the timberline. The relatively extensive use of leaf-fodder and the grazing by goats and cows in some parts of the area (around Laimoviken, Rensjön and Rautasjaure) may have also affected the forests at the timberline in these places. At the end of the 1930s, when there was a large reduction in the reindeer herds of the area, and when more or less all the cows and goats had disappeared, there must have been a considerable improvement in the conditions for an expansion of the birch forests.

One of the earlier authors dealing with the human impact on the Torneträsk area claims: "The keeping of cattle and goats has occurred intermittently since the end of the last century and was probably slight and restricted to relatively small areas" (Sonesson 1970), and "indications of former clearings and areas where hay was collected. Wood-cutting on a limited scale has probably continued since the Lapps first moved into the area. However, this could not seriously have influenced the timberline, since it was not combined with any cattle grazing until the end of the 19th century" (Sonesson and Lundberg 1974). Sonesson thinks that the overall change of the treeline of the area in the 20th century is almost exclusively a climate-dependent process. However, he has certainly only taken into account the effects of the modern type of extensive reindeer grazing and has neglected the influence of the "old" traditional husbandry practice.

However, several factors complicate this picture. One is the differences in the growth form of the birch of the area..In the eastern parts of the area, the growth form of the birches is probably more polycormic and in the western parts, more monocormic (Fig. 10). These differences have been related to the variations in snow cover (Sonesson and Hoogesteger 1983), which is generally thicker in the western than in the eastern part. However, it is possible that the growth form is responsible for the ability of the trees to withstand cutting and browsing thus reflecting the different former types of land use. The higher frequency of polycormic birches in the eastern parts may then be a result of a high frequency of tree cutting (compare the use of coppice woods in western and central Europe (Rackham 1980)).

Another complicating factor is the outbreak of the autumnal moth, *Epirrita autumnata* and the winter moth, *Operophthera brumata,* which can kill the birch forest. Tenow (1975) has shown that the outbreaks seem to be most devastating to the old, monocormic trees and to those at some distance from the timberline whereas those at the timberline are often unaffected. Climatic relationships have been put forward as explanations (Tenow 1975).

The open subalpine heaths
Sandberg (1963a) has pointed out that there are several subalpine heaths in the Abisko valley which may be related to the colder local climate here. Preliminary studies (Holmgren, pers. comm.) indicate that the heaths in the Abisko valley have a significantly lower soil temperature than comparable sites in the birch forest. In the early summer of 1985, I observed that the birches were developing poorly in several places in the Abisko Valley, Rautas Valley and Kårsavagge Valley. According to Holmgren (pers. comm.), the temperature of the soil at such sites was very low, even by the end of July, although the summer of this year was fairly normal. However, the snow cover of these sites seems to have been extraordinary thin and winter temperatures were abnormally low. The heaths may, to a large extent, be adapted to thin snow cover and therefore low soil temperatures, being unfavourable for the establishment of saplings. Also, frost movements in the soil should make the subalpine heaths unfavourable sites for larger shrubs and trees (Sandberg 1963a). However, were these heaths originally treeless areas or have they been deprived of trees in some way, and then lost their ability to keep a thicker snow cover?

The largest subalpine heaths in the Torneträsk area are situated in eastern Kårsavagga, just west of Lake Rautasjaure, at Sarva, west of Nakerjaure and at Råvvetievva (still inhabited in the summers), see Fig. 2. At all of these sites there were permanent summercamps or "storvisten", during the 19th century and at the beginning of this century. These storvisten were much used especially during the intermediate period between the old traditional reindeer husbandry when many small camps existed along the migration routes, and the modern reindeer husbandry associated with permanent settlements in the eastern part of the Torneträsk area (Fig. 6). It is possible that these large subalpine heaths were created by intense human activity. Between 4 to 10 families were living at these sites at the beginning of the 20th century. They still had some milking reindeer and also goats and, to some extent, cows. Large quantities of fuel and building and fencing material would have been used at these sites.

In such treeless sites, the snow conditions would have changed, resulting in an effect on the recovery of the forest. Another possibility is that the saami placed their camps on naturally existing open heaths, although this alternative seems less likely since they needed wood. Ruong (1975) says, for example, that the "storviste" Rensjön was moved three times at the beginning of the 20th century as a consequence of lack of fuel.

The species composition and structure of the forest
In Löfgren (1984) the theory is presented that the subalpine birch forest east of the mountain range in Lapland is not the natural "climax" forest. It is one out of several succession stages which is the result of climatical changes and different types of human impact. The pine should have had in many places a much more prominent position but it has been cut extensively by man and affected by severe climatical conditions. See also Grenegård (1958) and Kullman (1987).

In the light of this theory, it is interesting to note that large quantities of pine wood were documented as having been cut in the Abisko valley during the 19th century. The Abisko valley may have been covered to a relatively large extent by pine forest some 200 to 300 yr ago. There are no indications from pollen data collected in the area, that large pine forests existed in the Abisko valley in previous centuries (Sonesson 1970, 1974). However, the resolution in the available pollen profiles may be insufficient to settle this question.

In a number of photographs taken in the Torneträsk area during the period 1900 to 1940 (see above) it is possible to make detailed comparisons between the forest structure of around this time and the present day structure for about ten sites. At six sites, it is quite evident that there had been large changes in the forest. A number of new trees had filled in the spaces between the older trees. Sandberg (1963a) also mentions this development.

Today, we can only speculate about the probable reason for this thickening of the birch forest. Parallel to the discussion of the timberline, two main reasons can be suggested: more favourable climate and/or decreased grazing from reindeer, goats and cows. At some sites also regeneration of the birchforest after outbreaks of *Epirrita autumnata* and *Operophthera brumata* are possible.

The tall-herb meadows and Salix thickets
Salix thickets and tall-herb meadows are often found on topographically and altitudinally similar sites in the Torneträsk area (Vegetation maps 1979 to 1984). In the field, this is obvious at many sites. Sandberg (1963a: 903) shows two interesting pictures taken at the same

site on Mount Njulla in 1937 and 1959. These pictures clearly shows that a former tall-herb meadow (1937) has been replaced by thickets of *Salix glauca, S. lanata* and *S. phylicifolia* (1959). Hay meadows, which are today overgrown by *Salix* thicket, are documented from a number of sites. For example, Ruong (1937) describes hay meadows from the eastern end of Lake Rautasjaure which, in 1973, were to a large extent overgrown by *Salix*. On the mountain of Pakkapahutjåkka, not far from the former "storviste" at the western end of Lake Rautasjaure, there is a track which is now overgrown by *Salix*. However, the track is recognisable because it was marked by cairns although the cairns are now mostly covered by *Salix* bushes.

In 1984 on the northern side of Lake Torneträsk I found about 15 wooden constructions for drying hay on sloping ground inside *Salix* thickets.

It seems probable, therefore, that at least some present *Salix* thicket sites were hay meadows or grazing areas, previously dominated by tall-herbs and grasses. There may have been two ways in which these meadows developed from *Salix* thickets. One could have been the grazing and cutting of *Salix* around saami camps. The other could have been the deliberate, regular clearance of the thickets to create and maintain hay meadows.

Human impact on mire vegetation
There is much evidence that many mires in the investigation area have been used for haymaking (see Fig. 8). Persson (1961) and Sonesson (1970) mention the finding of remnants of wooden constructions for drying hay on the northern side of Lake Torneträsk and at Stordalen, 10 km E of Abisko. The total area of such managed mires is difficult to estimate. Figures varying between 700 and 4,500 ha are given above, based upon hay requirements. Estimates based on sites with remnants of wooden constructions for drying hay suggest an area of 700 to 1,000 ha. *Carex* species and *Eriophorum angustifolium* now dominate the areas formerly harvested. During the period from 1971 to 1985, it was possible to observe a marked invasion by *Salix* into *Carex*-dominated sites. Emanuelsson (1980) noted that breeding and displaying *Calidris alpina* and *Philomachus pugnax* were markedly reduced in numbers between 1971 and 1978 on sites below the timberline which were formerly used for haymaking. However, there was no reduction of these species on wet sites above the timberline which were probably never used for haymaking.

Conclusions

When summarizing the magnitude of the human impact on vegetation in the Torneträsk area, it is essential to realise that there are few areas of similar size, with such a limited human impact during the past 300 yr, in the rest of Fennoscandia. For example, reindeer nomadism probably developed later in Torne Lappmark than in any other region in Sweden (Lundmark 1982). Here, stock-raising and small scale agriculture were also introduced later than elsewhere (Bylund 1963: 105). However, the area was obviously not untouched by man.

During the 19th century, the climate in the investigation area was cooler than today, although established birches could survive at many sites at even higher altitudes than the present timberline. Intense grazing pressure, combined with the cutting of trees at the timberline, locally destroyed much of the birch forest. Regeneration was not possible until the climate improved during the 20th century. Regeneration was particularly favoured after 1940, when the grazing pressure decreased drastically.

In the Torneträsk area, there is an opportunity to observe, whithin a limited time span, how human impact on the environment starts (during the 17th century), how it successively increases and, finally, how it declines. In other words, we can follow the creation of a virgin cultural landscape from a wilderness, and thereafter (hopefully) observe as it reverts to wilderness. This is probably a very rare situation in Europe.

Acknowledgements – I thank M. Sonesson for stimulating me to write the present paper and for giving many valuable comments on It. I would like to thank N.-Å. Andersson, B. Holmgren and R. Berggård for valuable discussions on the subject. H.-G. Karlsson was very helpful in providing photographs of the saami sites from which old pictures existed. I am grateful to A. Rapp for giving me photocopies from the late O. Sjögren's private collection relating to sites close to the Låktatjåkka railway stop and to C. Callaghan for correcting the language. Finally I thank the personnel and colleagues at the Abisko Scientific Research Station for all help during the work.

References

Ahlström, G. 1966. De mörka bergen. En krönika om de lappländska malmfälten. – Stockholm (in Swedish).
Andersson, C. 1981. Kanans land vid Torneträsk. – In: Niemi, S. 1981. Lainio – vår hembygd. – Published by Lainio Hembygdsgille. Printed in Kemi, Finland (in Swedish).
Arell, N. 1977. Rennomadismen i Torne lappmark – markanvändning under kolonisationsepoken i fr. a. Enontekis socken. – Geografiska inst, Umeå Universitet Medd. no. 24. Umeå (in Swedish).
Asplund, C. J. 1905. Till Rautasvuoma lappar och Jukkasjärvis högfjäll. – Svenska Turistföreningens Årsbok 1905 (in Swedish).
Bäck, L. and Hedlund, L. G. 1982. Vandringsturismen i Norrbottensfjällen 1980. – Statens Naturvårdsverk PM 1572 (in Swedish).
Bagge, A. 1937. Stenåldern vid Torneträsk. – Norrbottens läns Hembygdsförenings Årsbok: 89–106 (in Swedish).
Brunnström, L. 1981. Kiruna – ett samhällsbygge i sekelskiftets Sverige. – Forskningsrapport nr 3 i projektet Norrländska städer och kulturmiljöer vid Umeå universitet. ISBN 91-7174-089-9 (in Swedish).
Bylund, E. 1963. Koloniseringen av Lappland. – In: Curry-Lindahl, K. (ed.), Natur i Lappland, Uppsala (in Swedish).
Campbell, Å. 1947. Från wildmark till bygd. En etnologisk undersökning av nybyggarkulturen i Lappland före industrialismens genombrott. – Skrifter utgivna genom Landsmåls- och Folkminnesarkivet i Uppsala Ser. B:5 (in Swedish).

Ekman, S. 1910. Norrlands jakt och fiske. – Uppsala (in Swedish).
Elveland, J. 1979. Dammängar, silängar och raningar – norrländska naturvårdsobjekt. – Statens Naturvårdsverk PM 1174 (in Swedish).
Emanuelsson, U. 1980. Människan och fjällfåglarna. – Fauna Flora 75: 49–54 (in Swedish).
– 1984. Ecological effects of grazing and trampling on mountain vegetation in northern Sweden. – Ph. D. Thesis, Univ. of Lund.
– and Wijk, S. 1979. Alajaureområdet – översiktlig naturinventering. – Länsstyrelsen i Norrbottens län. Planeringsavdelningens rapportserie nr 13 (in Swedish).
Fjällrenskötsel med binäringar. 1974. Översiktsplanering BD-län. – Länsstyrelsen i Norrbottens län, Planeringsavdelningen (in Swedish).
Fjellström, P. 1985. Samernas samhälle i tradition och nutid. – ISBN 91-1-853222-5. Värnamo (in Swedish).
Frödin, J. 1952. Skogar och myrar i norra Sverige i deras egenskap av betesmark för husdjur. – Inst. for sammenlignende kulturforskning, Ser B XLVI. Oslo (in Swedish).
Grenander, G. 1937. Lövtäkt i norra Sverige – Norrbotten. Norrbottens läns hembygdsförenings årsbok 1937: 61–78 (in Swedish).
Grenegård, L. 1958. Studier över barrskogens, speciellt tallens, förekomst inom Torneträskområdet. – Abisko Scientific Research Station. Unpublished mimeografed paper (in Swedish).
Hallström, G. 1932. Lapska offerplatser. Arkeologiska studier tillägnade H. K. H. Kronprins Gustav Adolf. – Stockholm (in Swedish).
Holmgren, A. 1912. Studier öfver nordligaste Skandinaviens björkskogar. – Stockholm (in Swedish).
Janson, S. 1960. Arkeologi och sjöregleringar. – In: Janson, S. and Hvarfner, H. 1960. Från Norrlandsälvar och fjällsjöar. – Riksantikvarieämbetets kulturhistoriska undersökningar i samband med kraftverksbyggen och sjöregleringar. Stockholm (in Swedish).
Kullman, L. 1976. Recent trädgränsdynamik i V Härjedalen. – Sv. Bot. Tidskr. Vol: 70: 2: 107–137 (in Swedish).
– 1979. Change and stability in the altitude opf birch tree-limit in southern Swedish Scandes 1915–1975. – Acta Phytogegraphica Suecica 65.
– 1984. Transplantation experiments with saplings of *Betula pubescens* ssp. *tortuosa* near the tree-limit in central Sweden. – Holarct. Ecol. 7: 289–293.
– 1987. Long-term dynamics of high-altitude populations of *Pinus sylvestris* in the Swedish Scandes. – J. Biogeogr. 14: 1–8.
Laestadius, P. 1831. Journal för första året of hans tjenstgöring såsom missionaire i Lappmarken. – Stockholm (in Swedish).
Lidman, H. (ed.) 1963. Fäbodar. – LTs förlag. Stockholm (in Swedish).
Lundholm, K. 1973a. Från stentid till järntid. – Norrbottens Museum. Luleå (in Swedish).
– 1973b. Norrbotten tar form. – Norrbottens Museum. Luleå (in Swedish).
Lundmark, B. 1973. Samer i gruvstad. – Norrbottens Museum. Luleå (in Swedish).
– (ed.). 1973b. Från skolkåtor och renfjäll – Terese Torgrim och Johan Tuuri berättar. – Norrbottens Museum. Luleå (in Swedish).
Lundmark, L. 1982. Uppbörd, utarmning, utveckling. Det samiska fångstsamhällets övergång till rennomadism i Lule lappmark. – Arkiv avhandlingsserie 14. Arkiv för arbetarrörelsens historia, Lund (in Swedish).
Löfgren, R. (ed.) 1984. Urskogar. Inventering av urskogsartade områden i Sverige. Del 5 Fjällregionen. – SNV pm 1511 (in Swedish).
Manker, E. 1947. De svenska fjällapparna. – Svenska Turistföreningens förlag. Stockholm (in Swedish).

– 1960. Fångstgropar och stalotomter. – Uppsala (in Swedish).

Mårtensson, O. 1956. Bryophytes of the Torneträsk area, northern Swedish Lapland. III. General part. – K. Sv. Vet. Akad. Avhandl. Naturskyddsärenden 15. (in Swedish).

Paulaharju, S. 1966. Ödebygdsfolk från Nordsveriges Finskbygder. – Natur och kultur, Stockholm (in Swedish).

Persson, Å. 1961. Mire and spring vegetation in an area north of Lake Torneträsk, Torne Lappmark, Sweden. I. Description of the vegetation. – Opera Bot. 6: 1. Lund (in Swedish).

Rackham, O. 1980. Ancient woodland, its history, vegetation and uses in England. – Edward Arnold, London.

Rosén, G. 1902. Förhållanden och missförhållanden vid Ofotenbanan. – Published by the author. Again published as Tornedalica Nr 21 1976. Luleå (in Swedish).

Rudberg, S. 1957. Ödemarkerna och den perifera bebyggelsen i inre Nordsverige. En diskussion av visse orsakssamband bakom fördelningen bygd-obygd. – Geographica Nr 33. Uppsala (in Swedish).

Ruong, I. 1937. Fjällapparna i Jukkasjärvi socken. – Geographica nr 3. Uppsala (in Swedish).

– 1975. Samerna. – Aldus/Bonniers, Stockholm,. ISBN 91-0-040105-6 (in Swedish).

Sandberg, G. 1963a. Växtvärlden i Abisko nationalpark. – In: Curry-Lindahl, K. (ed.), Natur i Lappland. Uppsala (in Swedish).

– 1963b. Vadvetjåkko nationalpark. – In: Curry-Lindahl, K. (ed.), Natur i Lappland. Uppsala (in Swedish).

SGU 1877. Underdånig berättelse om en ... år 1875 företagen undersökning af malmfyndigheter inom Gellivare och Jukkasjärvi socknar ... – Sv. Geol. Undersökning. Stockholm (in Swedish).

Sjögren, O. 1905. Abisko och utflykter från Abiskostugan. – Svenska Turistföreningens Årsskrift 1905: 203–235 (in Swedish).

– 1921. Abisko med omgivningar. – Svenska Turistföreningens Vägvisare n:o 51. Wahlström & Widstrand, Stockholm (in Swedish).

Sjulsson, K. 1979. Kristoffer Sjulssons minnen om Vapstenslapparna i början av 1800-talet. – Lund (in Swedish).

Sonesson, M. 1970. Studies on mire vegetation in the Torneträsk area, Northern Sweden. III. Communities of the poor mires. – Opera Bot. 26.

– 1974. Late Quarternary forest development of the Torneträsk area, North Sweden. 2. Pollen analytical evidence. – Oikos 25: 288–307.

– 1980. Klimatet och skogsgränsen i Abisko. – Fauna Flora 75: 1 (in Swedish).

– and Hoogesteger, J. 1983. Recent tree-line dynamics (*Betula pubescens* Ehrh. ssp. *tortuosa* (Ledeb./Nyman) in northern Sweden). – In: P. Morissat, P. and Payoth, S. (eds), Tree-Line ecology. Proceedings of the Northern Québeck Tree-line Conference. Nordicana 47: 47–55.

– and Lundberg, B. 1974. Late Quaternary forest development of the Torneträsk area, north Sweden. I. Structure of modern forest ecosystems. – Oikos 25: 121–133.

Steen, E. 1965. Reindeer grazing problems. – In: The plant cover of Sweden. Acta Phystogeographica Suecica 50.

Tenow, O. 1975. Topographical dependence of an outbreak of *Oporinia autumnata* Bkh. (Lep., Geometridae) in a mountain birch forest in northern Sweden. – Zoon 3: 85–110.

Vegetationskartor över Svenska fjällkedjan 1979–84. – Liber Kartor, Stockholm.

Vorren, Ø. 1980. Samisk bosettning på Nordkalotten, arealdisponering og resursutnyttning i historisk-økologisk belysning. – In: Badou, E. and Dahlstedt, K.-H. (eds), Nord-Skandinaviens historia i tvärvetenskaplig belysning. Umeå (in Swedish).

Wallén, C. C. 1963. Klimat och klimatfenomen i Lappland. – In: K. Curry-Lindahl, K. (ed.), Natur i Lappland, Uppsala, pp. 145–158 (in Swedish).

Zackrisson, O. 1986. Skogen och elden. – Sveriges Natur, Årsbok (in Swedish).

An important contribution:

336 pp, hard cover. Price DKK 370,00. Available from: Munksgaard International Booksellers and Publishers, P.O. Box 2148, DK-1016 Copenhagen K, Denmark.